THE SEX-LIFE LETTERS

G000242280

Also available in Grafton Books

The Sex-Life File
More Sex-Life Letters

The Sex-Life Letters

Compiled and with commentary by

Dr. Harold Greenwald and
Ruth Greenwald

Grafton
An Imprint of HarperCollinsPublishers

Grafton
An Imprint of HarperCollins*Publishers*
77–85 Fulham Palace Road,
Hammersmith, London W6 8JB

Published by Grafton 1974
Reprinted nine times
9

First published in the USA by
J. P. Tarcher, Inc.
Certain material contained herein has been
previously published by Penthouse Publications, Ltd
and Forum Press, Ltd

Copyright © Penthouse Publications, Ltd 1968
Copyright © Forum Press, Ltd 1969, 1970, 1971, 1972
Copyright © Forum Press, Ltd and
Harold and Ruth Greenwald 1972

ISBN 0 586 21006 7

Set in Times

Printed in Great Britain by
HarperCollinsManufacturing Glasgow

All rights reserved. No part of this publication may be
reproduced, stored in a retrieval system, or transmitted,
in any form or by any means, electronic, mechanical,
photocopying, recording or otherwise, without the prior
permission of the publishers.

This book is sold subject to the condition that it shall not,
by way of trade or otherwise, be lent, re-sold, hired out or
otherwise circulated without the publisher's prior consent
in any form of binding or cover other than that in which it
is published and without a similar condition including this
condition being imposed on the subsequent purchaser.

CONTENTS

PUBLISHER'S NOTE

THE letters contained in this book were selected from over 5000 published by Forum. the most widely read magazine in the world dealing with sexual behavior. The original selection of material for inclusion in the magazine was made by their Editorial Board, which includes internationally distinguished psychologists, doctors, lawyers, sociologists and anthropologists. A further selection was made by Dr. Harold Greenwald and Ruth Greenwald, with the intent of pursuing Forum's original commitment 'to give every voice an opportunity – every concept, attitude and opinion an equal chance to be heard'.

Dr. Harold Greenwald, after more than twenty years in private practice, is now a Professor of Clinical Psychology in California. He is past president of the National Psychological Association for Psychoanalysis, past president of the Association for Applied Psychoanalysis, and a member of more than a dozen professional associations.

Ruth Greenwald was Phi Beta Kappa at Columbia University School of Social Work. She is in private practice, specializing in marital and sexual problems, and supervises graduate students working toward degrees in counseling and therapy.

The comments by Forum's Editorial Board are followed by the letter *F*. Dr. Harold Greenwald's comments are noted by the letters *H.G.*, and Ruth Greenwald's comments by the letters *R.G.*

Some of the letters in this book describe practices that may be physically injurious and dangerous. The fact that these letters are published does not constitute a recommendation or an endorsement of such practices.

FOREWORD

AFTER over 20 years in private practice as a psycho-analyst, I have become accustomed to hearing people describe a wide variety of sexual activities, but even my experiences did not fully prepare me for these amazing letters. I was not only astounded by the inventiveness and complexity of the sexual choices made by the letter writers, but also by the fact that they were voluntarily writing about their private experiences in such a straightforward and frequently insightful manner. They were taking advantage of the great 'corner bar' tradition of telling a stranger those things they might not tell their most intimate friends (or even a therapist).

Nothing I have read or heard demonstrates more startlingly the nature and dimensions of the sexual revolution than this willingness to write openly and explicitly about these very personal activities. Revolutions involve a change in class behavior, and the sexual revolution is no exception. Whereas previously, extended sexual foreplay and complex variations were practiced primarily among the upper classes – such as the Roman aristocrats of Petronius Satyricon and the 19th century proper Victorian lords and ladies of the Hell Fire Club – today these behavior patterns have been democratized and are practiced, as *The Sex-Life Letters* clearly demonstrate, on all social levels. This readiness to engage in a wide variety of sexual activity and to share these experiences by writing letters for publication is a major result of the more permissive approach to the discussion of intimate experiences that exists today.

Even as a professor in a humanistically oriented university, I know that I risk harsh criticism from the academic world for becoming involved in the publication of material which many of my colleagues may consider sensational, and even sordid. Why am I willing to incur this risk?

I am willing because I am convinced that the reader of these letters can gain a greater understanding of himself and others by sharing the experiences of the letter writers. One important feeling expressed over and over again in the letters is the fear that the writer is unique in his particular problem and alone in

17

his particular sexual choice. Each of us believes himself to be unique and is proud of his feeling of individuality, yet we also desire to be like others and are afraid that being different means being wrong. This fear produces great guilts, which in turn can destroy what might otherwise be a far happier life. As a group therapy leader. I have seen that one of the greatest advantages of working with groups is the fact that the various members discover that they are not alone in their fears and frustrations, and that there are many others who have similar distresses in their lives and who make similar choices.

Many readers of this book, who hug some deep secret to their hearts – certain that it makes them at the very least odd, and perhaps worse – will discover that their sexual predilections are not so unusual. The relief that this offers is in itself ample justification for publication of the letters. Many of the letter writers themselves clearly document this.

Catharsis, the opportunity to purge one's emotions through the free and uncensored expressions of feelings, has long been recognized as a potential form of psychological therapy, as the Roman Catholic confessionals and psychoanalysts' couches remind us. But there also appears to be a considerable value in observed catharsis. In group therapy I have repeatedly seen people helped when someone else is able to discuss a subject with which they can identify. The letters offer only one writer the opportunity for the first catharsis – but they offer thousands of readers the opportunity for the second. The clearest expression of this benefit came, not surprisingly, in a letter to Forum which is not printed in this book: 'At first I must admit I was repelled, as some of the letters seemed needlessly explicit. I wondered why people would choose to express such things in print. But I found myself fascinated. The fact that people were able to be so open about those things I had never dared to talk about was enabling me to at least think about things that I had kept secret.'

Many individuals are compulsively driven to engage in behavior that they do not consciously like. The opportunity to discuss or read about such behavior may well act as the means to help them give it up. Some people are driven to engage in activities that they do not approve of in order to be different and to make themselves feel important. When they discover that these activities are not unique, they sometimes regain the capacity to choose whether or not they wish to continue them

18

and are thus able to replace compulsive behavior with voluntary behavior.

A corollary of the greater self-understanding and acceptance that can be derived from reading these letters is the growth of one's understanding of others. In commenting on the letters, we (and Forum's experts) have tried to avoid the 'advice to the lovelorn' approach. Instead we have attempted to clarify what leads the writer to act the way he does and why, for him, a seemingly bizarre choice may in fact be quite reasonable. It is important to remember that many of these letters do not represent problems but are merely descriptions of behavior from which the writer is, in many cases, deriving more excitement and fulfillment than the reader may be from his 'normal' sex life.

It is by now a truism that, because of ignorance, fear and guilt the great majority of married people in our country, if not in the entire world, are deriving only a fraction of the potential joy and pleasure that they could receive from their marital relationship. Many people who deal with these problems professionally would say that only one marriage in ten has a truly satisfactory sexual relationship. The world would be a better place if we changed this statistic. Of course, one cannot look at marriage or any of its variations as being solely a sexual relationship; however, it has been said that although good sex is only 10% of a marriage, bad sex is frequently 90%.

Most husbands and wives know exactly how their spouses like their steak, eggs or coffee, what movies they will or won't enjoy, what political candidate will or won't appeal to them, but they have far less information about their mates' sexual preferences.

Both Ruth and I have been most impressed with how often readers state that the mutual reading of these letters opened channels of communication by bringing up subjects that had never been raised before, because one partner feared that it would shock the other. By reading and discussing the letters together and moving from the general to the personal, they have been able to finally say, 'I've often wondered what it would be like to try that,' and frequently have discovered that their partner, too, had secretly been wanting to do the same thing.

It has frequently been our experience that when people are unable to talk about their sexual experiences with each other, they find difficulty in other communication. As they begin to

19

speak more freely in this area, they generally find that it improves relations in other areas. Sexual relations cannot be divorced from other ways of interacting, and many of the so-called sexual problems presented by the letter writers are merely symptoms of more basic problems with intimacy, closeness and love.

People frequently write Forum to say that reading such frank discussions has helped uninhibit them. Since it would be pointless to fill the book with testimonials, comparatively few of these letters are included, but the files are jammed with them. A great many expressed the opinion that being able to free themselves of restricting taboos has not only helped them improve a functioning marriage, but has saved a dying one. By encouraging imagination and a willingness to try new things, the letters may well have a beneficial effect in liberalizing formerly restricted behavior.

Lastly, although this book is not a sex manual, there is no question that the variety of sexual techniques described here will enhance the reader's knowledge and perhaps his ability for personal giving and receiving in his sexual life. Many readers who have few other information sources available may find ways to cure their problems, or at least discover ways to live with them with greater contentment.

The Sex-Life Letters also offers a rich source of material for professional researchers and therapists interested in the wide range of sexual behavior being practiced today, especially as many writers have included material to show what they believe to be the origin of their behavior. It is true that the writers were not chosen as a representative sample of the population, but like most samples of people whose sexual lives have been studied (including the monumental studies of Dr. Kinsey and Masters & Johnson), they are self-chosen.

Before agreeing to work on this book, I examined many of the letters and answered for myself many of the objections that occurred to me.

I questioned the editors of Forum about the genuineness of the letters. Robert Chartham, Ph.D., a noted English psychologist who is on Forum's editorial board, answered, 'Let me scotch the notion right from the start that the Forum letters are not genuine. Forum has no need to invent letters, since it receives many more than it can print, all dealing with every aspect of human relations from the commoner sort to the most bizarre. I can personally vouch for this. Not only have I seen the originals (whose authenticity is checked), but I myself, because of my books, personally receive about 60 letters a week of a similar nature. Thus it makes all the sense in the world that a journal of Forum's reputation with an estimated two million readers will receive a great number of letters.'

Dr. Chartham, of course, does not preclude the possibility that some of the letters are writers' fantasies – put-ons – sent in by humorous contributors. I agree. Although the experience of professionals in the field would indicate that the behavior described by every letter has actually taken place with a far larger percentage of people than most readers would expect, the letters were not published in Forum Magazine originally unless, in the opinion of the magazine's consultants, they seemed genuine, and they would not have been chosen by me unless I had felt they represented realistic sexual behavior.

A second objection that one occasionally hears with regard to material of this kind is that some people reading this material will 'get ideas'. Of course, this is a possibility, and in many instances the ideas will help them achieve more fulfilling relationships. As former New York City mayor Jimmy Walker once said: 'Nobody ever got seduced by reading a book.' My experience (and I am sure the reader's) has shown that no amount of reading about something is going to persuade me to even experiment with an activity that I find personally unattractive. The only effect may be to make me more tolerant and understanding. Nobody has ever produced evidence that airing material of this kind increases its incidence.

A third complaint is that these letters do not contain a true picture of sexual attitudes and experiences today, that they present an unbalanced emphasis on unusual sexual behavior. This would have validity if we were claiming that these letters represent a statistical survey. We are not. Certainly, the emphasis is on unusual practices (although any professional in the field will tell you that unusual behavior is more usual than the general public believes), and it is just because such practices cause more guilt and trouble that they deserve to be brought into the open where people can learn to deal with them.

A fourth objection is that some of these letters display a separation of tender emotional feelings from sexual feelings. Unfortunately, this is an expression of the alienation to which modern man is particularly susceptible. I should hope that

21

seeing this dimension in others will lead some to recognize the problem in themselves and encourage them to take steps to deal with it.

The emphasis on physical sex is not due to any particular editorial bias – nearly all the letters received by Forum are on that topic. Most other aspects of human experience can be expressed and shared through established social channels. It is difficult, indeed, to find a place where one can freely reveal the physical side of one's sex life. Forum Magazine offers its readers that opportunity and they have taken it.

One other objection frequently heard is that letters of this kind raise false sexual expectations and that the reader will come to accept the idea that, as far as sex is concerned, anything goes. This may lead to a great deal of unhappiness among otherwise contented couples who feel an obligation to experiment in order to keep up with the Jones's.

We are living in revolutionary times, and these levels of expectation are being raised in every area – political, educational, economic, and sexual. We did not make the sexual revolution, but we are aware that these rising expectations can be met only when people understand the nature of their own sexual desires, the sources of their frustrations and the methods by which they can find fulfillment within the context of more loving relationships.

The publication of these letters may well be an important contribution to that understanding.

HAROLD GREENWALD

La Jolla, California
July 1972

*   *   *

When my husband asked if I would like to collaborate on a book, I was delighted and told him so. Our previous collaborations – 35 years of marriage, two grown sons, and a certain amount of joint counseling – had worked out well. However, when he explained that the project involved responding to the Forum Magazine letters, I began to have doubts and considered my initial reaction more carefully.

I gave special consideration to the problem of how my own

sexual preferences and prejudices might get in the way of my commenting openly on the correspondence. The letters evoked many feelings in me: identification with the women who complained about the restrictiveness of their upbringing and their difficulties in accepting themselves as people with a full range of sexual options; compassion for those who could not come to terms with their desires; at times, simple incredulity.

I began to realize that although it was comfortable enough for me to hear and respond to recitals of sexual behavior in the privacy of my own office, I might be uncomfortable being publicly identified with descriptions of such activities – just as many readers who no doubt will enjoy reading this book may also be ashamed of that pleasure and embarrassed if they are 'caught' doing it.

I mentioned the project to a few friends, people who consider themselves to be cosmopolitan and liberated. Their reactions were mostly smiles and smirks with such comments as 'What a turn-on for you and Harold,' or 'You'll make a mint on it – people love to read kinky stories.' There was little or no mention of the implications of this kind of book or its possible value. It was these comments which helped me realize that unhappily I, like many of my friends, was not as liberated as I wanted to believe and certainly as I wanted others to believe. We have all heard and read a great deal about changing attitudes and changing sexual behavior – about a greater acceptance in our society of 'doing your own thing'. Certainly some of this is true. However, in my practice, in the letters, in my friends' comments and in myself I could see that guilt about deviating from the usual roles and concern about enjoying different sexual activities still exist in abundance. Too many people continue to ask, in the words of T. S. Eliot, 'Do I dare disturb the universe?' It was in order to help formulate an answer to that question that I decided to go ahead with the book.

A colleague raised another area of concern. She commented that since my own sexual experiences were comparatively limited, how could I understand what the letter writers were experiencing? I was ready to agree with her when I realized that Harold's and my purpose was neither to give nor to refuse the Good Housekeeping Seal of Approval or to make ourselves judges of anyone's activities. Most of us have to struggle with too many judges in our lives already, and we do not wish to become another in that forbidding pantheon. Our purpose is, rather, to help the reader broaden his understanding of human sexual behaviour and enjoy the sexual choices he has made.

RUTH GREENWALD

La Jolla, California
July 1972

The Sex-Life Letters

THEIR OWN BUSINESS

Whoever originally said 'ignorance is bliss' should have had his head examined. My ignorance concerning sex was anything but blissful.

Brought up as I was in a small midwestern town, my only preparation for marriage was an accumulation of dirty jokes about marriage plus one old-fashioned, moralistic marriage manual. Normal sex with one's wife was usually the missionary, man-on-top position; in other words, one's love session consisted of a brief preliminary bout followed by intercourse. As far as I was concerned, that was it. Anything else was wrong and was indulged in by perverts. I'm not kidding. This is exactly what I thought and I know my friends felt the same way.

Today, at the age of 54, as I look back on my marital life, I am not only sad, but also angry. Angry that I was cheated out of so much pleasure, due mainly to my abysmal ignorance about sex. Oral love, for instance. I once broached the suggestion to my wife and was immediately put off by her attitude. She referred to it as degenerate, and I went along with her views. I had never read about such love practices although I first came across the idea when somebody told me a dirty joke involving 69. From then on, I could only relate to it in terms of a dirty joke.

As far as I was concerned, such things as blue films, sex aids, mutual masturbation, making love at any hour of the day, group sex, troilism, etc., were purely and simply wrong. Peculiarly enough, I never asked myself why they were wrong. It was something I just took for granted. No doubt due to ignorance and the same type of Victorian upbringing as everyone else in my town.

Today, after 32 years of marriage, it's too late for my wife and me to change our ways. Needless to say, the brainwashing we were inflicted with as children is deeply ingrained. While intellectually I would love to be sexually permissive, emotionally I am a sexual cripple.

The reason for this letter was not to cry over spilt milk. Rather, it was to point out to those young people who are just starting out in marriage that between a man and woman, everything goes, just so long as you don't harm one another physically or force your partner into doing something she doesn't want to do.

What two people do sexually is no one's business but their own. No government or religion should have the right to tell a man and his wife what they can or cannot do in the privacy of their own home. As an extreme example, if they both prefer oral sex to intercourse, that's their business and they should feel no guilt about their actions. If they enjoy making love with another couple or couples, and it helps in keeping their sex lives stimulated, well, why not? Who are they hurting?

God, what I wouldn't do to be 22 again!

C.L.

PEEKING PERKS

I notice occasional letters in Forum from women whose husbands want them to make love to other men or expose themselves.

Two years ago my husband went this way. He implored me to undress in front of his friends. He said how proud he was of me, etc. It became an obsession and he was so persistent that after a lot of thought I decided to do something about it and meet him halfway.

Although I didn't fancy standing naked in the presence of his friends, I felt that it might be quite exciting to be spied upon. It does give me a little thrill and keeps my husband happy. This is how it works.

I am told by my husband when he is bringing a friend back from the pub in the evening and the exact time. I am always just about to take a bath when they arrive, saying to my husband that he should have told me he was bringing a friend back. I am always in my nightdress and dressing gown and apologize for my appearance. I cut them some sandwiches and make coffee and tell them I am going to carry on with my bath if they will excuse me.

My husband immediately asks his friend if he would like a bit of fun and the answer is always yes.

26

We live in an old house with a loft and it is quite easy to get into. A few steps inside and one can look right down into the bathroom through a steam ventilator fixed in the bathroom ceiling.

My husband leads his friend to the ventilator where he can stare down at me and I carry on taking my bath in complete ignorance, so to speak, of what is happening.

The fun really starts when I have finished and I stand up to dry and powder myself. Several times I have ended up by masturbating. When they go downstairs again I join them shortly and I'm tickled at what my husband's friend is thinking!

My husband always makes wonderful love to me when this has happened and if only for this I feel it is worthwhile.

Mrs M.P.

The enjoyment of peeping must be universal and surely stems from childhood curiosity and sexual excitement and the satisfaction of having furtive glimpses of the parent of the opposite sex, or both parents, dressing or undressing. Only when it becomes someone's sole sexual preoccupation should it be called voyeurism.

Obviously the enjoyment of spying on someone naked is not quite the same as watching striptease or nakedness openly, but clearly both have a far, far wider appeal to most 'normal' people than the pretense that the interest exists only as a deviation suggests.

The motives of a man like your husband who enjoys exhibiting his wife's charms to others, may be many-sided. But, in general, in our perverse, patriarchal society, beautiful women are male property to be shown off to others, rather like a new car or any other possession. The object is to arouse envy and admiration. The owner of this beautiful woman may even use her as a kind of clothes horse on which he hangs the expensive fur coats and jewelry that demonstrate his wealth and power and, ultimately, his sexual potency.

Of course, women enjoy the material proofs of affection too and fully enjoy displaying them and their own charms to the envy and chagrin of their less fortunate sisters. And they not only revel in the masculine admiration they receive but experience it as a powerful sexual stimulant.

You remark that several times you have masturbated while being watched but do not make it clear if this was done to excite

27

the men or satisfy your own aroused feelings. Your husband's intent seems to be primarily to raise his sexual tensions, and yours, by creating a triangle situation in which another man is sexually aroused by being allowed to look at you naked and in sexually stimulating movements. It is not, apparently, your husband's intention that this man should touch you. But he knows and enjoys the fact that he must envy him. Your husband is filled with glowing self-satisfaction that, having shut the other man outside your house, he is going to have full and satisfying possession of you sexually.

This may be seen as an enactment of the Oedipus fantasy situation where the rival man, who sexually desires the same woman, is defeated and the desired woman taken possession of sexually. The same theme appears heavily disguised in so many childhood dreams and fantasies where, in the case of a boy, the father is the original rival and the mother the desired woman. – F.

A BIT DIFFERENT?

My husband and I have been married now for some three years and in addition to regular and frequent copulation my husband still likes, on occasion, to be persuaded to orgasm by hand.

At first I thought that perhaps I was inadequate, but he assures me that this is not so – he merely likes to be governed in this way occasionally.

The bedroom is never used at these times and although various positions are used I am always required to remain clothed while he is completely naked.

I must stress that our marriage is a happy one and I am pleased to fulfill him in this way (in truth I obtain pleasure from promoting and witnessing this wonder of nature). But I confess to wondering if other wives are called upon for similar acts of love or whether my husband is simply a bit different.

Mrs. J.R.

HUSBAND MASTURBATES

I left my husband 14 months ago because after only being married six months I found out that he masturbated quite frequently in the early morning. He told me that this was normal and that lots of men did it, but I found this very hard to believe when there is a normal healthy wife who is willing to have sex anyway. This continued for four years. Each time I was confronted with evidence that my husband had masturbated I asked him to see a doctor, but he always refused. When I asked him if I was sexually satisfactory to him, saying he was making me feel inadequate, he said that he was more than satisfied with me as his wife in every respect.

As time went by our sexual life came to a standstill, and during our last year together we had sex about once a month. Then I left him. I was and I still am sexually frustrated but I have no interest in taking another man as I am still very much in love with my husband and he with me.

We both would like very much to live together again but not under the same conditions as before. We are both willing to do as much as we can to try and make our marriage work again and would even like to see a psychiatrist if this would help.

Mrs. E. L.

I can understand this lady wondering whether she was not satisfying her husband when she discovered that he masturbated as well as made love to her.

Her husband is quite right – quite a large number of happily married men who, have regular and satisfying sex lives masturbate once or twice a week as well as making love three or four times. I know a couple of highly sexed men in their early 30s who make love seven days a week – sometimes more frequently – and who also masturbate daily. They find they have to, to relieve the buildup of sexual tension. They are both married to average-sexed wives for whom a frequency of seven times weekly is high. Though both wives have adjusted to this frequency and have been happy to do so, the husbands feel that it would be asking too much of them to increase still more; so they masturbate. – F.

A SENSIBLE WIFE

May I say, in answer to a question very frequently raised, that masturbation on the part of married men is so frequent as to be normal. However affectionate a wife, there will always be times when she is too busy or too tired to attend to her husband's 'needs', and she will be a fool if she takes exception to him having a little extra pleasure on the side.

But there is more to it than that; few men achieve orgasm without fantasy – a plain wife becomes a big-breasted film star, a demanding mistress becomes a slavish concubine, at the moment of orgasm, and using the hand offers opportunity for a different set of imaginings. As the sailor said when they asked him why he preferred tossing off in his bunk to visiting the brothel: 'You get a better class of girl.'

Any sensible wife will prefer that her husband seek 'variety' in his own bed rather than someone else's, and offer him every encouragement.

A.J.

VENUS IN FURS

The thing that really sends me is fur. Fur works me up to such a degree that I often masturbate looking at photos of models clad in furs.

I am wondering if this is passed down from father to son because I have, when I was very young, entered my parents' bedroom in the early morning and seen my mother's silver fox fur on the bed.

I also remember on a couple of occasions my mother tickling my father's chin and neck with the tail of this particular fox. Although I thought nothing about it at the time, I am sure it has had some bearing on my life.

When I got married, which was only three years ago, I was able to discuss with my wife my likes and dislikes about sex. She asked me one night, 'What really makes you feel sexy; would, in fact, a nude woman appeal to you?' I said it would, but if she was lying on a bed of fur or was wearing a fur of any kind it would be more attractive to me.

'I had better get myself a fur then,' she said, laughing, 'and after that a wheelchair to wheel you about in, because they say too much sex makes you weak.' I then told her that even talking about furs made me feel very sexy.

That night she commented on the fact that I felt much bigger in her than usual and she had three orgasms.

A week later, just after we got into bed, she said, 'Do you feel like intercourse?' I said that being married to such an attractive woman I always fancied it.

'I bet you I could finish you, even without touching you with my hands,' she replied. She then stripped and went to the wardrobe where she took out the most beautiful pair of silver fox furs I have ever seen. I could not believe my eyes as she stood there wearing nothing but silver foxes, moving the furs over her body so that they stroked her breasts lovingly. Next she took a fox tail in each hand and slowly tickled my body, starting at my neck and working down to my knees until I could contain myself no longer and grabbed her. We really had a night of loving after that, only stopping for a short time between bouts.

I am happy to say that since then furs have always been a part of our loveplay and intercourse up to this day.

I bought a book called *Venus in Furs* just recently which we both enjoyed very much. Also we both went to see the film 'Midnight Cowboy' and were thrilled to see one of the actresses making love in a beautiful red fox coat. My wife tossed me off when we saw this in the pictures, as I was so worked up, but seeing this action without the furs would not have had the same effect.

Surely there must be many other people who are as affected by fur as I am?

B.R.

WHEN THE FUR FLIES

I enjoy intercourse only when the woman is wearing furs, or I am wearing them myself. I like the fur to be thick and soft. Persian lamb, ocelot and leopard fur are of no use. The most effective are deep fox fur, lynx, chinchilla and bearskin. Mink is acceptable, but curiously enough, I prefer beaver, lamb or bunny fur.

Fake furs are definitely out. I find that a garment with a fur collar is better than no fur at all – at a pinch, a coat with fur collar and cuffs will do.

As far as the garment itself is concerned, jackets which just stop short of the vital front and back lower regions are excellent, as are capes, which meet in the center of the breast cleavage.

One of my most exciting experiences was with two girls – one wore a blue fox cape round her shoulders, the other a fur stole round her hips. I recall one girl for whom I bought a silver fox cape: she was so delighted that she always wore it whenever we had intercourse. I have found that most women accept the idea without enthusiasm, but do not seem inclined to refuse to wear fur.

I have come across only one woman who had been asked to wear fur during intercourse prior to meeting me. Most women are surprised by the fact that I cannot obtain an erection without the additional warmth of fur. I wonder if other men feel this desire, but are too reticent and shy to express it? I pose this question because I have noticed that when I wear an overcoat with fur lapels, so many men touch or stroke the fur.

I wear furs on every possible occasion. The coat mentioned above has a beaver lamb fur lining and phantom beaver collar. I also have a suede coat lined with Hungarian lamb with a baby beaver collar. I have a scarf lined with muskrat and a camel's hair scarf lined with Lucca lamb. My wardrobe is completed by a beaver lamb tie, a grey mink cravat and a lynx collar. All these articles can be used for massage and stimulation either when I am alone or with a girl. I possess an album of 'Fur Pin-Ups', the best exposing the breasts surrounded by cozy fur.

Although I am not aware of what caused this fetish. I must admit that I don't want to stop it. I really enjoy fur. In my opinion, every desirable woman is made infinitely more desirable by wearing furs – especially with a turned up fur collar hugging the cheeks.

Sex manuals pay scant attention to this little known fetish, although I did once read of a man caught masturbating amongst a pile of furs.

Looking back, it was a camel scarf which first caught my eye. As a boy I used it when masturbating. I then obtained a pair of large gauntlets lined with fur, and used them both. Cashmere was next to catch my attention. To see a bulging breast pressing against cashmere is a delightful sight. However, it is really fur which I find irresistible. I even touch it as I walk by a wearer in the street.

At present, my girl friend has a lynx cat suit, with a huge collar. Holes have been cut so that her breasts and nipples are gorgeously exposed, and there are three wide slits at the back and front for easy access, when the fun starts and the fur flies – all on our big fox overblanket. In my opinion, fur seems more agreeable as a stimulant than whips, rubber or leather which are much more popular fetishes.

Is fur fetishism unusual?

F.C.

Fur fetishism is not as unusual as one would think – though of course, it needs considerable financial resources to indulge. Sacher-Masoch's classic book was called Venus in Furs *and Edwardian ladies were known to enjoy making love on tiger skins. Nor is there anything reprehensible or harmful in it if you can afford such pleasures. Erotic stimulation in this respect is based on the sense of touch – which is actually three complete senses, detecting, respectively, heat and cold, pressure (including rough and smooth) and pain. Fur fetishism involves the first two of these. The sense of touch (or the triple sense) is a highly refined, sensitive and discriminating faculty which offers infinite possibilities of new stimuli. Experts have pointed out that the sense of touch conveys sexual suggestion faster and more directly than does any other sense.*

Fur affects women differently; very few women are insensitive to the sensuous feeling of fur against the skin. This may be because fur is a natural material evoking memories of childhood contact with the mother's body and hair: some psychiatrists believe that one of the main reasons for keeping cats and dogs is the psychologically reassuring feeling, and the physical pleasures, that stroking them gives their owners. Another reason why a woman will generally be far less reluctant to wear furs for her lover than, say, rubber is that the wearing of furs, in this culture, is a common way of enhancing sexual appeal. Few women, on the other hand can feel sexy in themselves (as opposed to in their partner's eyes) while wearing rubber or other common fetish materials. – F.

PRO-PUBIC SHAVING

My wife, whose strong sexual desires equal my own, finds that cunnilingus as foreplay is virtually essential to her final satisfaction. She is exceptionally heavily bushed, in which decoration her pride is equalled by my own admiration. But, some phobia causes me to revolt at the contact of pubic hair with my lips.

For nearly two years I had forced myself to do what was necessary without enjoyment, but finally I managed to induce my wife to sacrifice this badge of her sex and allow me to shave her. The effect has been remarkable. Now, not only do I greatly enjoy cunnilingus, but my greater freedom and lack of inhibition doubles, so she says, my wife's enjoyment, and certainly her behavior tends to confirm that this is not an exaggeration. But it has had another and unforeseen result. Now, cleanly mown, the lovely curves of her mons veneris, hitherto masked, are brought to view and afford such a finish to a lovely figure that I have only to glimpse her nakedness to react almost instantly.

Whether or not they have similar difficulties to mine, I urge other spouses to follow my example. Those few who have already done so, on our advice, have blessed us.

T.F.

ANTI-PUBIC SHAVING

May I strongly condemn the exhortation to women to shave the pubis. They should no more think of doing so than of shaving their heads.

I suspect that anyone who recommends it is certainly one of a small minority and wishes a girl to look as though she has yet to reach puberty because he finds this stimulating.

I think you will find that most men react to a desirable display of pubic hair with a pretty quick erection.

Since I started showing girls how to shampoo, dress, comb and scent their pubic hair, their comments have left me in no doubt concerning the value of this grooming. Previously, during cunnilingus, my mouth inevitably collected a few hairs which can be annoying if they reach the back of the throat, but after this beauty treatment I have yet to have this happen. The girls' pleasure at the increased incidence of cunnilingus and the endearing compliments received afterwards are only equaled by mine in its performance. Truly, their genitals are now so much more appetizing, while the hairdressing has developed into a sort of foreplay. So, don't cut it off, cultivate it!

Now I also dress my genital hair in a similar manner, and even girls who had never before performed fellatio now do so of their own volition.

R.B.

KEEP YOUR HAIR ON

Nature, and the development of the body, intended pubic hair to be there, just the same as human hair on the head. My wife had her pubic hair shaved off just for a trial and she thought it was horrible, and so did I.

There is nothing so exciting to a man during loveplay than to run one's fingers through the pubic hair prior to inserting the finger into the vagina – it's a must during lovemaking prior to intercourse.

I am sure all male readers will agree with me. So ladies, if you want to keep your lovers, keep your hair on!

G.W.

THE SPICE OF LIFE

My wife and I believe that variety is the spice of sex life, and during a period of six happy and faithful years of marriage we have developed a number of stimulating sex games which insure against the possibility of monotony occurring through adherence to a basic pattern of straightforward intercourse.

To begin with, my wife is multi-orgasmic and to assist her to reach two or three climaxes before actual sexual union we obtained a rubber dildo with which I masturbate her in the preliminary stages of our lovemaking. This instrument, which is a great source of satisfaction to her is a beautifully made and accurate replica of the erect penis with a hollow rubber bulb at its base which holds about a third of a cup of fluid. It is filled by squeezing the air from it and then dipping the tip of the dildo into a glass of warm milk or cream; the liquid is expelled by pressure on the bulb, ejaculating it in rhythmic squirts into the vagina in simulation of the male orgasm.

Soon after we had acquired it my wife discovered, by experiment, that she could excite herself during my daytime absence by 'wearing' the dildo inside herself, holding it in place with tight latex rubber briefs. Thus inserted and maintained in position, only the bulb protrudes into the crotch of her briefs. These latter, being of stretch material, allow a slight in-and-out movement of the dildo as she moves about, and at the same time they provide a pleasantly erotic sensation in the general sexual region. (The feel of tight latex rubber panties alone is sufficient to bring my wife to orgasm when she is in a sexy mood.) In this manner she can enjoy a leisurely, prolonged, and controlled period of self-stimulation as she goes about her housework and shopping, and when at last orgasm cannot be held back a moment longer the dildo may be made to squirt its fluid by squeezing the bulb tightly between the tops of her thighs.

Needless to say, climaxes have occurred in some pretty unusual situations, such as at a bus stop and in a supermarket, but these occasions my wife regards as being exciting rather than embarrassing, enjoying, as she does, the secret pleasure of experiencing ecstatic sexual bliss unknown to the people around her. This pleasure is heightened by the fact that she is obliged to keep a tight rein on her physical response to the moment, though she finds a slight rhythmic movement of the hips to be inevitable.

This 'game', however, takes on its plural aspect when it takes place with my knowledge and in my presence among the company of others who are not, of course, 'in the know'. We both find it to be a most stimulating practice for my wife to wear her dildo when we have friends in for drinks or dinner, especially if I have had the pleasure of inserting it for her before they arrive. During the course of the evening, as she becomes more and more worked up by the movement of the dildo in her vagina and by the tactile stimulation of her rubber briefs, I note with rising excitement the tiny telltale signs of her increasing response, and when at last, slightly flushed, she smiles at me and indicates by a sign that orgasm is imminent or squeezes my hand and whispers 'Darling, I'm coming – now!' my own reaction brings me close to the heights of a climax in turn. Believe me, by the time our guests have departed we are more than ready to strip each other nude and to consummate our excitement in an act of furious coupling.

Our 'games' are numerous, and, we believe, keep our interest in each other fresh. We are both highly sexed (and glad to be), and are both totally honest with each other as to our sexual desires. Variations in customary sexual techniques include, for example, making love on a rubber sheet, having intercourse while I wear my wife's suspender belt and stockings, using a candle with its end rounded off and oiled with hand lotion to masturbate my wife's anus, and concluding intercourse by my wife wetting herself – i.e. by urinating – at the moment of orgasm. This last is a particular source of satisfaction to my wife, who finds the act of urination in a sexual situation to be highly pleasurable and indeed, in a state of extreme tension, often gains momentary relief by voluntarily wetting her panties.

The point, however, is this. Contrary to the conclusions that may be drawn from the above, neither of us is a rubber fetishist; nor is my wife a latent lesbian, an anal erotic, or a urolagniac; nor am I a transvestite. None of these things is *essential* to our sexual activity, which consists for 95% of the time of ordinary sexual congress. At the most we believe ourselves to be sensualists, enjoying the feel of tactile stimuli, whether from objects, clothing, or certain acts, as an enhancement to normal sexual appetites and satisfaction. And our games are not an end in themselves, a substitute, but are rather the salt and pepper of an honest and faithful sex life. We do nothing that we do not both enjoy, and we commend our attitude to married couples who seek happiness in this sphere.

P.B.

PING PONG PING

With reference to P.B.'s letter saying that his wife wears an erect rubber penis inside herself during the day – my wife does much the same, but uses a small soft rubber ball, about the size of a ping-pong ball. This she places between the lips of her vagina, so that it presses against her clitoris, and holds it there by putting on a pantie girdle. She gets the most exciting feelings, especially when she walks up and down stairs.

What I would like to know is, is there anything a man can similarly wear or use during the day?

W.H.

TRAVELING PLEASURE

I make secret preparations before setting out on any long journey by car or train – or, for that matter, on any occasion when I know I shall be in a sitting position for any length of time.

Inside my briefs I insert a large-size sanitary pad, positioning it so that it covers my testicles and penis. Apart from being extremely comfortable, one can, by occasional gentle pressure of the thighs, stimulate the penis embedded in the soft cushion of the pad. Moreover, one can reach the point of ejaculation without fear of soiling one's clothes – the sperm being soaked up by the pad.

I am extremely interested in the design of men's underwear

but feel that the most comfortable garment for covering the testicles and penis is yet to be discovered. The material I prefer is toweling, which fortunately is just beginning to be used.

P.S.

UROLAGNIA

I recall an evening almost 20 years ago when my husband and I first indulged in urolagnia, not long after our marriage. The strange thing is that before I was married I very often spent an uncomfortable, sometimes agonizing, few hours with my boy-friend, later my fiancée, because I was too shy to go to the lavatory, or, if visiting friends or relatives of his, to ask where the toilet was.

On one occasion, I remember I wet myself in the toilet when I arrived home. I couldn't get my panties down in time and perhaps it was this subconscious memory that led us to watching each other empty our bladders.

My husband and I had been to a party and he had had a few beers. In those days we had a motorcycle combination and it was a very chilly October evening. When we arrived home his hands were frozen and he was dying to get rid of some of that beer. He was so cold he could hardly unbuckle the belt of his stormcoat outside the toilet. I helped him, unbuttoning his coat for him. He went into the toilet and I could see he was desper-ate. Something made me follow him in. Aware of the urgency, I undid his fly buttons and reached into his trousers. While hold-ing him, easing back his foreskin, watching him urinate, I became so excited that I felt myself lubricating. When he had finished I told him I must go too and pulled up my clothes and took down my panties. I asked him if he wanted to watch me, and I peed standing, my clothes held high as he bent his head to watch. Needless to say we hurried immediately afterward to the bedroom, both of us highly excited.

Since that evening we have often shared the toilet. He loves to pull my panties down. This excites him so that it sometimes leads to his masturbating me as I sit on the toilet.

I have excited him by peeing into his hand in the bathroom when he has begun loveplay after my bath. I have never leaked during intercourse, not even when my bladder was full. If I happen to mention to my husband during intercourse that I want to go to the toilet, then he comes almost at once and his coming off brings me off. I seem to get a more intense orgasm when my bladder is full.

We have often wondered if this love game of ours is harmful? We do not indulge in it very often. It began when one or other of us read somewhere that the urge to urinate began when the bladder content reached the half-pint mark. We wondered how much we could hold and I bet that I could hold more than he. I don't suppose we have done it more than a half dozen times, but I can always hold more than he. We measured by using a pint bottle and a plastic funnel. My maximum was just over three pints, while his is just over two and both of us had to play with ourselves in order to hold so much. I actually masturbated to orgasm on several occasions and once my husband did the same in an effort to win the bet.

Mrs. V.T.

From babyhood we are taught, often with threats of violence or of the withdrawal of parental love if we don't comply, to urinate and defecate in the 'right' place at the 'right' time. The ways we are forced into this type of rigid (though socially acceptable and even necessary) behavior are often destructive. There are probably many people who, deep down, would like to urinate in the 'wrong' place for a change, and preferably on those who coerced them to do it in the 'right' place when they were too young to fight back. (In most marriages, of course, the wife carries something of the connotations of the mother for her husband, and the husband something of the connotations of the father for his wife.).

When young and fit one takes the most extraordinary liberties with one's body and no harm will come of it. To hold one's water in such a way after the age of 45 would be to court disaster – someone, somewhere will, sooner or later, be unable to empty the bladder at all and medical help will be required.

Owing to the pelvic congestion induced, many people find their sensations increased if they indulge in sexual intercourse with a distended bladder. Equally, many others interpret the increased sensation as pain, and so make sure their bladder is emptied beforehand.

In general, the answer to any such query is this – if uncomfortable or undesirable symptoms appear after performing such an act, then it is better avoided. If not, then no harm is likely in the young and fit. – F.

39

GOOD CONNECTION

My wife and I have only been together for five and a half years, but in that time my wildest dreams have been realized sexually. Both of us have had previous experience, talk openly about it, and agree quite fervently that this is marvelous. And it is.

For me, the whole sexual field changed about three years ago when my partner asked, quite unexpectedly, what I thought about self-masturbation. I was completely knocked out of my stride – for in all my experience (and I am no chicken) no woman had ever talked of this subject before. I replied that I didn't think it was necessary, and got the shock of my life when I was asked why. I then went on to give all sorts of fanciful reasons, and stayed quiet for the remainder of our car journey. My wife had replied in the negative when I asked if she had ever masturbated.

Several days later, my wife telephoned me at my office and confessed that she had masturbated, and still did.

I was shattered, my ego confused. I immediately thought that I wasn't satisfying her. She then convinced me not to take it this way. That night, sex was marvelous. When she rolled on top of me after several climaxes and whispered 'stay still', I did so. I could feel the slight movement of her buttocks as she moved up and down on me – and then where I normally place my fingers on her clitoris, I felt her hand slip in between us and start to move very slightly. In roughly 30 seconds she started gasping at the approach of her climax, and the feeling of excitement in me was uncomfortable. I could withstand her climaxes usually, but not this one. This was sex unlimited. We crashed through the barrier together. And it is always like this when we do it this way – although we never plan it – for if that is the way it is, then that is the way it is.

One morning the phone rang, and it was my wife, at home 25 miles away. In the course of conversation, during which we thanked each other for the marvelous session of the previous evening, matters were discussed very quietly and intimately, and I could feel a mounting excitement. I decided to seduce her vocally, if I could. After about 20 minutes of gentle subtle persuasion. I had her going enough for her to admit that if I was there I would only need to touch her and she would climax. I asked her to touch herself. There was no reply – just a gasp and a further gasp and then the sound I knew so well – the moan of pure pleasure as she started to go. We climaxed together and we were 25 miles apart ... who the hell wants group sex?

M.M.

MUTUAL MASTURBATION

In 20 years of marriage, and 25 years of making love together, my wife and I have practiced mutual masturbation for the past 13 years.

Our attempts at lovemaking were the shy fumblings of adolescents. I always achieved orgasm, but I now know that my wife never did, although in her inexperienced way she felt satisfied. After marriage our techniques improved and we tried various positions, but still my wife did not come off properly, although we didn't realize it.

During her periods she used to masturbate me, but I never thought she could do it to herself until shortly after the birth of our first child I read a book explaining the function of the clitoris. That night I asked her if she had ever masturbated and her reply was negative so I suggested she try stroking her clitoris. Although hesitant at first, she quickly found the right spot and away she went. When she was really wet she asked me to mount her in the usual way, and as I reached my climax so did she. I think she nearly went out of her mind with ecstasy at her first proper orgasm in nearly eight years' experience.

When she knew what she wanted, we eventually found we could reach a simultaneous climax without the preliminary masturbation and sometimes if I had been drinking she would have two or even three orgasms before I had mine.

After the birth of our second child about 13 years ago, my wife was told that to have more children would be extremely dangerous, so we continued our sex life using the contraceptive devices available and masturbation.

After preliminary slight petting and sometimes intercourse short of my climax, my wife lies on her back and I on my side facing her. I insert my thumb two inches or so into the vagina and leave my other hand free to play with myself when required. She stimulates her clitoris with her forefinger in a rapid side to side movement. During this time I whisper erotica into her ear varying from sweet tenderness to outlandish fantasies.

Originally I wanted to move my thumb in and out to simulate penile penetration but she prefers it to be still until she starts her orgasm. During this time she lies with her legs close together and her buttocks taut, gripping my thumb as tightly as possible. As she reaches her peak of clitoral stimulation, she moans in ecstasy and when she starts to come she opens her legs and moves her buttocks slowly up and down, drawing my thumb in as far as it will go. As we both start moving together the pace increases until she reaches her orgasm, at which time I can feel her vagina pulsating. She then either masturbates me to my climax, or I finish myself off while she tells me similar fantasies.

Although our original reason for mutual masturbation was mainly health, we now realize that we can have a satisfactory release even if we are too tired to indulge in the intense physical activity required to copulate properly. Couples should have no guilt about masturbation, especially if it brings pleasure to both.

F.J.

THE COMPLETE TREATMENT

Readers may be interested in my recent experience when, at the suggestion of a correspondent abroad who knew of my interest in correction and rubber fetishism, I visited the establishment of a very enlightened lady in the West End of London. I had been given a telephone number, and on contacting Madame, I was given an appointment for noon. I must say that I was a little apprehensive at this venture into the unknown, but my curiosity was sufficient to take the plunge.

The house was situated in a cul-de-sac off a busy street. I went up to the first floor as directed and was admitted by an elderly servant and shown into a waiting-room like a doctor's or dentist's with a table of journals. The only difference was a number of striking colored plates of ladies in latex rubber garments on the walls.

After a brief wait, I was invited to meet Madame on the next floor. I had been told she was about 40, so had not expected a girl in her early 20's. She turned out to be a friendly person with whom one could discuss one's interests without embarrassment. The room was her boudoir and was bulging with garments of all types in rubber and leather. In fact, it was almost like a boutique in Carnaby Street! She told me her collection was worth over $1700 and one leather outfit, illustrated in a photograph on the wall, cost over $250.

On this occasion, Madame was simply dressed in a heavy latex rubber short-skirted black dress with buckled shoes and black stockings. She asked me what treatment I wanted, and I told her I liked to be corrected with the cane. We then went up to the next floor and at the top of the stairs was a large cupboard which she told me was the punishment cupboard. Opening the door, she pointed out the various securing straps, etc., and told me that usually the client would be dressed in latex restrictive clothing, bound and gagged, and shut in the cupboard to reflect on his misdeeds and the punishment he would soon receive. I did not sample this treatment on my first visit, but Madame explained that punishment should always be linked to misdeeds and that the right atmosphere should be created before she gave a whipping. She also suggested that to relax in rubber garments and read some suitable literature before she appeared would be helpful in creating the right relationship.

We then entered the punishment room and I immediately realized that Madame was a dedicated exponent of the art. The walls were lined with every type of punishment – canes, whips, switches, cats, birches, etc., and also line drawings of whippings and torturing! As to equipment, the room was full of it, the place of honor in the center being the whipping horse, a heavy metal frame with rungs and a mirror at its head. There was also a chromium apparatus for stretching out the victim, rather like the historic rack. Two other pieces of apparatus I did not discover the use for, made of wood, were near the walls. There was also a couch which I suspected could be stripped to reveal some other piece of apparatus.

Madame told me to undress and put on the pair of thin latex briefs I had brought with me and then left the room so that, after doing as I was told, I had the chance to look round. On this occasion, she did not dress up in her more striking equipment nor did she dress me in any of her rubberwear. But when she returned, she carried a latex mask which she put over my head and fastened tightly round the neck. I was then ordered to stand at the foot of the whipping horse and bend over it. She strapped on leather wrist straps and a leather collar round my neck. I was on tiptoe as she secured my legs with other straps and tightened a thick cord round my midlde. She then told me she would give me a warming up with the cat across my bottom to make it tingle. This she did most efficiently and I found the stinging pain quite stimulating.

Madame then said she was going to give me 50 strokes with the cane. She started with a thin one over my briefs, using it hard and efficiently until she found it was cutting the skin. She then removed the briefs and continued with a thicker cane avoiding the damaged areas. This was the most severe treatment I had ever had, but I did not cry out or beg for mercy. To complete the treatment she gave me massage with an electric vibrator before releasing me.

Her fee was very modest and her personality such that I looked forward to visting her again. I anticipate relaxing in rubber, trying the dark cupboard treatment, asking to be tightly corseted, and for her to wear more bizarre rubber garments.

She obviously felt that the session would be more exciting for both parties if a realistic fantasy setting was introduced and if there was a misdeed calling for corrective treatment. In such an atmosphere she would give the punishment under strict discipline, counting strokes and repeating some penitential phrase with additional strokes if mistakes were made. She also said she would require the client to kiss the cane or whip.

This lady told me she would never give treatment just for money; she had to enjoy the session herself and she was quite prepared to refuse treatment if the wrong approach was made. One could feel that she was sincere, out to give what the client wanted, discreet and very honest.

V.H.

Sadomasochism is one of the most interesting and puzzling aspects of human sexuality. Many people cannot understand how there can be so much pleasure in pain; yet many others find it almost impossible to achieve sexual pleasure and release without this experience. Frequently the pain is only symbolic; occasionally it has to be severe. Similarly, there are those who can achieve sexual pleasure only by giving pain.

Sadists can range from the man who heightens his own and his partner's sexual pleasure by biting or playfully slapping, to the individual who has to use whips, canes and other pain-inflicting devices to derive sexual excitement. Many sadists need to feel in complete control and also to experience a response,

44

and the infliction of pain certainly produces a response, from the receiver. Within control and kept at a more or less symbolic level, a bit of sadism, or un peu-sauvage as the French say, can be a stimulant to lovemaking.

Masochism similarly runs the gamut from the desire to be bitten playfully to the need for very strong pain to obtain gratification. The desire is actually not pain, but the pleasure of release. Pain, like other strong physical stimuli, is closely associated with sexuality, so while the pain is endured, the goal is still pleasure.

A great many people become involved in this kind of sexual play at an early age when they are beaten across the buttocks, sometimes while placed across the knees of the punishing adult. In such a position the genitals are in contact with the knees. Slapping the buttocks, which are close to the genital area, causes an engorgement of blood in that area which produces the sexual excitement. Having experienced this excitement in childhood, many people remain fixated at that level and continue to look for the same excitement in sexual activity later in life.

Some children even court the displeasure of their parents in order to enjoy the voluptuous feelings of being slapped. The French philosopher Jean Jacques Rousseau, for example, relates that when he was about 10 years old he got so much sexual pleasure from being spanked by his governess that she became aware of his response and had his bed removed from her room because she was so embarrassed.

Another explanation for the prevalence of masochistic fantasies and desires is the feeling of guilt about sexuality which so many people still suffer from. The masochism then serves a triple purpose: (1) The masochist considers himself the victim of another person's sexual assault. (2) He feels he is being punished for his sexual feelings. (3) He has physical stimulation which leads to sexual release. The masochist may also really be a 'secret' sadist and derive pleasure from identifying with the one who administers the beating.

Sadism and masochism, while most commonly associated with sexuality, can also be found in many popular sports – for example, bull fighting and cock fighting, as well as boxing and wrestling – which involve a strong sadistic element. The onlooker obtains pleasure by identifying with the person administering the pain, or if he is masochistic, by indentifying with the recipient of the pain. – H.G.

SADDLES HUSBAND

My husband thinks he's a horse. Well, not all the time and he certainly has no aspirations to win the Grand National. But he's a horse alright. At least five nights a week. He'll strip naked, get down on all fours and having already dressed in jodhpurs and riding cap I'll throw a saddle over him, straddle his waist, and duly mounted we ride around the room. I'll also cut his flanks with a riding crop and it is all a prelude to sexual intercourse when in fact I am mounted by the 'horse.'

I'll admit to enjoying this which gives me sexual satisfaction but until I read Forum I was worried about the deviation. Is it normal for male partners to associate themselves with animals? Perhaps my husband carries it too far for he'll ride around the room for perhaps an hour whinnying to the whip. Lately he's also asked permission to build a special stable in a corner of the bedroom in which to store his equipment and stock. But the real fly in the ointment is, am I doing wrong by jockeying along?

Mrs. J.R.

The 'Horse' fantasy is one of the most common masochistic obsessions and is so old that an early medieval woodcut depicts Aristotle as being ridden by a famous Athenian courtesan. Your husband, therefore, is in ancient and honourable company.

We assume that your husband still spends most of his life on two feet rather than on four legs and that he hasn't taken to consuming hay instead of steaks.

But you might try to cut the one hour to rather less – or he may become too tired to come to the point. – F.

TALLYHO!

It is difficult to fully understand the motivations of these men who prefer flagellistic practices as a prelude to intercourse instead of the highly erotic and stimulating art of female adornment. I find this to be an anomalous situation, inasmuch as the wearing of pretty or provocative clothing is so much more sexually stimulating than being laid into with a whip.

As for me, I find my wife's wearing of riding clothes to be a most powerful sexual stimulant. My wife took up this worthy sport sometime ago and for the purpose, bought herself a skin-tight pair of fawn breeches and a pair of long black leather boots. She wears these with a white shirt, appropriately close fitting over her breasts and, beneath all, a pair of long stretch nylon panties of a charming light blue color.

The immediate fear of bankruptcy due to the high cost of getting astride the noble beast was at once mitigated by the sight of my wife, a comely woman with an hourglass figure and deep breasts, clad in this sheath-fitting attire which was enough to set my eyeballs bulging. In fact, it so much enhanced our love-making, she only has to dress the part, whether to ride or not, and we have achieved a new and exciting relationship, and this after 17 years of marriage! From my wife's point of view, the stimulation of opening her thighs to get astride a horse and the subsequent jogging motion often arouses her desires to the pitch where only a long session of lovemaking can assuage them.

Thus, the innocent sport of horse riding has stimulated our desires in a way we find wholly delightful

J.K.

VOYEUR

My husband is a Peeping Tom. Not a very serious crime, you may think. To most people it's just a rather funny thing to joke about. If the women who are peeped at are annoyed they can always close their curtains. But living with someone who's quite preoccupied with peeping as a pastime involves a lot of problems that are not obvious to the outsider. Living with my husband is slowly driving me mad.

We have been married eight years. For the first year or so I wasn't even aware of his peculiarity. He used to complain of insomnia and stay up after I went to bed. I used to think it helped his headaches to sit in the dark alone until, one night, I felt so sorry for him I decided to get up and sit with him in the living room. To my amazement I found him in the darkened room gazing intently into a neighbor's window.

His secret out, he invited me to join him. In just the right position we could see between the opening of the curtains a couple making love. I was frankly a bit peeved that we weren't doing likewise. Anyway, I didn't say anything and he started telling me of the activities of all our neighbors; some of them people I hadn't even noticed before. But he knew who left the bathroom window open when they went to the toilet, the teenage boy who masturbated with his light on, and the young girl

47

opposite who had two boyfriends. He was almost in a frenzy the night she entertained them on the bed in a threesome.

We spent hours sitting in the dark at the open window. I might add that none of these entertainments added to our sex life; they seemed sufficient excitement in themselves. He watches and then goes to bed happy. Soon after watching the sexy threesome, he invested in a pair of quite expensive binoculars with the money we had been saving for a new couch in the living room. I was upset, but it didn't really matter because we moved soon afterward. We have moved five times in the past eight years; always because he's had a row with one of the neighbors, or it's been difficult to travel to work, or the flat is too cold, etc. I know better now. It's when he's exhausted the local viewing.

Over the years we've not only wasted a lot of money we can't afford in these moves, and a lot of effort, but I never can feel my home is secure or permanent. Every time I get the place somewhere near what I want, we move on again. And, of course, he's been buying bigger and better binoculars and a telescope even. He has found a flat on the tenth floor of a block and is thinking of moving again soon.

At this point I've become quite desperate. Trying to reason with him has got me nowhere.

Is there any cure for a Peeping Tom?

Mrs. R.B.

Voyeurism, also known as scoptophilia or mixoscopia, is one of the commonest deviations. Peeping Toms find satisfaction in watching the 'forbidden'. In many cases it isn't even necessary to see the act itself performed, at least not under normal conditions. For some voyeurs, the sight of the genital organs of a member of the opposite sex is sufficient. Others are satisfied by the simple fact of seeing a woman clambering up a steep place or balancing herself in an armchair in a provocative position. Others find pleasure in watching the copulation of animals, still others in watching defecation or urination.

On the whole this is the most innocent of all abnormalities – because it is very difficult to draw the line of demarcation between normality and the first symptoms of the morbid state. Nor are there any guiding principles for the treatment of voyeurism – since the same reactions are produced as a rule in different patients by various causes; the first task of the phys-

ician is to discover that cause. It seems to us that you could try to get your husband to seek professional help. – F.

SEX GAMES

I have been reading Forum for a year, and am surprised that there is not more correspondence on games one can play. My wife and I have made up a game which takes the form of a draw. My wife writes down on pieces of paper the many different ways she enjoys having sex and I do the same. We then toss up to see who has the first draw. Of course we also have a joker on each set, so it may backfire on the person who thinks what they want is going to happen. We play this game often and find that it brightens our sex life.

J.C.

BREASTFEEDING PLEASURES

I am a young woman aged 20. I was married when I was 16, my husband then being 22.

My case centers around my breasts; I am not very tall and rather slim but I have a full 35-inch bust. My breasts are not enormous but they are very prominent, set high on my chest and are firm. I have never needed the support of a bra which I have never yet worn. My breasts were well developed by the time I was 13 and even at that age I had large prominent nipples.

I started going out with Jack my husband when I was about 15 and I soon realized how sensitive my breasts and nipples were when Jack began to fondle me in the cinema or out in the fields and woods at weekends. I always became very excited when he fondled my breasts, and my nipples always grew large and firm. After a period of kissing and fondling in this way a few light touches of Jack's fingers on my clitoris were sufficient to bring me to orgasm. In fact I would sometimes climax when he stroked between my thighs or round the lips of my sex, and many times he made me come off several times in an evening. Jack always liked to bare my breasts and see the nipples grow, and he always remarked on how lovely they were. He said that it got him randy to see them.

When we got married soon after I was 16 we got our cottage out here in the country and since then we have always enjoyed our sex. With constant handling from Jack my breasts seemed to become firmer than ever and the nipples grew even bigger so that they always protruded and were distinctly visible through my dresses and sweaters.

During loveplay my breasts and nipples were always very sensitive and the nipples received a lot of attention from my husband until they became really enormous. He loved to roll and suck them which gave me great pleasure and always made me ready for sex in a very short time. In our rather secluded cottage I often went about naked or at least naked above the waist knowing that Jack liked to see me like this. After a time we decided to have a baby while we were young and I became pregnant and had my darling baby boy just before I was 18.

I fed my baby myself right from the start and I found it to be very satisfying and lovely. When I first came into milk my breasts had filled out to a full 38 inches which looked gigantic on a girl of my modest size. I soon found that I became sexually roused when I fed my baby, Peter, and I frequently played with myself.

As Peter became a little older I began to play a game with him when feeding him, particularly in the afternoons before he had his sleep. I would take him upstairs and lie naked on the bed and allow him to crawl over me. He quickly learned where to find his feed and I let him feed on me as he liked. I still feed him a couple of times a day and always in the afternoon.

Sometimes I lay him on the bed and kneel over him with my breasts hanging down over his face and I let him feed on me like this. This always gets me excited and I play with myself. Sometimes while I am kneeling over Peter when he has finished milking me I play with him, blowing raspberries on his chest and tummy, and he chuckles and giggles with glee.

My husband has been working as a truck driver for the past year, and he is away most weeks from Monday to Friday on long distance runs, often going over to the continent. While we have a very full sex life most weekends I still miss his attentions during the week, and my pleasure from feeding Peter doesn't make up for this although it goes part way. Jack keeps telling me that I should stop feeding Peter now, but I enjoy it so much and Jack likes my nipples in their present state of fullness so much that I don't want to stop.

Could you advise me if it is good to go on feeding a child who is now two, as I am doing? Will it affect my health or breast size and shape? Will my nipples revert to their previous size if I stop? Also is it good for Peter to allow him to feed on me for so long? Will it make him a breast fetishist in later life?

Mrs T.M.

The fact that you become sexually roused while breast-feeding your son is not particularly surprising, neither is it difficult to explain. The breast, and especially the nipple, is one of the body's erotogenic areas. Other well-known erotic areas include the lobes of the ear, the small of the back, the genitals, and the inner aspects of the thighs.

To varying degrees most women respond with sexual arousal when some or all of these areas are manually stimulated. Like you many women enjoy breastfeeding and quite a number become sexually roused. However, most mothers accept the sexual pleasure as secondary to the main object of the exercise, which after all is providing the infant with nourishment. For you the exercise has become purely sexual – after all, there are no nutritional reasons for breastfeeding a small boy until the age of two. Furthermore, the fact that you feed him while naked and masturbate yourself, very clearly has nothing to do with his dietary requirements.

Constant stimulation of the type you describe, of your breasts and nipples, might produce a very slight enlargement of these organs, but I would stress that appreciable increases in size would be unlikely unless you were receiving almost constant stimulation throughout most of the day. For your professed requirement of an erect full nipple, such time-consuming activities are not required since like the erect penis, the erect nipple bears little relationship to its nonstimulated size. You appear to have exceptionally sensitive nipples and breasts, which respond promptly and erotically to manual stimulation.

If your intention is to further increase your breast size by feeding Peter, then you are largely wasting your time. You will, of course, enjoy the experience since, on your own admission, you simply like having your breasts and nipples caressed. If you stop your activities there will be a tendency for both your breast and nipples to become smaller. However, this again will be negligible since following pregnancy and lactation there are permanent structural changes which preclude the breast from returning to its pre-pregnant state.

Regarding any possible untoward effects on Peter, it is theo-

retically possible that later on in life he might become obsessed with female breasts, but this is by no means certain. It is unlikely that he will remember being breastfed providing you stop now.

If it is important to your husband and yourself that you have prominent nipples, you could massage them daily using a little lanolin. While not increasing them in size from their present dimensions, it would tend to keep them physically in good condition. Your husband could augment your efforts by spending more time fondling your breasts and nipples during lovemaking. – F.

MALE NIPPLE SENSITIVITY

As a boy I used to get acute tickling sensations when my nipples were touched by clothing or, if I was not wearing a shirt, by the wind blowing across them. I could not bear to touch them under any circumstances, and washing in that area, or the touch of the doctor's cold stethoscope, were excruciating. I used to pray that this sensitivity would vanish as I got older.

But now I'm deeply grateful that this didn't happen! I've just recently discovered that I get fantastic sexual pleasure from having my nipples tickled by my girlfriend. It gives me a wonderful erection and a sensual feeling all over, though I cannot come to orgasm by this alone. Is it unusual for a man to be sexually stimulated in this manner?

D.B.

Your highly 'eroticized' nipples are not so unusual as you might think! Although the phenomenon is generally more apparent in females who, for obvious biological reasons, have bigger and more developed nipples, structurally the nipple is homologous (comparable) to the male penis. Thus it becomes erect in precisely the same way and to the same type of predominantly tactile (touching) stimulation as that organ. It is this structural and behavioral similarity of the nipple to the penis which makes the former's erotogenicity more understandable.

Masters and Johnson reported in Human Sexual Response, *'As a source of erotic stimulation male breasts and nipples seldom are manipulated directly during heterosexual activity. However, breast stimulation does constitute a significant seg-*

ment of male homosexual activity. As a result, the nipples and even the anterior chest wall develop erotogenic qualities seldom found in the heterosexually oriented male.'

On reading this, I could not see why homosexuals should be thus sensitive and not heterosexuals; and it occurred to me that perhaps the latter could develop such sensitivity by regular stimulation. I asked 15 of my heterosexual friends, who sometimes help me with experiments but who had never thought of their nipples as a sensitive zone, to undertake some research for me. At the end of three months of daily stimulation of the nipples, 11 reported that theirs were definitely sensitive, four that theirs were not at all. The 11 manifested varying degrees of sensitivity, from bringing about erection by nipple-stimulation only, to extremely pleasant erotic responses only after erection had taken place. Six found that they were nipple-sensitive at the first trial, but increased the degree of sensitivity with regular stimulation. Three began to be aware of sensitivity at the end of the first week; two not until several weeks of perseverance. Three, who were highly sexed, could be brought off through nipple-stimulation alone.

In my view, it is well worth trying to develop nipple-sensitivity, because if it can be achieved, it adds a new experience to lovemaking. – F.

EROGENOUS ZONES

Every man knows about the part a woman's nipples and clitoris should play in lovemaking, so I was surprised, when I first started sleeping with my present girlfriend, to find that caresses in these areas, though pleasant, did not produce any marked effect and that she really only became aroused when intercourse began. This did not prevent her having an orgasm; but obviously there were difficulties in penetration since she would not be lubricated.

When I finally got up the courage to ask her whether there were any particular caresses that would excite her, she said that the sexiest thing anyone could do to her was to bite her ears and kiss her throat, preferably with a day's growth of stubble, also scratching the back of her neck, or clutching and biting it, during lovemaking. It certainly worked!

Now, having read Desmond Morris's *The Naked Ape,* I see

that my girlfriend's sensitivity in these areas is not so surprising. Morris believes that the only function of the ear-lobes is sexual; apparently they are composed of erectile tissue. He also points out that among many animals the male bites the back of the female's neck during coupling.

Her nipples were not responsive to gentle caresses – she tended to giggle, if anything, being rather ticklish and I had more or less given up playing with her breasts until I read the recommendation to stimulate them by hard pressure with the flat of the hand. This technique gave her the first specifically erotic, rather than merely pleasant, sensations in the breasts and as a result, they are now becoming more sensitive to more orthodox forms of caress.

P.H.

DEFINING 'NORMAL'

Several nights ago, my friends and I had a most vociferous session – the theme being, what is 'normal' when it comes to sex. One group insisted that sexual normalcy depended on the particular mores of the culture in which you live. Thus, in Great Britain, the sexual practices and beliefs of the majority decided what was normal and what was abnormal.

I was very much against this view, I strongly feel that there is no such thing as 'normality' when it comes to sex. Each human being should be free to decide for himself what he considers 'normal', and so long as he does not cause any pain, injury or embarrassment to himself or to his partner, whatever he does will be 'normal' by his standards.

U.L.

The criterion of normality is one question which the psychiatrist, along with his fellow behavioral scientists, the psychologist and the sociologist, cannot answer. One hears talk of statistical norms and moral norms, of personal norms and social norms. But no matter how we slice it, a norm is a relative thing.

The sexual thinking of early psychologists and psychiatrists tended to follow religio-legal lines, and by today's standards would be considered as archaic. For example, pioneer sexologists Krafft-Ebing and Havelock Ellis considered masturbation 'shameful', 'perverted', 'degenerate' and 'disgusting' –

terms straight from the moralist's lexicon. Indeed, in Psychopathia Sexualis, *Krafft-Ebing goes so far as to suggest that an adult's indulgence in masturbation is a 'functional sign of degeneration' and the result of his 'moral sense' being 'too far gone to allow consideration of the moral significance of the act, and resistance to the impulse.'*

Our view is that sexual normality and abnormality are personal and subjective concepts. What is unnatural to one man is natural to another. What is abnormal under certain circumstances may be completely normal under others. And, in any event, to be different is not necessarily to be wrong, or to be 'sick'.

This does not mean that sexual behavior is never pathological. However, if we are to take it upon ourselves to pronounce an act as sick or abnormal, let us take care to meet the same standards which we observe with respect to physical illness. We treat a sore throat or a broken arm not because it is 'abnormal' or because it is 'immature'. We treat it because it hinders the patient's functioning. Let this, then, be the criterion by which we judge sexual behavior.

If the performance of a specific sex act hinders a person's functioning, then therapy is called for. However, if the performance of an act does not hinder the individual's functioning, let us recognize this act as 'His choice', though it may be considered by society as anti-social or even immoral. – F.

PRIVATE PARTS

I could never show my private parts to a man and the thought of 'explorations' fills me with revulsion. A woman's organs are not attractive and why any man should want to poke around down there except for perverted pleasure mystifies me. No man can find it a thing of beauty.

I like sex as much as anyone but no man is going to use my private parts to get a cheap thrill. Perhaps it is unfortunate that that part of a woman is made that way but the fact is that it is a very unpleasant looking, smelly and messy part of our body. A woman is better keeping it to herself.

Miss H.W.

It is unfortunate that so many women have come to regard

55

their genital area as somehow unclean. Much of this feeling relates back to (1) the attitude that sex is unclean and all parts of the body connected with sex are dirty, and (2) the idea that women in our society are sometimes considered inferior, therefore their organs are inferior. Consequently many women project on to their male partner the same feelings of disgust with the female genitalia. Those men who have been able to overcome this feeling find the female genitals, particularly of the woman they love, highly acceptable and exciting parts. – R.G.

A FRENCH LETTER

I have noticed that several of your female correspondents were worried about the odor of genitalia which they considered to be repugnant. At the same time, many men have stated that they would indulge in cunnilingus only on the condition that it is preceded by a very complete intimate toilet.

I would now like to give the French point of view which is very different from those of your readers, and that is, this is a 'sacrilege'. For a real man, what perfume can be more delicious, more exciting, more tantalizing than the 'parfum naturel' of the female?

What pleasure can one experience with a woman who emits from her sacred place the odor of soap or eau de cologne? One might as well make love to a sponge or wash cloth!

J.I.

EROTIC ODOR

I think J.I. can be reassured that many Englishmen do enjoy to the full the savoring of their beloved's *parfum naturel* as he so delicately puts it. Surely many must enjoy the ecstatic delights of cunnilingus and find it an experience second only to orgasm itself.

There is the classic story of the lover who prevailed on his mistress never to wash those parts which were most dear to him but to allow him to use his tongue for all such ablutions. At the other end of the scale is Van De Velde's requirement that the genital kiss shall only occur where scrupulous cleanliness exists. I cannot help feeling for many men that the woman is at her most attractive when in a condition halfway between these extremes. Surely there can be no doubt that the actual reason for performing cunnilingus is the overwhelming desire on the part of the man to savor by smell and taste that most endearing and most responsive part of woman. A freshly washed, and worse, shaved vulva can only be compared with a gorgeous rose which has no scent: the experience of either is a great disappointment. Whether we realize it or not, the sense of smell has a great deal to do with love, and this is certainly so where cunnilingus is concerned.

The worst offenders against that happy state of possessing *parfum naturel* are those who believe correct hygiene demands twice-daily vulval washing and those who seldom wash anyway. Nylon pants and tights offend by preventing the natural evaporation of sweat so that bacterial activity on the skin increases and leads to unpleasantness. My ideal girl will, therefore, perform a careful vulval toilet on alternate days; she will wear cotton pants (or in warm weather, none at all) and she will at all costs avoid that newcomer to the toilet range, the vulval and vaginal deodorant.

Lastly, may I give a word of advice to my fellow man. Having savored the delights of cunnilingus, be careful to remove all traces of the *parfum naturel* from your face before continuing intercourse. Most women are fastidious enough not to relish a face-to-face encounter with their own *parfum*, however *naturel* it may so wonderfully be.

Dr. L.S.

USE OF THE SENSES

I was very interested to read the comments of Dr. L.S. on erotic odor, and I heartily agree with him. I have proved the increase in sexual appreciation by using to the full the senses of touch, smell, taste and vision. The subtle tastes and smells that linger are happy memories and stimuli to greater delights.

Ironically, I learned to appreciate the importance of the senses in lovemaking from two women who were sharing a flat. They received stimulation from every one of the senses, and for sheer physical delight, they utilized my 'services' from time to time, and taught me how to enjoy all the nuances of sex, an area in which few men are learned.

One particular bit of loveplay I'll never forget was as follows. They placed me naked on my back across a narrow divan with a cushion under my buttocks and my head slightly lower than my body, resting on a stool. One of the women would kneel across my face, away from me, presenting a truly wonderful view. The other woman would mount and face her friend, kneeling astride my face. As she worked herself further and further onto my penis she would lean slightly and press my legs down, causing me to seesaw upward and forced my face and nose deep into the soft sexual parts of the woman over me. This heightened her excitement and was, of course, very pleasurable to me. When my forehead contacted the base of the spine and took some of her weight off her knees she thrilled and came to a climax.

Needless to say, they had great imagination – an ingredient sadly lacking in most people. If lovers used their senses and imaginations to the full, they would experience sexual sensations they never knew existed.

D.P.

Some of the newer therapies, particularly the nonverbal ones, are concentrating on the fuller use of all the senses. They hold that through increased awareness involving all the senses a person can experience greater feelings of aliveness, being, joy and sensuality – certainly one aspect of which is the increased sexual appreciation described by D.P. – R.G.

DOUBLE COUPLING

My husband and I are on our way back home from a delayed, but most exciting honeymoon. We stayed at a beautiful hotel just outside Athens. It has its own private bay around the perimeter of which are a number of delightful, furnished bungalows serviced from the hotel. It was in one of these bungalows that we were installed.

On the evening of our arrival we swam and sunbathed and made the acquaintance of another very young English couple. They occupied the next bungalow to ours and invited us in for a glass of champagne before we changed for dinner.

When we arrived at their bungalow the girl was reading an article about sexual behavior. Before long, with more champagne to break down inhibitions, we began discussing the varied range of subjects which come under the theme of sex.

Another factor which enhanced our mutual interest was our

difference in coloring. I am a true platinum blonde, my husband is very dark, the girl a chestnut redhead and her husband fair.

Before parting for the evening, we touched on the subject of male anatomy and were of the opinion that the penile statistics we had read about were below normal. We tried to persuade the two men to let us take their personal measurements, a suggestion to which they eventually reluctantly agreed. However, the conditions were that the measuring would take place on the following evening and that we girls would do the measuring. Next day we met our friends, while sunbathing, and my husband and I felt very shy about what had been said the previous evening. This was not true of our friends, who said how they were both looking forward to the return party in our bungalow that evening.

Champagne is a wonderful substance – by 6.30 p.m. our friends were with us, and the girl had brought along a tape measure. They were ready for anything.

Removing our dressing gowns we two girls took each man separately into the bedroom and quickly confirmed our views.

My husband was first and his dark hair seemed to thrill the other girl to such an extent that she encouraged him a little, and this caused his already erect penis to extend well over an inch more. After this we felt it only fair to take him the whole way.

Then we brought in the girl's husband. He admitted that he had been watching us and this showed clearly because of his massive erection. Again with a little encouragement, from me this time, we produced the same effect as with my husband.

To reciprocate my encouragement, he insisted on kissing me and with his wife aiding and abetting, we did a supreme '69' while his wife looked on, her hands active between her thighs.

With the 'Ice' so well broken after only two days, we spent all our evenings together. While sunbathing during the day, we devised many geometrical patterns to find positions for two men and two girls, to produce orgasms simultaneously.

Every evening was a super thrill, particularly our last night together, before the other two had to return home. We devoted the evening to what we called 'ménage à trois' – the two girls and one man or one girl and two men.

The sensation of having two large organs inside at the same time, I shall never forget. The other girl was so excited, we thought at first that she would pass out. The men were equally thrilled and while talking about it afterwards over more champagne, they gave evident signs that the evening was not over.

No doubt many people will consider our actions to be immoral or even degenerate. We couldn't disagree more. The four of us agree that there is nothing immoral about the sheer, unadulterated, uninhibited enjoyment of sex if those involved are not forced into it or hurt in any way, and are doing it because they enjoy what they're doing.

My husband and I are very much in love with one another, and we derive great pleasure from sex. It was especially stimulating for me to see the tremendous enjoyment he got out of our sexual activities with the other couple. Rather than detracting, it enhanced our love for one another.

What we disapprove of in marriage is the infidelity whereby one of the partners has sexual relations with a third party, without the consent or knowledge of the mate. We feel that this type of sexual activity can be destructive to a marriage.

Mrs. P.C.

MILD ZOOPHILIA

I live in a mobile home and have traveled all over Britain and the Continent. I have come across more than one instance of zoophilia in my travels.

In fact, when I and two of my sisters were in our early teens we did much the same thing with our dog; I don't think we came to any harm.

I have a particular lady friend at the moment who practices zoophilia with her dog, a large mongrel. Often she strips naked while doing her housework and allows him to excite her from any position she happens to be in, sometimes making a paste of chocolate powder, sugar, and milk and spreading it on her breasts for him to lick off. She takes the precaution of wearing a kind of plastic apron which is a yard long and two feet wide, behind her, to act as a safeguard if the dog tries to mount her.

Sometimes she has a session with the dog lasting several hours; but on the other hand she may go for weeks without anything at all.

One woman friend of hers also enjoys these practices and comes to stay with her every three months or so for a couple of days merely to enjoy the dog's attentions (she is a married professional woman in the early 50s).

Only once in all the years I have known them do I remember any accident happening: a couple of years ago my friend had discarded her apron and the dog coupled with her 'all the way'. She douched herself afterwards.

My experience leads me to believe that zoophilia, especially in milder forms, may be more common than people think.

C.R.

There is insufficient explanation of the confinement of sexual activity to contacts between females and males of the same species. However, evidence is accumulating that individuals of quite unrelated species do make interspecific contacts more often than biologists have heretofore allowed. It is probable that the human animal makes interspecific sexual contact less often than some of the other species of mammals primarily because he has no close relative among the other mammals and secondarily because of the considerable part played by psychologic stimuli in limiting his sexual activity. It is particularly interesting to note the degree of abhorrence with which intercourse between the human and animals of other species is viewed by most persons who have not had such experience.

Human contacts with animals of other species have been known since the dawn of history. They are known among all races of people today and they are not foreign to our own culture. Far from being a matter for surprise, the record substantiates our present understanding that the forces which bring individuals of the same species together in sexual relations may sometimes serve to bring individuals of different species together in the same type of sexual relations.

Kinsey found that only a fraction of one percent of the total number of male orgasms within the whole population of the U.S.A. came about through animal contact. It was estimated that only one male in 12 or 14 ever has sexual experience with animals. It was, however, discovered that the significance of interspecific relationships becomes more apparent if calculations are confined to that segment of the population which has access to animals, namely to those raised on farms.

Among boys raised on farms about 17 percent experience orgasm as the product of animal contacts occurring sometime after the onset of puberty. As many more have contacts which do not result in orgasm. A fair number of city-bred boys do at some time have animal contact, with household pets, par-

ticularly with dogs. In fact the animals involved in these contacts include practically all the domesticated species on the farm or kept as pets in the household. Because of their convenient size, animals like calves and sheep are most frequently involved. Practically every other mammal that has ever been kept on a farm enters into the record, and a few of the larger birds, like chickens, ducks and geese.

Vaginal coitus is the most frequent technique employed, but it was found that in certain parts of the U.S.A. fellation of the boy by the calf is not uncommon and occasionally the household pets, particularly the dog or the cat, are induced to perform. Masturbation of the animal by the human subject is almost as frequent as vaginal coitus, either on the male or female animal, but most common with the former.

Some 3.6 percent of Kinsey's female sample had sexual contact of some sort with animals after adolescence. In addition to overt experience with animals one percent had animal fantasies while masturbating and a similar sample had dreamt of having animal contacts. In 25 out of 5,793 adult case histories the human female had been brought to orgasm by her sexual contact with animals, chiefly as a result of the animal's manipulation of her genitalia with its mouth. There were six females, each of whom had reached orgasm more than 125 times with animal contacts, and there was one female who had reached orgasm perhaps 900 times with such contacts.

In England, as in most European countries and the United States, there are laws in respects to animal contacts, and prosecution is not uncommon, especially in rural areas. – F.

FELLATIO

I would very much like to know more about the subject of fellatio as my husband, being dubious at first, now permits this occasionally, but fears being hurt. He has twice come to orgasm this way with great pleasure, but on ejaculation is *extremely* tender. Are all men?

I would very much like to perfect the technique and would like to know more about the most sensitive areas to titillate on the penis, whether the tongue or lips or sides of the mouth should be used, and how best to swallow the semen without retching?

Mrs. E.W.

The penis of many men is tender after they have an orgasm, some more so than others, but it disappears within a short time.

To bring the penis to erection by fellatio, the man should lie on his back, his limp penis pointing up towards his navel and the foreskin drawn right back if he is not circumcised. Beginning at the base, near the scrotum, the partner should run the tip of her tongue up the shaft of the penis, pause at the frenum and stimulate it for a few seconds, then begin again at the base of the penis.

After the penis has become erect, either the frenum, the tip just below the opening and under the rim can be titillated with the tip of the tongue, or the penis-head taken completely into the mouth and sucked vigorously, or the two techniques combined. Great care must be taken not to scratch the penis-head with the teeth. Some men also like to have the shaft stroked rapidly with the fingers while the head is being sucked.

If the fellator is sexually roused, she will be making so much saliva that she may not be aware of the semen spurting into her mouth, and she will swallow it with the saliva. If she does retch, it is the result of the imagination. – F.

Experimenting with techniques thought up by the partners is really more satisfactory than a written description.

One of the problems in following written instructions is that many people see this as a mechanical performance rather than something that the individual has thought of spontaneously and enjoys. – R.G.

DEFINITELY SAFE

I am not able to feel confident in sexual relations, because I cannot trace any information on the following subject.

If stimulation is continued to orgasm, my wife occasionally receives semen in her mouth. While I have been advised that digestive juices will dispose of semen which is swallowed in the course of sexual relations, I realize that out of the hundreds of millions of individual sperm, one or two may still be carried into the bloodstream and thence find their way to the ovaries and, at a period which is not 'safe', could cause a pregnancy.

Not desiring an unwanted pregnancy, and as my GP is unable

to *assure* me on it, can you advise me if I should refrain from letting this happen at a period which is not safe'?

P.C.

I can assure P.C. unequivocally, categorically, positively and quite definitely that sperm ingested by the mouth cannot ever reach the bloodstream or the ovary.

Pregnancy cannot even result from oral contact and the swallowing of the ejaculate.

Oral-genital contact is quite safe (from the pregnancy point of view) at any time in the menstrual cycle. – F.

VENEREAL DISEASE BY MOUTH

As a practicing homosexual I am quite often requested to perform fellatio. I don't mind this, but I am worried by the fact that sometimes, not always intentionally, I find that I have swallowed the whole or part of the ejaculate.

Is the risk of venereal disease greater in this manner? How would it show itself if I were to catch it – in the usual manner through a discharge from my own penis? I would very much appreciate guidance on these matters.

J.H.

In general, the ejaculate is curiously free from infections which can be transmitted, provided there is no ulcer on the penis or urethral discharge. As a rule, if the genitalia look healthy, then they probably are free from active infection.

The most dangerous contacts are casual ones, made clothed, under poor conditions, when neither party is known to the other, and no visual examination is possible in a good light.

Because of the discharge and the obvious unhealthiness of the genitalia, few people with active gonorrhea are likely to be subject to oral contact, hence the rarity of oral lesions in this disease. – F.

LESBIAN EXPERIENCE

I have been happily married for six years and my husband and I are suited sexually: we have intercourse at least three times a week. For the past four months, however, my husband has been in the hospital and, as a result, I have been very frustrated sexually.

My friend, Jean, whom I have known since schooldays and who is unmarried, came to spend a weekend with me as I was alone in the house. On the first night after I had had a bath, I put on a mini-dress with nothing underneath and I was sitting in an armchair in front of the fire drinking sherry. My friend was sitting in front of me on the floor with her head resting against my knees. We had both been drinking too much and were rather drunk. The conversation gradually got around to sex and I was telling how much I missed my husband. She asked me if I masturbated and I told her I did but that it brought very little relief. She said 'I don't like to see you like this. Do you think it would help if I relieved you?'

I didn't answer. I had never thought of anything like this before. I know I should have refused but it seemed as if I was helpless. Still squatting on the floor in front of me, Jean turned and faced me and slowly pushed my knees apart. She was very surprised that I was naked underneath. She began rubbing my genitals, gently pulling the lips apart, then squeezing them together and rubbing my clitoris, until I reached a state of excitement I had never known with my husband. She did various other things to me including the insertion of a candle for masturbation purposes. We made love the entire weekend.

After this experience, does that make me a confirmed lesbian or can I recapture the enjoyment I have experienced with my husband when he returns from the hospital?

Mrs. M.T.

Having a sexual experience with another woman does not make a woman a lesbian. Many men and women have had occasional homosexual experiences and have still been able to enjoy heterosexual love. – R.G.

TRANSVESTITE HUSBAND

Could Forum possibly be responsible for putting ideas into people's heads? Your stories of bondage and transvestism seem to have exposed a secret longing in my husband.

I knew he always had a funny interest in these things, because

I could sense his interest whenever he saw a story about transvestites in the newspapers, and also he liked to take me to pubs with drag acts. I tried to ignore this, because I did not want to believe he might have a desire to wear women's clothes.

He has bought Forum since it came on sale, bringing it home for me to read. Again I could feel his excitement whenever we read a letter about transvestism, or about women controlling their husbands.

I worried about this a great deal, but then decided that I might as well know the worst. I reasoned that if my feelings were correct and he did have this quirk, I had better find out now rather than years later. In which case I would then have to decide whether I could tolerate it.

Matters came to a head while discussing a letter in Forum suggesting that men wear panty girdles as a 'chastity belt'. I began to tease him, saying that I should make him wear girl's panties to keep him faithful. He would then be too ashamed to have an affair lest it be discovered that he wore lingerie.

Although it started as a joke, his reaction left me in no doubt that he liked the idea. I began to insist that he put them on, accompanied by nylons and suspender belt. When he agreed to this I was sure of my ground. After he had worn these garments under his normal clothes for a few weeks we began to discuss the subject openly. He admitted his desire to dress up, but hesitated to do it voluntarily. He likes to feel that he is being compelled to dress in women's clothes.

I decided to go to the limit, and thus 'made' him wear skirts and blouses around the house, and nighties in bed, and also bought a wig and women's shoes in his size.

I thought I would be repelled by having a husband in dresses but this was not the case. Our sex life has improved dramatically as he gets intensely sexy when dressed up. Although I would have preferred my man to be normal, I find that his oddity does not make me love him any less.

If matters remained at this stage, I would not be worried, but I am concerned that his desires could become stronger. Our sexual games involve him being tied to the bed in women's clothes, and me on top, where I tease and masturbate him before making love.

Sometimes we pretend that he is really a girl and has no penis when we fondle each other until he can resist the urge no longer, and we then complete the act of love. At these times I

66

threaten to throw away all his male clothes and keep him permanently in skirts, when the words almost always bring him into instant orgasm.

He also gets tremendously excited at the idea of having his beard removed and having hormone treatment to give him breasts.

This is my concern, for while I do not mind (and rather enjoy) the present state of affairs, I'm not sure that I want matters to go any further. As long as his dressing up is a private matter at home I am prepared to tolerate and even encourage it. Yet if the urge within him gets stronger, and he begins to want to live as a woman all the time, then our families, our employers, friends and neighbors would all make our marriage impossible.

Therefore I hope you can offer some advice on the matter, as I dare not ask my doctor.

D.R.

It is difficult to know precisely whether you condemn or congratulate Forum for your present situation; probably it is true to say a bit of both. Certainly you indicate, in glowing terms, that your sex life has improved dramatically, although at the same time you express concern over your husband's increasing desire to assume the 'female role', even to the extent of growing breasts, etc. On the information presented it would appear that your husband is progressing beyond the stage of transvestism into transsexualism. This is characterized not only by a desire to dress as a female, but to assume the appropriate physical and psychological attributes as well (this applies both to non-sexual as well as sexual situations). Indeed, as you probably already know, both male and female transsexualists have submitted themselves to extensive surgery and hormone treatment to become equipped with the external (but not internal) genitalia of the opposite sex. These 'sex change' operations, however, cannot change the biological sex of the recipient; normally this is determined at the time of conception and remains fixed throughout life. In short, it is not biologically possible at present to change a man into a woman, and vice versa.

Patterns of behavior are either established, or extinguished, according to 'reward-punishment' principles. Simply, this means that any behavior which is gratifying or pleasurable, in some way tends to be repeated, and established as permanent. This is certainly true for sexual behavior and there is the possibility that your obvious encouragement of your husband's sexual practices, coupled with the intense satisfaction it brings you both, may enhance the possibility of the development of the complete transsexual syndrome.

While apprehensive, your letter appears to suggest that you wish the status quo to be retained. This is just possible and may possibly be achieved by offering no further encouragement than at present. However, if you wish a reversal to former patterns of sexual behavior, it will be necessary to frankly discourage him from pursuing his present behavior, although this may have the complication of pushing him into seeking gratification elsewhere. Notwithstanding, this is a risk you may decide to accept. If things get out of hand and you are resolved to seek a change your best bet is professional help.

In conclusion, it is in my opinion unlikely that any magazine or newspaper story has caused your husband's transvestism. Sexual identity and practices are apparently laid down in early life and tend to become fixed by late adolescence. It seems likely that with your approval and encouragement, former tendencies have re-emerged. – F.

PORNOGRAPHY PLEASURES

My husband loves photographs of couples having sex and has a large collection showing every possible position. He also enormously enjoys books and films on the same subject. He thinks I share his interest but I merely go along with this because we have wonderful sex together afterwards and because I love him.

I wish you could explain this enjoyment of pornography to me. Most men enjoy it in all forms – but perhaps a lot of women don't because of their strict upbringing. I'm not in the least puritanic. I love sex and had more than a few affairs before I was married but I really do dislike 'dirty' pictures. It tends to put me off rather than excite me.

I think I would enjoy a film with a competent, attractive actress playing opposite a good actor, both enacting a believable love story, the film following through with both going to bed and passionately making love together. But unfortunately all the sex films I've seen are made with frowsy looking whores playing for a few minutes at being housewives, then when some dirty looking grocery boy or such-like knocks on her door, she immediately drops her drawers. They have uninspired sexual contact, deliberately moving as directed for the best view of their genitals. Could it be that men have a greater imagination than women and transform this crude material into something better than it really is?

Mrs. R.R.

PORNOGRAPHY AND ART

One of the most pathetic sights I know is that of a married man furtively secreting a packet of pornography and saying with a smirk, 'I mustn't let the wife see these or she'll go crazy.'

Why not let her see them? Art is the exercise of imagination on our environment, distilled through imagination and experience into paintings, books, plays, films, music etc., for our mutual benefit and satisfaction. It heightens our appreciation and understanding of the world we live in and provides us with essential relief from the increasing tensions of modern living. Because of twisted social and moral attitudes, sex in art, which is all that pornography is, has been driven underground and its standard is therefore appallingly low. If it became accepted and our obscenity laws were swept away, then Mrs. R.R. would not have to look at films of tatty little whores and spotty grocery boys. The standard would rise to a level that she would find acceptable and, as she suggests, enjoyable.

It is a truism that without the civilizing influence of a woman, a man produces abject behavior patterns and quite twisted attitudes. Sexual art has been one of the worst sufferers and if the furtive little man would attempt a real relationship with his wife (which would include his interest in pornography), not only might he be surprised at her reaction but he might help to raise pornography above the dismal level where it has languished.

A.T.

NUDES FOR WOMEN?

An event occurred in our office the other day which surprised me in many ways.

A woman brought an American nudist magazine into the

69

office and it was not very long before some of her female friends were invited to look at it, which they all did. I observed that they did not skim over the pages but looked at every one carefully, sometimes making observations such as 'Isn't he nice' and 'Don't they look cute'.

During the day every female in the building looked at this magazine and some of them, on the excuse of showing their friends, went through the pictures two or three times. This surprised me as some of them were married and had often stated that they were not interested in the human male's form.

Dr. Kinsey has stated that 83% of females were just not interested in nude pictures. On the strength of my evidence that day I would say that 100% of the female sex were definitely interested.

I would add that the pictures were all in color and unretouched and I would also add that it was quite clear that all the males were circumcised. I did not see a single foreskin and that may have proved a point of added interest. It was most noticeable that the picture most of the females kept looking at again and again was of a male showing a very clear and detailed picture of a very large and very red glans. A little later an English nudist magazine came into the office showing the male form. Not one male was circumcised in the whole book. In contrast the females showed no interest in this magazine.

The comparison of the magazines of the two countries did prove to me beyond a shadow of doubt the difference of opinion on the subject of circumcision held by these two countries.

The above report should make every circumcised man just that bit more 'cocksure' of himself.

J.W.

BREAST FIXATION

I just cannot become permanently interested in a partner unless she has very large breasts (and I mean very large), a circumstance which has brought me considerable unhappiness. I am in my early thirties, considered not unattractive, reasonably successful, with all the trappings which go with this, and consequently I've never been short of attractive girlfriends. My last girlfriend had a 40-inch bust and 25-inch waist.

Once I thought a great deal about someone who did not meet

70

my physical requirements, and although I tried hard to put down my feelings the results were disastrous.

I have within me this all-consuming urge to find anyone who might be the right partner, and I find physically a tremendous reservoir of affection building up for someone, who because of my peculiarity/fetish, call it what you will, I will never find. Hence my unhappiness. Is there any explanation for this powerful attraction to large breasts?

F.K.

THE BIGGER THEY COME

Like most other men, I become very stimulated when I meet a woman or even see a picture of a woman with large breasts. As a matter of fact, a large bosom is the one thing that will arouse me more than any part of a woman's body when it comes to lovemaking.

I recently met a very beautiful girl and I think I'm in love with her. She's very intelligent, has a great sense of humor, and has everything that I've ever wanted in a wife – except for the fact that she has very small breasts.

I know it sounds silly and really should not matter, but somehow the fact that she doesn't possess a big bust makes me fear that I will not be able to get the most out of our sexual relations if we were to get married. She has made it plain that she will not consent to our becoming intimate until after we are married.

Is there such a thing as a breast fetishist, or am I mistakenly putting an undue amount of importance on the value of large breasts?

M.T.

The writer M.T. is dealing with a fixation and not a fetish. Interest in women's breasts is certainly very widespread in our society, as exemplified by the rapid growth of topless entertainment and by the large number of movie stars whose talent, in some cases, has consisted chiefly of their ability to fill a D cup. Throughout history, as shown in all the visual arts, there has been considerable interest in women's breasts.

Psychoanalysts frequently explain that because the breast is the first source of nourishment, many men are still symbolically searching for the giving, nurturing woman.

I have found that fixations of the kind described by M.T. can

71

frequently be treated most effectively through satiation. Thus, I have encouraged men who could only find satisfaction with large-breasted women, not to fight it but enjoy it. When so encouraged, the compulsive nature of this fixation frequently diminishes, and they can begin to enjoy and be stimulated by more varieties of shapes and sizes. The problem with all fixations, as the author of the letter indicates, is that it severely limits choices.

Women with large breasts react in various ways to the response which their endowment arouses in some men. Some are pleased at the attention, while others protest. The main objection some of these women have to being admired for their breasts is the depersonalization involved. They feel that men who are so stimulated by their breasts are not interested in them as people, but merely as erotic objects. As one young woman explained, 'Of course, I want men to find me attractive – especially when I like them – but that's not the same as looking on me as just a thing with big boobs.' – H.G.

'BOTTOMS MAN'

When it comes to appreciation of the female shape I am indeed a 'bottoms man'. Breasts are puny in comparison to the lovely fullness, the sensual voluptuousness of the average female bottom.

Whatever fashion has done to conceal or reveal this lovely piece of cleft curvaceousness, the bottom has come thrusting through, bringing delight to man through the ages. Thus, I disagree, after playing with, spanking, or titillating the buttocks of a nicely proportioned female, that it becomes necessary – according to some of your readers, and your 'experts' too – to turn her over. Surely it makes sense to pay the bottom the final compliment?

J.T.

PLAIN TALK

People should be encouraged to use terms native to their locality and natural in their everyday speech. So, the rather prim 'penis' should be dropped and the wide ranging fruity bunch of eloquent alternatives be more properly used: 'cock', a fine flaunty word; 'prick', derivatively obscure but mighty powerful when used in an evocative phrase such as 'dirty big prick'; 'dick', coarse and uncompromising. Perhaps this expression is now confined to juveniles, although women enjoy playing with it lingually as an exercise to prove their emancipation from the shackles of an unfortunate Victorian upbringing.

When it comes to superseding 'vagina', a word full of connotations of timid middle-class compromise, the alternatives are legion.

The word 'cunt' is almost universally loved. It is so deliciously snook-cocking at all the sickening prudishness which has emasculated society since the early nineteenth century. Sexually aware etymologists should be commended for their powers of invention for producing such a word as 'quim', a synonym of cunt. Cunt is a plain, direct, universal word of the female orifice in repose. 'Quim', connates the cunt in a certain anticipatory state, prior to copulation and as a word is a piece of sheer inspiration.

Richness of language in any sphere is a mark of the civilized man and the lively mind. Every word implants an image in the mind. As the image changes so should the word, otherwise the truth of the matter is not conveyed.

Consider, for instance, the word 'fuck'. It seems that people do not realize that in the English language we do not have an adequate simple, transitive verb for The Act. When a woman in excess of intense eroticism, near the culmination of preliminary loveplay, sheds all her verbal propriety and cries out – 'Fuck me – fuck the ass off me,' she is merely expressing in verbal violence the indescribably intense desire to be savagely 'tupped' (yet another earthy verb). But what if she had to submit for this highly satisfying verbal flagellant the 'proper' expression – 'Have intercourse with me – have intercourse with me until my posterior is parted from my torso.' Well, not quite the same is it? And the image ...

Finally, do you know of that marvelous piece of Chaucerism: 'He swived her good and deep'? Beautiful isn't it?

Language, drawn on from its rich mines of imagery, can be a powerfully piquant ingredient of any love feast.

N.F.

PLEASURE BY ENEMA

Since I was a girl of nine (I am now a widow of 39) I have

73

held the view that an enema is a pleasurable experience. When I was a schoolgirl I spent a week in hospital after an operation. During that week I received several enemas. Although I felt embarrassed and humiliated, I actually enjoyed the experiences in a manner that is now difficult to recall precisely.

So lasting was the impression that I have never forgotten it and I have tried to relive it many times since. Between nine and 19 I used to dwell on every detail and it was my principal fantasy when I masturbated. The mere sight of an enema syringe in a surgical store was enough to excite me.

I purchased a syringe when I was at college but self-administration was quite unsatisfactory. I had a girlfriend who was a nurse and the first person to whom I confessed my unusual interests. When she offered to repeat the treatment, I accepted willingly and I found the experience very satisfying. After several occasions she proposed we switch roles so that I became the 'nurse'. I found this so very satisfying that I surprised myself and began to wonder what was wrong with me.

By now I was enjoying normal sexual relationships with men and I began to realize that I had still one step to go to achieve my real desire. I wanted a man to administer the intimate enema treatment, but I could not bring myself to discuss it with a male friend. Then, one evening I was at a party where there was a fair amount of sexual activity going on. I found myself in a bedroom with a partner who put me across his knee, took my panties down and gave me a playful spanking which I enjoyed very much. He became more intimate, separated my buttocks and inserted a vaselined finger up my anus. I could not disguise my intense sexual pleasure and when he asked if I was enjoying it I admitted I did, 'because it felt like being given an enema'.

He proceeded to cross-question me and extracted my first full confession to a man. To my delight he was completely understanding and offered to provide me with the full treatment just as I had described it.

I could scarcely wait till the following evening when I visited his apartment. The anticipation was almost unbearable. After a fantastic half-hour across his knee we went into the bedroom where he gave me a large, warm, soapy enema just as the nurse had done when I was a child. The only difference was that as he syringed me he masturbated me. The sensation was indescribable, I came almost immediately and by the time the enema was finished I had had several orgasms.

74

He was very experienced and I learned for the first time that other women derived sexual satisfaction from the same treatment though very few cared to admit it. We subsequently had intercourse and before I left I had a second enema, even more exciting than the first.

I continued to visit him about once a week and on the third occasion we reversed the roles of 'nurse' and 'patient'. He enjoyed both roles but his preference was for the active role and mine for the passive.

Two years later I married another man who had no interest in my 'special' activities. We had a normal relationship and were happy. I was never unfaithful in the accepted meaning of the word but I did very occasionally visit my former partner only to repeat the treatment that had affected me so profoundly.

My husband was killed in an automobile accident and I am now a widow with no children. I indulge in my former pursuit when the opportunity arises, which isn't often, but I still get tremendous anticipation whenever the day arrives. The same acute, mixed, bittersweet sensations are always there; being undressed, intimately examined, having my buttocks separated and my anus vaselined and finally being thoroughly syringed and masturbated simultaneously until I don't know which urge to obey first.

Although I now know that my reactions are not unique, I always wonder how many other women have and enjoy similar experiences. And when I hear someone say they dread the prospect of an enema I feel they just don't know what they're missing!

Mrs. E.G.

WAXING SEXY

We live in a small town where sexual aids are difficult to come by. Many magazines advertise fun items to send for but you always have to forward money first. If resources are scarce you just don't order.

We've always had a great sex life with no inhibitions, and one thing that always interested us was the use of the dildo. It always sounded like fun but we never sent for it. A few weeks ago my imaginative hubby was busy making candles, a hobby of his. He had one in a rather large mold and took it out before it was completely hardened. While in the process of discarding it his mind conjured up an image of a dildo. With a few squeezes and a bit of whittling he made a very realistic prick – glorious knob and all!

Imagine my surprise when he pulled that out! I have always been able to experience at least one great orgasm during each lovemaking session but with our little friend it's usually three or four and this little plaything only makes the 'real McCoy' feel even greater.

So you don't have to live in a city or be rolling in dough to enjoy little pleasures. All this one takes is a 49-cent box of wax and your imagination. Fun unlimited! Thank goodness for imaginative husbands.

Mrs. C.A.

ASSIST IN CLIMAX

My wife and I are both 44 and have been married 21 years. We are both very happy and love one another very much. Our problem is that my wife only reaches her sexual climax on very rare occasions when we make love.

My wife said she would like to use a dildo to see if it would help in our loveplay and assist her in reaching her climax more often.

Are dildoes usually effective in helping women attain an orgasm?

R.O.

The orgasmic response depends on so many factors that it would be impossible for me to make a simple prescription and say, 'Use the dildo.' The major value of the dildo is that it prolongs sexual foreplay, which is what many women need for orgasm.

However, when great emphasis is put on the climax, it is much more difficult to achieve with or without mechanical aids. – H.G.

FANTASIES

My husband becomes sexually excited by fantasies of watching another man making passionate love to me, although so far this has not happened.

It all started after we had watched a blue movie at the house of some friends. The main actor was a man of huge proportions which I found very exciting. That night all my husband could talk about was the sight of that huge penis thrusting in and out of the woman, as he was fondling me. Still being sexually aroused, I was absolutely wet – more so than I can ever remember before.

As our lovemaking progressed he spoke about seeing that huge penis penetrating into me, giving such descriptions and details that I was quickly brought to a shattering climax.

Now, whenever we make love (about four or five times a week) he excites me, and himself, by saying how much he would enjoy watching another man make love to me. He would like to see a penis of huge proportions enter fully into me and to watch the expression on my face.

The thought of being made love to by another such well-endowed man does have an attraction but how does one approach another man and say 'make love to me while my husband watches'? Although my husband says he would like to see such a performance, how would he really take it if the fantasy became reality?

Mrs. V.M.

One of the problems of sexually adjusting in marriage stems from the fact that so much of sexuality is not concerned with reality, but with fantasies.

Some people find that acting out a fantasy is often a disappointment and reduces the stimulating potential of the fantasy. There is no way to predict what your husband's reaction will be. However, in my experience I have known men who, after encouraging their wives to engage in sex with other men, were furious when the wife had the temerity to enjoy it. – H.G.

... WHO HELP THEMSELVES

I have read with interest cases about women who are unable to achieve orgasm due to excessive masturbation during their girlhood. This was the case with me, and I was unable to climax during intercourse until my husband hit upon an idea. He asked me to rub my clitoris during our lovemaking sessions, while he kept just the head of his penis in my vagina. I found that I could bring myself to climax and, upon my command, he would insert his penis all the way in.

We now employ this method every time we make love. I alternate my masturbation between my clitoris and the right side of my vaginal lips. This also gives my husband an enormous erection, and stimulates him to tremendous orgasms. I suggest this method for any woman who finds herself unable to come during intercourse.

Also, we have found that using so-called dirty language during the act of lovemaking brings us to new heights. I especially tell my husband to 'fuck me now' when I am ready to come, and we tell each other to 'fuck me' during this stage. Saying things like this can be a marvelous aphrodisiac.

Mrs. M.S.

This is an excellent and widely used technique for the many women (perhaps the majority) who are unable to come during ordinary intercourse.

We should like to make the point, however, that the inability to reach orgasm through intercourse alone has nothing whatsoever to do with 'excessive' masturbation during girlhood. It is a pity that this out-dated and disproved Freudian view of female sexuality is still so prevalent. Freud held that a woman could have two kinds of orgasm: clitoral and vaginal. Masturbation could cause the woman to become dependent on clitoral orgasm and unable to make the transition to the 'more mature' vaginal orgasm during intercourse.

Since there is in reality only one kind of female orgasm, the clitoral (as Masters and Johnson have proved), the distress this false doctrine caused can readily be imagined. Thousands and thousands of perfectly normal, loving, sexually responsive women were brain-washed into believing that because they could not be satisfied by penis-vagina contact alone they were abnormal, immature, or repressed.

So ingrained was this dogma, in total contradiction of the anatomical facts, that doctors even performed operations to bring the clitoris nearer the vagina, having found that in many 'frigid' women they were widely separated. This operation, of course, only worked because in its new position the clitoris was more likely to be stimulated by the penis during intercourse. But this obvious fact seems to have escaped the experts, who believed that they were thereby helping 'frigid' women to achieve the non-existent vaginal orgasm!

Perhaps it is also worth saying, yet again, that the concept of 'excessive' masturbation hardly holds up in practice, since the body sets its own limits in this field, and that it is now believed that adolescent masturbation in girls establishes a habit of sexual response and teaches the girl about her own sexuality – knowledge that is useful if not almost essential in later marriage. – F.

PENILE PROBLEM

While much has been written by qualified authorities reassuring men with smaller-than-average-penises, little or nothing has been said to allay the fears of men who run to the other extreme. I am 29 years old with normal, healthy sexual drives, yet because of the acute embarrassment I feel as regards the staggering dimensions of my penis – I am a virgin.

Although I bear no rancor toward them, I cannot help feeling that my own parents are partly responsible for the crippling sexual self-consciousness that I have. By the age of ten, my member was already larger than that of a well-endowed adult and my mother and father (usually after they'd had a few drinks) were fond of bringing me into the livingroom and 'showing me off' to their friends. I'll never forget the resulting titters and gasps, the looks of incredulity and stark wonder – they are, unfortunately, burned into my brain.

As I got older my problem grew – literally and figuratively. In High School I did my level best to guard my monstrous secret, exercising extreme caution at urinals and in changing rooms, but all to no avail. One day I was 'spotted', and after that life at school was pure hell. I was the butt of constant, not to say coarse, schoolboy jibes ('why don't you tuck it in your socks?', 'hey, does that thing bite', etc. etc.) – and nicknames such as 'Dipstick', 'Pete the Prong' and 'Jumbo Joint' flew thick and fast.

By the time I graduated from high school (cum laude) I figured that most everyone in my hometown of Ocala, Florida (pop. 61,000) must have known about my outside endowment: you see, my parents and their friends were spreading the word in one age bracket, and my schoolmates were spreading it in another. To put it blandly, my penis had bridged the generation gap. It had also made me a legend of sorts in my own town. People sniggered and pointed me out in the street,

Complete strangers gave me knowing looks. Soon I could bear it no longer and left Ocala to settle in Miami. It was here, at the age of 20, that I had my first – and last sexual encounter with a woman. To make a long story short, she picked me up in a bar, and after a few drinks invited me back to her place. Maybe it was the drinks, but for once I overcame my embarrassment and shyness and decided to have a go. When we got to her apartment we began kissing and soon I was in a state of total arousement. We then repaired to the bedroom and commenced to take our clothes off, back to back. When we were stripped, she encouraged me to turn around and face her. With my heart in my mouth, I did so. The next few seconds were the most terrible in my life. The woman took one look, and emitted a sort of strangled scream. Needless to say, I broke all records getting back into my clothes and I fled the apartment.

Ever since that humiliating experience, I have quite understandably, I think, steered well clear of women, fearing a similar action. Most men, I understand, would like to be endowed with prodigious weapons, but believe me, in my case, an overlarge penis has caused nothing but heartaches.

P.G.

WHO'S AFRAID OF THE BIG BAD WOLF?

Let's get one thing about penile size sorted out once and for all. I am only five foot two and fairly small with it. My boyfriend is six foot three and 224 pounds. His penis is 9¼ by 5¼ inches (I know having measured it). Now I'm not saying that this isn't a great size for a prick to be, and I appreciate from statistics that we are lucky – but I both saw it and took it into me without batting an eyelid. There was neither any pain nor any trouble – nor did it occur to me either that there would be or that this size was unnatural, although I am only 18 and not widely experienced.

In his time my boyfriend has had intercourse with many women, and, although I have no doubt that they all appreciated his cock, none of them showed amazement, horror or any similar emotion. Surely all these men who testify to such reactions are either indulging in wishful thinking – or mixing with women who don't want it at all!

Miss W.S.

ALL IN THE MIND

I agree that technique matters more than penis size. However, it does not require a great deal of ingenuity to devise techniques adapted to the larger than average penis, and which give enhanced pleasures to the man while also protecting the woman from damage; and of course one derives considerable satisfaction at being able to give this additional satisfaction to one's partner. Although I am of average build I have myself accommodated a penis a little over nine inches long – he insisted on measuring it! – without discomfort. In this case one's hand (or one's partner's) can be used as an extension of the vagina as it were, which must give the average woman an extra psychic thrill while of course providing additional stimulus for the man. Size is not all-important but a large erect penis is certainly good for the female ego since it has an inevitable suggestion of greater desire! It certainly turns me on.

Miss J.H.

PSYCHOLOGICAL FIXATION

The perennial subject of penis size occurs so frequently that it runs the risk of being exhausted, but a recent TV program stated that psychological testing in America found that over 90% of males suffer from a sense of having too small a penis.

I happen to be homosexual, so I can claim a considerably wider experience of the erect male organ than can most heterosexual males. The size of the penis does have added psychological significance for a male homosexual quite simply because of its attributes of much-desired 'maleness'.

One's sense of inadequacy can be totally without physical foundation, and entirely a psychological 'fixation'. My own case proves this. My organ is eight inches in length and two inches in diameter, yet through my late teens and early twenties I was convinced I was under-endowed, even though I saw that most of the men I met were smaller.

What has gradually become obvious, however, is that although I am fairly fortunate in this respect, the tenderness and mutual trust of a loving relationship are of far more value than physical dimensions in establishing potency; I am sure this applies to male-female relationships as much as to male-male ones.

R.P.

THE CLITORAL POSITION

Isn't it time that men woke up to the fact that there is no such thing as a vaginal orgasm (they can read Masters and Johnson as well as Kinsey if they have any lingering doubts) so that their sexual attention should be focused on the real orgasm-producing area – the clitoris?

Just because the vagina is a convenient hole for them to park their 'weapon' (as they revealingly call it) there is no reason for women to continue being passive recipients of their target practice. Their monotonous thrusts are useless if no effort is made simultaneously to stimulate the clitoris. When women don't respond in many of the 'standard' positions which favor men's pleasure, but not women's, they are labeled 'frigid' and are left wondering what's wrong with them. This is ridiculous since the position of an individual woman's clitoris is very important in assessing whether she is anatomically suited to stimulation from the penis going in and out of the vagina. If her clitoris is a particularly low one, then the chances that the penis will rub against it while making its thrusts are good. If, however, it is located higher up, then ordinary logic would tell anyone that the so-called 'normal' thrusts of intercourse won't do much good.

Men are always going on about ways of accommodating their varying sized penises, how to achieve maximum penetration, how to make a small penis go a long way, etc. But no thought seems to be given to the clitoral position and how to train a man to use his penis to reach this highly sensitive area.

Some women do claim to have a vaginal orgasm. What they actually feel are strong repercussions of their clitoral orgasms – the contractions, the bursting pleasure, the pulse-like beating. Like fireworks bursting from one particular source and quickly spreading over a large area, the clitoral orgasm too reaches further out the moment it explodes.

Many men continue to resist this idea for various reasons. Their egos can't stand up to the idea that their penises are not exactly the last word in pleasure, and that the quarter-inch calculations they've been making to assess their penile grandeur (or lack of it) don't make that much difference to the recipient. Since the penis's greatest advantage (for a woman) is just being there when the orgasmic contractions want to grip on to something to increase intensity, then the width rather than the length would seem to be of greater importance.

Men often equate their penis size with their manhood. Women have fallen for this idea, seeing their own womanliness in terms of how much 'manhood' they can accommodate. The psychological effect has been for women generally to prefer a large penis (believing it feels better) since it makes them feel 'more of a woman'.

Also, understanding of the true situation leads many men to conclude that two women could satisfy themselves just as well on their own. Any idea that even hints at the fact that men might not be indispensable to women is enough to send shudders up any man's spine. Unlike male homosexuals, women wouldn't even have the problem of hemorrhoids.

And then there is the small matter of ease. Of course it's much easier for men not to have to bother about the old clit and just get on with their own enjoyment, half-hoping that the woman they're with is getting something out of it. This kind of hit-or-miss situation just isn't good enough any more. No one is asking them to be contortionists, but before intercourse even begins the man must consider the woman's clitoral position so that a true meeting occurs. Otherwise why should she bother?

Mrs. L.P.

LITERARY IMAGININGS?

I have recently been reading some of the old erotic classics, like *Fanny Hill* and *My Secret Life*.

Time and time again in such books the proof of a woman's enjoyment of a sexual encounter is described as a 'spending' analogous to the man's. The woman's 'juices' are said to flow copiously and mix with her partner's semen, and after manual stimulation these 'effusions' are said to run down over the man's hand and wrist.

Admittedly I have had experience with far fewer women than the indefatigable heroes of these books. But although I know full well the necessity for a nicely lubricated vagina (and have usually managed to induce this state of affairs), I have never experienced the state of orgasmic female flooding as described in these books.

Did these authors know what they were talking about? Have I been missing something?

J.C.

Until comparatively recently it was believed that women ejaculated something akin to that of the male. This idea, like the one that the male was born with a certain quantity of semen which was stored in his spinal cord and decreased with each ejaculate, is, of course, nonsense. It was, however, fostered to a certain extent by the presence in many women of very copious Bartholin's gland production, and by the expulsion of a kind of mucous plug from the neck of the uterus which some women claim they actually feel happening during orgasm.

Everything in this type of book is always exaggerated. Penises are always really outsize in dimensions – the only exception I can think of is My Secret Life, *in which Walter is always worrying about the smallness of his – vaginas are always wide and long or beautifully tight, and the sexual capacity of both men and women is always such that they are capable of attaining orgasms dozens of times a day.*

This trait of exaggeration is also seen in blatantly pornographic drawings and sculptures, especially in ancient Greek, Roman and Japanese works of this kind. Modern pornography follows the same fashion. – F.

FEMININE FLOW

Some women do ejaculate during intercourse. I have known four women, including my wife, who frequently or occasionally ejaculate.

These women all possess libidos of above average strength, but even in their case 'flows' only occur with the more voluptuous orgasms.

The fluid is definitely not urine. It is like water – freeflowing, colorless, tasteless and does not possess any lubricating properties. The amount ejaculated seems to be very comparable in volume to that produced by a male ejaculation of semen. My wife and I are not sure of its point of issue but think that it flows from the vagina.

It is excessively pleasurable to me to have my crotch (or face) soaked by this sudden 'flow'; take it from me, if the writer of *Fanny Hill* mentions 'feminine flow', he knew what he was writing about!

G.P.

Feminine flow is also affected by the menstrual cycle so that the flow may be minimal or copious at different times in the cycle. – H.G.

CLITORIS IS EMBEDDED

My fiancée and I have a problem with which we hope you will be able to help us. We have been courting for three years and have been having regular intercourse for most of that time. She is now on the Pill, and we have a happy and exciting sex life, but she can only achieve an orgasm by laying on top of me and by working and pressing down on me. In this way, she can have up to five or six orgasms.

Her clitoris is embedded and covered, so it never emerges from beneath the skin. Knowing other women can have an orgasm through intercourse and by manual and oral stimulation worries her and makes her wonder if she will ever achieve an orgasm any other way.

When we were first courting, before we started having intercourse, she had her first orgasm when we were petting heavily, and she was lying on top of me. Since then, she has always satisfied herself in this way. We were wondering if it is because she has become so used to satisfying herself in this way, she can't achieve orgasm any other way?

J.S.

It is very difficult to give a satisfactory answer without having more detailed information. From his description of his partner's clitoris, it would seem lesions prevent the head from emerging from the hood when the organ is erect. This is not an uncommon occurrence and can be put right by a fairly simple operation.

I am not clear from what J.S. writes whether his penis is in his partner's vagina when she lies on top of him, working and pressing down on him. If not, what part of his anatomy does she press her clitoral area against? But whether or not the penis is in the vagina, I can see no reason why the same results should not be obtained in the reverse position with him on top. If the penis is not in the vagina, he should press down on her clitoral area with his erect penis and stimulate the area with pelvic movement. If the penis is in the vagina, he should not make backward and forward movements, but keep his penis at maximum depth, and pressing his pubic bone against his partner's bone, making circular movements with his pelvis, which should bring her off without fail.

For some time, more enlightened sexologists have been declaring, only in very rare cases, where the organ is abnormally large or somewhat strangely positioned, does the clitoris actually touch the penis during coupling. Masters and Johnson have proved this view to be right by their discovery that, during the woman's orgasmic phase, the clitoris actually withdraws backward automatically away from the penis. With this discovery, they also discovered stimulation of the general clitoral area either during masturbation or lovemaking is perhaps more effective in bringing the woman off than direct stimulation of the clitoris itself.

I can well understand, if the clitoris is covered by lesions, there can be no response to oral stimulation but I am puzzled his partner does not react to manual stimulation. When she was a girl, did she never masturbate by stimulating the clitoris with a finger? If she did, and successfully brought herself off by this means, then it does rather seem she might have become psychologically fixated on her present method in the way he suggests. – F.

HIDDEN CLITORIS

I have been prompted into writing this as a result of a letter by J.S. since it appears we may have a similar problem. My fiancée and I have been having intercourse now for about 18 months and although we both enjoy it and are satisfied, there is one thing which is lacking in our relationship.

My fiancée has not yet experienced an orgasm, a fact which we are beginning to believe may be associated with her clitoris being hidden in some way. I must confess to being somewhat ignorant as to the shape and physical size of the clitoris (literature on this topic seems somewhat limited) but there does not appear to be any region which responds particularly well to my caresses, and I am apparently not capable of making her attain orgasm by manual means.

We spend considerable time on the preliminaries but if this continues for more than ten minutes or so, I have great difficulty in maintaining her excitement. The same thing applies when we are actually engaged in intercourse; if we remain coupled for more than ten minutes her excitement seems to wane.

Is it possible that she could not have a clitoris at all, or is it more likely to be hidden? You mention in your reply to J.S. that a simple operation might be the answer but can we arrange for this in any way, bearing in mind that it will probably be two years before we are married?

I must stress that my fiancée is not frigid, since she gets excited during the early stages and she does enjoy intercourse so long as it is not prolonged. However, this is worrying to both of us and particularly to her since she is suspecting something may be wrong with her because of the fact that she does not really become more and more excited as we progress. Also she is aware of the fact that other girls become enormously excited when their clitorises are stimulated by their partners.

In your reply to J.S. you say you are rather surprised that she cannot be brought off manually and inquire whether or not she used to masturbate by stimulating the clitoris with a finger. My fiancée and I have discussed this point and she says that she has never masturbated in this way and has never reached a climax, presumably because she did not find anything to stimulate which excited her.

M.T.

It is possible but extremely rare for the clitoris to be completely absent. It is very much more common for it be covered by adhesions. These may be of any degree; from minor adhesions due to infection, to major adhesions of the labia minora present at birth and which may be so severe that there is difficulty in passing urine.

A simple physical examination will make the diagnosis without doubt. Minor adhesions can be freed under local anesthesia but, of course, the more extensive ones may require surgical treatment. – F.

KICKS FROM BOOTS

Why does a person suddenly, out of the blue, become hyper-addicted to a particular article of clothing? And is there any chance of such a fixation getting out of hand?

My reason for asking is that I have developed what seems to me to be an exaggerated and quite unreasonable attraction toward girls in white boots, not the short Courréges type but specifically the tall, tight-fitting variety that are beginning to be fashionable again. My addiction goes back to last winter, and the fact that I can find no logical reason for this passion shames and troubles me greatly. I find girls in white boots completely distracting and utterly irresistible. I have taken to following women wearing white boots (even long white socks that look like boots until you get up close) and after losing sight of them I often have to duck into the toilet to relieve myself. I sat opposite a girl wearing a pair the other day in the tube, and by the time she got off I had an erection and was weak with emotion. I have a scrapbook full of newspaper cuttings of girls in white boots and spend hours looking at them and masturbating.

How does a kink like this begin? Although I naturally appreciate miniskirts and am wild about black boots, no other article of female attire has this effect on me. I have never suffered from such an obsession before and it strikes me as distinctly unhealthy. I just hope I am not turning into a fetishist. I have never been to a prostitute, but I think if I did I would reach orgasm simply by touching her white boots. Is my addiction unusual?

A.M.

I agree that girls in white boots can be very attractive, but so can girls in brown boots, black boots and even in sneakers.

Many attempts have been made to explain the phenomenon of fetishism, one of the most studied and least understood of sexual anomalies. One reason for this lack of understanding is the frequent confusion between fetishism and fixation.

In fixation, an individual becomes strongly sensitized to a particular part or aspect of the opposite sex. As is evidenced from many of the letters in this book, for example, a number of men are fixated on breasts, buttocks, and feel great sexual arousal and excitement by a certain size of breasts or shape of buttocks.

In fetishism, on the other hand, an individual becomes attached to an object worn by a member of the opposite sex, in the case of the heterosexual, or of the same sex in the case of a homosexual. The fetishist becomes so attracted to the object that he no longer needs the person. He may, for example, find great stimulation from a pair of silk panties even when empty. However, association of the woman, or her image, with the panties is essential.

Fetishists may become involved through any one or a combination of the five senses. Some are aroused by the tactile stimulation of silk, fur or corduroy, to mention just a few; others by the sight of varied objects, i.e., white boots, high-heeled shoes or a particular kind of underwear. Similarly, there are those who are turned on by a special odor, a particular sound or taste.

Some psychoanalysts have explained the fetish, following Freud's hypothesis, as a substitute for the penis; others, as a substitute breast. While such explanations may be significant in some cases, in my experience I have found it most helpful to look at the particular behavior in terms of conditioning. Pavlov's dog was fed at the same time that a bell was rung. In a short time the dog salivated at the sound of the bell, without the food. This is conditioning. Similarly, the fetishist may be originally excited by a woman who is wearing a special article of clothing such as a pair of high-heeled boots – then later becomes excited by the boots themselves.

While fetishists rarely come for therapy since many of them frequently enjoy their attachment to the stimulating object, I have come across fetishism in patients who came because of other problems. One young man, considered quite attractive by many women, preferred masturbating into a pair of silk panties which he would purchase. In therapy he remembered quite clearly how excited he became the first time he was with a woman and removed her skirt and saw her blue silk panties with the pubic hair faintly visible through them. Since he was also a person who had difficulty with close relationships, his choice of an object rather than another person for sexual stimulation was understandable. Many of the fetishists I have treated came for therapy because of their difficulties in dealing with intimate relations, and I have found it often necessary to help them overcome their problems with personal relationships.

Some authorities believe there is a link between crime and fetishism. This is not to say that all fetishists are criminals but many seem to get added pleasure from the fetish-object if they steal it. Kleptomaniacs, for example, frequently get sexual pleasure just from the act of stealing a particular object.

Pyromaniacs are also sexually stimulated not by an object,

but an act. To many of them fire is apparently an externalized symbolic form of the sexual fire within their bodies. To a male who feels inadequate, the ability to create a huge roaring fire is frequently a substitute for the burning passion he feels incapable of igniting in a woman.

Another puzzling aspect of the whole pattern of fetishism is the lack of reported cases of female fetishists. I would agree with the speculation that this may largely be due to the difference in society's expectations of behavior from men and women. In general, women have been raised to be more passive and not openly express their sexual feelings. The feminine woman has long been thought of as one who responds, rather than initiates. However, along with different changes taking place today, more cases of female fetishists are being reported.

I am frequently asked, 'What is the difference between a strong preference and a fixation?' The answer lies in the compulsivity of the feeling. Many of us have strong preferences, but we can be aroused, stimulated, satisfied by many different stimuli. In the case of the fixated person, the stimulus for excitement is very specific and the person has great difficulty being excited by anything other than the fixation. – H.G.

NEW STYLE BIKINI

Little mention is made in sex books of the absorptive powers of the vagina and penis. If the penis is thrust fully into the vagina and held there, the secretions tend to be absorbed, and so the penis and vagina adhere. If movement is minimal and care taken not to spread any remaining secretions the penis and vagina move as one resulting in clitoral stimulation as stretching takes place on thrust.

As an aid, my wife bought a pair of close-fitting bikini type panties in a nonstretch semitransparent nylon. She removed all the elastic, substituting tapes of correct length. Both sides were cut and fitted with 'hooks and eyes'. In front an aperture was made and this was fitted with a draw-string.

Before intercourse, the penis and scrotum are passed through this aperture and the draw-string is firmly tied. After intromission – woman above astride position – the bikini is fastened in the usual way.

Withdrawal is now impossible and the limited movements and deep penetration give rise to some unusual sensations affecting the glans and the cervix.

J.T.

BONDAGE

A great deal has been, and is being, written about the sexual act – particularly in reference to its surroundings, its performance, and so on – but, as some of your correspondents have remarked, the act is the fulfillment of a longer or shorter period of preparation. And to my mind, it is this preparation which is by far the most important aspect of lovemaking.

My wife and I have been married now for nearly 16 years, and we find that bondage is the most exciting parcel in which to wrap the center.

New and exciting ways and means were tried, to be discarded or improved upon, during the early days of our marriage, and over the course of the years we have built up a store of varying equipment, dress, etc., which almost fills a complete chest of drawers. What we did find in our early days was that cords, however soft they were, were not satisfactory. Apart from the fact that the wearer may be able to manipulate a sharp blade to cut herself free, we found that if the cord was tight enough to be really effective, it was too tight to leave for any length of time; while if I tied it loosely enough not to interfere with the circulation, then it was completely ineffective and my wife would be free in a trice.

So, in our wanderings, we picked up a couple of pairs of police regulation handcuffs and two pairs of leg irons, and these – together with any number of lengths of chain and padlocks – have been our standby for a number of years. Without the keys, they are completely inescapable, and they are 'comfortable' enough to wear for days at a time, if the occasion warrants it – certainly for many hours. And the time was when we would never go out in the car for a picnic, or evening drive, without at least one pair of handcuffs in the glove compartment.

However, we have now found that our old cord technique was all wrong, and we have gone back to the occasional use of cords but applied differently. This business of the heroine in books being 'bound cruelly hand and foot so that the cords dug deep into her tender flesh' may be alright in fiction but is quite unnecessary. I can now tie my wife's wrists together, first of all 'acrossward' and then 'up and down' (at right angles to the first) – as loose as you please. The trick comes in winding the rest of the cord between the wrists in the 'third dimension', thus drawing the other cords into some degree of tightness. When the last bit of the cord is pulled as tight as you want and knotted on top of the bound wrists, and thus away from prying fingers, I can assure you it is absolutely secure.

If the ankles are also to be tied, then again wind the cords between the legs as well and tie the knot in front, so that the bound hands cannot reach it. What you do in each case, in fact, is to make two quite effective cord handcuffs! Tied in this way, my wife has literally spent hours and hours in helpless bondage without undue discomfort.

My wife and I can both thoroughly recommend this pre-act bondage play, which, if reasonable care is taken, may transport a mere 'rush job', as it so often is, into a whole evening's wonderful delight.

M.R.

MARITAL GAME

Readers may be interested in a rather novel form of marital game practiced by my friend and his wife.

She has made a leather collar, with one end threaded through the other with a length of thread attached. The collar is fitted over her husband's penis just behind the glans. He tells me that it is quite a snug fit and normally causes no discomfort, but pulling on the thread his wife has complete control of his movements.

Used indoors, his wife first of all undresses him, then ties his hands behind him. The collar is then fitted on and the thread used either to tie him to the bed post, where he is left until his wife feels fit to release him, or used to lead him about the house at her whim.

Used outdoors with the thread suitably threaded as to be inconspicuous my friend is often led through the street, or occasionally tied to a park bench while his wife goes for a walk.

The thread can be manipulated to give either pleasure or pain as desired.

When my friend told me about this form of restraint, which both he and his wife enjoy immensely, I thought that it was just a tall story he had made up. However, since reading of the many extraordinary techniques employed by married couples to stimulate their marriages, I feel now that it could be true.

J.L.

Yes, it could be true, but before you go into mass production of those collars and threads you might think of doing a more extensive market survey to see how many people would enjoy this kind of game. – H.G.

THE INITIATION

Shortly before the war, my parents sometimes spent long weekends in London and on these occasions left my young brother and me (aged 10 and 13 respectively) in the care of a village woman who used to 'do' for my mother. She was in her middle or late twenties, her husband was away in the airforce and there were rumors that she was behaving promiscuously in his absence with a number of other men.

A boy at school lent me a well-thumbed and dog-eared book of 'girlie' pictures one day on the condition that I pass it on to the next eager reader at breaktime the following morning. After supper I was very anxious to get to bed, and I threw myself into a frenzied bout of masturbation, gorging my eyes on the photographs, with the blankets pulled over my head, and a torch in my free hand. I was scared out of my wits when a few minutes after settling down to my solitary orgy, the bedclothes were suddenly yanked back, and there, staring down at me in all my shame, stood my guardian. Evidently my eagerness to get to bed had puzzled her. 'I might have guessed you'd be up to something revolting like this,' she said. 'You're a little pig.'

I was rigid with shame and fear. She locked the door and returned to the rumpled bed, telling me that rather than report the incident to my parents, she had decided to rid me of my desire to abuse myself in 'that disgusting way'. She was a big hefty woman and I was powerless to resist as she sat heavily on the bed, and leaning her whole weight across me, took my still erect penis in her hands and began to manipulate it vigorously, though not too roughly. Throughout this extraordinary form of correction, she continued to reprimand me, and catalog all the dire consequences of self-abuse. I soon experienced two or three orgasms in quick succession, each a little less violent than the

93

last, until I was feeling utterly wrung out. Without ceasing her terrible ministrations for an instant, she continued and induced a further ejaculation before unpinning me.

Completely exhausted, with a raw red penis, I was forced to sob my apologies for having been wicked and sinful. For this I was rewarded by my now flushed, and clearly stimulated assailant with a plethora of kisses and lewd caresses all over my body and warned, before she finally hurried from the room – to relieve herself, I suspect – that I could expect far worse if she ever caught me 'at it' again. The following morning I was dejected and jaded and could never bring myself to look in her face again.

Degrading though the punishment was, it was also unutterably exciting, and my onanistic fantasies from then on invariably involved my being forcibly restrained and sexually violated by some attractive woman of my acquaintance. A few years ago, I was reminded of my ignominious ordeal when I read Gustave Mirabeau's lurid description of the 'torture of the caress' – an identical, but far more lethal experience than that to which I had been subjected – in his novel *Le Jardin Des Supplices*. I wonder whether others have been the victims of similar succubine assaults?

J.F.

No, but I wish I had. – H.G.

THE BEHOLDER'S EYE

So far as visual pleasure is concerned, I suppose at one time or another all parts of the human body have had their fair share of praise or blame. I have heard the female nipples denounced as ugly protuberances detracting from the divine curve of the breasts: other parts of the body that can be praised – or criticized – include the feet, knees, buttocks and armpits. Nowadays it is not customary to admire the male genitals as things of beauty; but it was not always so. The early Greek sculptors and the great artists of the Renaissance such as Michelangelo and Donatello saw nothing unaesthetic about the male sex organs.

In fact, to the Greeks, all parts of the body were equally beautiful; the suggestion that any one part of the human frame was ugly or offensive to the eye would have been regarded as sacrilegious – as an insult to the Gods. In one of Aristophanes'

94

plays a character comments quite openly on the beauty of a young man's penis; such a remark heard today on the stage of any Western theater could only provoke unseemly titters – to a Greek audience it would have seemed a perfectly natural thing to say.

I am not suggesting, of course, that the private parts of every man are invariably pleasing to look at; any more than that all women's breasts are things of beauty. On the contrary – they can be very ugly indeed. However, from my own experience of seeing hundreds of naked men, women and children at naturist camps both at home and abroad, I would say that the penises of young boys are nearly always pleasing to the eye; and while the genitalia of adult men vary enormously in size, shape and character, it no longer surprises me to hear my wife say of an attractive nude young man that 'he has a handsome penis'.

The same kind of reasoning surely applies with equal force to the female genitalia. Readers of Walter's *My Secret Life* will recall how that connoisseur of the vagina could derive intense pleasure from merely looking at a woman's sex organs – sometimes for long periods of time. Few of us, in the nature of things, can have the wide experience of Walter in these matters; hence one wonders whether the intense controversies that have raged in the columns of some magazines about the beauty (or otherwise) of the pubic hair are not due to simple ignorance on the part of the disputants.

This again is a matter on which I find it most difficult to generalize. I am inclined to take the view that the pubic hair is a normal, natural and decorative feature of the feminine landscape; I never find it objectionable and sometimes I think that it is quite charming; and I can find little that is beautiful in the shaven pubis. But these are matters of taste!

For me, one of the most delightful of all forms of contact is where the man lies on his back and the woman kneels over him, reversed – so that her bare buttocks come close to his lips. In this position she can take his penis deeply into her mouth, while her partner's tongue wanders happily from anus to vulva and back again. And the visual satisfaction is truly rewarding. I know of no rose in my garden so sweet as the dewy, soft-petaled flower that hides secretly between my woman's thighs, only to be revealed in the foreplay of love.

Other civilizations less inhibited than our own have unmistakably asserted the view, in sculpture, woodcarving, painting and the like, that the vulva and the erect penis are the most beautiful things in God's creation. It is a view, which I for one, do not feel disposed to dispute.

W.T.

PILLOW TALK

Many years ago I enjoyed the company of a superb girl, married to one of my fellow officers; she was born for loving and erotic sex, being very sensual, and she delighted in using sexy talk to spur me on. I found it a very powerful aphrodisiac which always led to our lovemaking reaching fresh heights of joy.

What made our hours so glorious and breathtaking was her complete knowledge of what made a man randy – the power of ecouteurism. As we lay on the sofa together she would whisper and relate how her husband had sex with her, stimulating me with all the details of her past sex life.

She would describe for my benefit the old double bed at her parents' home, how it squeaked and rocked and shook as she was being fucked at night when they stayed there. She would describe how in Germany a brother officer used to call on her when her husband was away on duty at other stations: 'We always had it naked, as he liked me nude, while my husband liked me in my sexy underclothes.'

What a contrast between making love to that girl and the usual dismal silence most women seem to prefer in bed. The experiences I had with her were the most erotic of my life. Surely I can't be the only man who is so powerfully affected by 'ecouteurism'?

R.D.

EROTIC SOUNDS

Until two months ago my wife and I had spent the majority of our married life living in crowded blocks of flats or with parents. However, now that we have eventually moved into a rather remote but very beautiful little cottage out in the country, we have found that not only has our general mode of living become more relaxed and easier, but also that our sex life has taken a surprising new direction.

We have always enjoyed lovemaking and began our sexual

relationship six years ago, three years before our marriage. We have been through all the various positions and methods of loveplay and quite honestly didn't consider that things could get much better. Both of us were always perfectly satisfied.

But as I have said, we always lived in fairly close proximity to other people, and on suddenly finding ourselves the only people for miles around, we discovered the erotic stimulation of sound. The second night that we spent in our new home is one I will never forget. We began to make love and I remember noticing that my wife was reacting somewhat noisily, then as she approached orgasm she began to scream and shout with pleasure. It was so unexpected and so stimulating that I too immediately came to orgasm with her.

Talking about it afterward my wife revealed that she had always felt the urge to do this but was inhibited by the fact that either our parents in the next room would hear, or when we were living in a flat even the next door neighbors would be treated to a spot of ecouteurism through the thin walls. Thus, almost unthinkingly we always made love without raising our voices above a murmur.

From then on there has been no stopping us. We discovered the delights of chasing one another through the house laughing and shouting. Sometimes my wife will go to bed before me, and we will hold an erotic conversation while I stand at the foot of the stairs. I then leave her for about half an hour and excitement mounts while she waits for me. I too have found it a wonderful experience to let forth with all I have, especially during orgasm. During mutual orgasm, our combined sound must be quite intense, but it provides a wonderful sense of utter abandonment.

Loveplay is also enhanced through laughter and all the other erotic sounds which signify pleasure. Of course it would perhaps be exhausting to act in this way continually, although we have found that nowadays when we do make love in silence it is deep and meaningful because it is a contrast and because it is not forced upon us through inhibition.

It seems such a shame that many people living in our over-crowded cities, piled on top of one another in high rise flats, will probably never know the sheer joy of employing their lungs and vocal cords as further aids to both the mental and physical pleasure of sex.

M.L.

97

INHIBITING NOISE

It happens to me during lovemaking that in the final and almost unbearable intensity of orgasm I am overwhelmingly impelled to groan and scream out loud. My own efforts to restrain this, plus my husband's attempt to muffle the sound by pressing his hand over my mouth, have always detracted a little from my full enjoyment. Naturally, with our teenage children in the house we normally have to accept these restrictions, although, of course, on the rare occasions when we can be sure of being alone and can make uninhibited noisy love, it is a supreme experience for me which also gives intense pleasure to my husband.

Mrs. M.C.

TAPE RECORDER TACTICS

I am 33 and share a flat with a boyfriend. We have a small tape recorder which we secrete in our bedroom when we invite a sexy friend or friends along. The tape lasts an hour. We never let them know it's on but after they have gone we play back the session. As we go in for many kinds of 'tricks' the recordings are pretty exciting.

One evening we had a mild spanking party among four of us. You can hear the swish of the cane onto the bare bottoms of us all in turn and the odd remarks that were made! We have two friends who do the same at their flat and we exchange tapes regularly. (Of course we do not know with whom they were performing as only first names are ever used.) We find that it is tremendous fun to get into bed, cuddle up, turn on the recorder by the bed and masturbate one another. Visualizing the scene makes us both so terribly stimulated that it is not always easy to hold back. But the 'oohs' and 'aahs' are enough to bring us both off without much trouble.

Sound really seems to have been neglected as an erotic stimulant – but now that tape recorders are so easy to come by it's something every couple can experiment with. It's certainly added a new dimension to our sex life.

Miss M.B.

FAKING IT

I would like to pass on to your female readers a simple bit of advice which might benefit their marriages as much as it has mine. My husband has a thing about bringing me to orgasm. If I don't come during one of our lovemaking sessions, he gets terribly upset and morose.

There are times when we're making love when I just can't seem to come to a climax. This usually happens when I have something on my mind or when I'm terribly tired and agree to sex only to please my husband. Despite the fact I assure him I am enjoying our lovemaking and it makes no difference to me if I do not have an orgasm, he still insists I have one. I am certain it has something to do with the male ego and his wanting to prove his masculinity.

One night when I was extremely tired and was not able to reach a climax, out of desperation, I made believe I was having one. Immediately after that, my husband had his orgasm after which he peacefully fell asleep. Since that night, I have done the same thing whenever the occasion called for it.

I personally do not feel that what I'm doing is wrong or harmful to my husband in any way. As a matter of fact, it has improved our marital relations. There are times when I have feigned multiple orgasms and this excites him so his climaxes reach their peak levels. It's wonderful for his ego and his pride and for the following few days, he's closer and warmer to me than ever. As a result, both of us are happier and our marriage is strengthened.

If my 'little white sexual lie' can help me in my marriage, there is no reason why it couldn't help other wives who are in the same predicament.

Mrs. F.L.

This letter surely deals with a universal phenomenon. Men also can – and do – fake. If people felt better about just plain fun, they wouldn't feel guilty about not having orgasms. – R.G.

PITFALLS OF EXPERTISE

I wonder if one can become too sexually expert for one's own good? That may seem a rather peculiar question to ask when we are continually deploring the lack of sexual accomplishment in lovers. But I have found that with greater experimentation and variety of technique, the ability to achieve orgasm is maintained, but to a great extent, spontaneity is lost. When the actions of loving become too calculated, a great deal of the enjoyment goes. True, there is the satisfaction of perceiving the enjoyment one is affording one's partner as one strokes and manipulates her flesh, but often one's own sexual excitement is absent to a great degree.

After the final ejaculation and one's partner's orgasmic response, one has a good sense of sexual achievement and there is, of course, the satisfaction of sexual release, but a great deal of the lovemaking must be premeditated and often a repetition. There are the occasional unforeseen acts by one's partner, but even these give less stimulation than did unexpected responses when one was more sexually naïve and inexperienced.

We do lose a lot, I think, as the years pass. We become expert lovers but lose some of the almost unbearable excitement of youthful sexual encounters. I well recall the prolonged agitation of expectation when in my youth a girl showed sexual interest in me.

I had no academic interest then in the tentatively exploring fingers of my girlfriend, nor the now more or less purely aesthetic appreciation of her breasts and buttocks. We fought for each other's flesh as a drowning man fights for air. We would not be denied, each wanting to use the other to the utmost to relieve the animal passions which possessed us.

Sometimes, of course, the orgasm was missed because the actual finding was inexpertly done, but a limp penis could always be coaxed back to hardness and the lovemaking continued. Now, the orgasm is expertly achieved and very satisfying, but the preliminaries seem rather *too* expertly accomplished.

How can one blend the expertise of the mature with the spontaneity of youth? Or must we accept that maturer love must necessarily be more the enjoyment of a connoisseur?

J.J.

Dr. Stephen Neiger, Fellow of the Society of the Scientific Study of Sex, wrote on this problem: 'Too much variety can be just as deadly for sex as is monotony. In fact, continuous experimentation often is just another form of boredom that will keep someone from building an intimate relationship.'

My objection to many of the 'how-to' sex books on the market is their focus on techniques alone. Of course we need *education and information, but sex as an activity – whether for pleasure, fun, or intimacy – involves another human being. In these manuals there seem to be no people, just parts–legs, arms, penises, clitorises, organs. How unfortunate it would be if our technological age produces only master sex technicians. – R.G.*

BISEXUAL WIFE

My wife appears to be bisexual as for several years in our married life she always became most excited when during loveplay we discussed what it would be like to have another woman in bed with us.

This never failed to excite her and just talking about it was almost enough to bring on an orgasm. Neither of us ever expected to put these fantasies into practice but were in fact most surprised and delighted when the opportunity arose.

The husband of one of my wife's friends sent abroad on business a short time ago and June, her friend, came to stay with us for a fortnight. After she had been staying with us for a few days she decided to give us a treat for a change and one morning brought us a cup of tea in bed. She sat down on the edge of the bed drinking her tea and I could tell that the sight and nearness of her in a quite revealing nightie excited my wife. Quickly finishing my tea I slowly stroked my wife's thighs before gently caressing her pubic hairs.

The effect was even more pronounced than usual and by now I had an enormous erection. It was obvious to June that we were both in a high state of arousal. I felt that things were going a little too far and suggested that she might prefer to leave us. To our astonishment she said that she did not feel at all embarrassed and was in fact becoming quite worked up herself. Within a matter of seconds she joined us in bed.

What followed was the most exhilarating sexual experience any of us ever had. Nothing was barred and we all felt intense pleasure. How grateful I was that my wife never hid any of her bisexual feelings from me and felt free enough to indulge in sex with another woman right next to me. And how happy she was that I never showed distaste for this side of her nature

R.K.

HOOKED ON FISH

As one who is highly sexed, I am also stimulated greatly by the sight and smell of wet fish. When at school, I was errand boy for a fishmonger and his wife. She embodied all that seemed sexy in a woman, large firm breasts and two lovely long legs. One day she caught me masturbating and, as a result, on occasion did it to me, while in turn, she made me kneel and put my head up her skirt and perform cunnilingus. There was a delightfully warm fishy smell in the shop which was analogous to the odor of her genitals.

So now whenever I pass a fish shop with the fish glistening on the slab, I get a terrific erection. Would this reaction be considered a fetish?

G.P.

Smell is a very important sexual sense, and olfactory stimulation has developed into the vast perfumery industry, largely based on musk and ambergris. But like all senses, individual likes and dislikes play a considerable part. Your friendly fishmonger's wife has obviously given you something of a fixation; it would become a fetish if the smell of a fish shop would be the only stimulant in causing your erection. – F.

MOTHERS TEACH DAUGHTERS

It never fails to amaze me in this so-called civilized community, we gently raise and educate our daughters to the age of puberty and then leave their defloration and possibly future mental health and happiness to the mercy of the first fumbling inexperienced lout with audacity enough to get their pants off.

Sex, love, call it what you will, is to a woman her whole existence and has been said to be so through the ages. To a man, it is a thing apart. However we leave our daughters' awakenings in this respect in the hands of some youth experienced more in the arts of driving fast cars or fishing than he is in the handling of women. What he does know of women, he has learnt through trial and error, more through boredom than interest.

Is it any wonder, then, that women in the western world are still searching well into their thirties and after, not knowing what it is they seek, until eventually they meet up with the expert midway through life? What a waste of time and energy which profits none but the tourist agencies and airlines.

We can't educate the louts until they are done with their cars and other playthings, so better we educate our daughters and who better to choose as a tutor than their mothers, who, midway through life must surely have met one man with enough experience and patience.

If only more mothers, having sought and found what they were looking for, were generous enough, or perhaps sure enough, secure enough in themselves, to help their daughters experience early in life what they themselves may have taken a lifetime to acquire!

P.K.

FAMILY ALBUM

Most people today use the camera to record important things in their lives which they want to remember – weddings, their children growing up, holidays, outings and so on.

Providing you can do your own developing and printing – and even developing color film is not all that difficult – your family album can be much more complete. As well as having pictures of your radiant bride in her wedding gown, you can have photographs of the blushing bride at home later – in the nude. If you set your camera up on a tripod and use the delayed action setting, you can photograph yourselves in the nude together, kissing, cuddling, caressing or copulating. It can add a new dimension to your lives, rather like having a third person watching your moments of intimacy but without the embarrassment! And what delightful reminders to look back on in the future!

Although I have photographed many beautiful professional models, the pictures which mean most to me personally are those of my wife, which is why nude photography should not be kept in a separate compartment from personal photographs.

My wife is pretty without being glamorous but she is a shy girl who doesn't relish being photographed with her clothes on, let alone without them. She needed considerable persuasion before she finally posed for me in the nude. I well remember the first occasion. I had set up photoflood lights in our living room one evening to take some portraits of her. To add variety to the pictures, she changed her dress several times during the session

103

and when she had exhausted the clothes we had got out, I went upstairs to see what else I could find for her to wear. When I came down again, I brought with me her nylon nightdress and asked her to pose in that. She refused. I spent ages talking to her, cajoling and coaxing before she allowed herself to be persuaded. Only after I had pointed out that the nightie was not particularly transparent did she get undressed and put it on. I took a number of pictures of her in the nightdress, but when I asked her to take it off, I got a point-blank 'No.' Clearly nothing was going to persuade her, although normally she never minded me seeing her naked. I took a last couple of pictures of her in the nightie and then asked her to change to another seat, coming forward to place her in the position I wanted. Then before she realized exactly what I was going to do, I gently took hold of the hem of the nightie and pulled it up over her head. To my surprise she didn't stop me taking it off, although she was saying something to the effect, 'No, I don't want to.'

She sat down and I stepped back and started clicking away again while she was still protesting halfheartedly. She looked so shy and selfconscious as I took those first nude pictures of her that I realized why she had been so reluctant to pose. She didn't object to uncovering herself in front of me, but the camera seemed to her like a third person staring at her nakedness. It took a time for the atmosphere to thaw but eventually I got a photograph in which she was smiling. But when I asked her to open her legs, she looked disgusted. How I finally persuaded her to I can't remember, but it was only a brief movement, enough for one click of the shutter, and she wouldn't repeat it.

We now have pictures of us in the nude together – pictures of her kissing my body; playing with my penis; and even pretending to suck my penis (which she will not do). There have been pictures of her with her legs spread wide with my fingers stroking her, and also with me kissing her genitals. It took some time to get a picture of us having intercourse, because I often lost my erection while setting the camera. But eventually we managed a shot which records our union; and on remote beaches we have taken off our swimsuits for outdoor nude shots together.

I wonder how many keen photographers use their cameras, as I do, to record the really intimate moments in their lives for their own private albums.

O.T.

DAYDREAMER

Before I was married I used to have a daydream. I was attracted to the man I was working for (I don't think he was even aware of me as a woman). I used to masturbate thinking of him carrying me off to his private love-nest, tying me down and blindfolding me and slipping his penis inside me when I least expected it. This idea developed with him also having a couple of his friends present and all of them would take me and when they wished. I wouldn't know which one it was. This thought became such an obsession that I would find my mind wandering to it and visualizing the whole scene at work, oblivious of what was going on around me. My workmates thought I was a bit vacant at times.

I was always a daydreamer as a youngster. I used to love to imagine I was invisible and that I could go into any shop I fancied and take toys and sweets and money from the till. No one could ever catch me because they couldn't see me. In my teens I would wander around department stores and imagine what it would be like to shoplift, to take all the clothes and makeup and jewelry that took my fancy. I used to have recurring dreams of shoplifting and wake up very elated.

It's been years since I've indulged in any serious daydreaming until recently. I must stop it. I've been very down to earth since I got married and I want to stay that way. It's rather frightening to think what could happen to the world if everyone acted out their daydreams. What chaos could be caused! Perhaps it is basically wrong to have complete sexual freedom and maybe we should feel guilty if we go beyond a certain limit. The question is who is wise enough to set that limit?

Mrs. L.R.

Sexual fantasies are a common element of the experience of most human beings. In a survey conducted by Professor Paul Cameron of the University of Louisville, Kentucky, over 4,000 persons were interviewed, varying in age from 8 to 99, and it was found that among males sex crosses the mind about every other minute from the teen years through young adulthood and then diminishes to 1 minute out of 5 in middle age and then to 1 out of 10 in old age.

Female frequency is generally less and of shorter duration. Female teenagers report sex on their mind about 2 out of every

5 minutes, dropping to 1 out of 3 minutes in young adulthood, 1 out of 10 in middle age, and 1 out of 20 in old age.

This is some indication of the frequency of sexual thoughts, of which a great many are fantasies. Unfortunately some people become uncomfortable when thinking about sexual matters. Sometimes this discomfort results from lack of knowledge, anxiety caused by deeper fear of the unknown or anxiety caused by conflicts arising from sex-negative child-rearing practices. When a person believes that sex is dirty and evil, he also believes that sexual fantasies are dirty and evil. Some persons, like the author of this letter, find their sexual fantasies unacceptable because they consider them antisocial.

Actually, fantasy is frequently an aid to maintaining faithfulness in a relationship. Since many of us are sexually attracted to others, as well as to our mates, it enables us to 'enjoy' others without crossing over into overt behavior which would cause difficulties in our relationships. Also, it allows us to indulge in a wide variety of forbidden behaviour (masochism, incest, group sex, etc.) without incurring any risks. Many of the people who actually act out activities which may be hurtful to themselves or others are people incapable of fantasy.

When people can relax and accept their sexual fantasies, and enjoy them either as a prelude or an accompaniment to normal sexual experience, they tend to heighten the experience rather than to cause any difficulties. There is a great difference between fantasy and reality, and the freedom to experience fantasy and to know that it is not reality helps to develop mature sexual attitudes. – H.G.

TOO CLEAN SEX

One of the qualities which first attracted me to my wife was her immaculate appearance and the great care she took with her grooming. To me, such careful attention indicated a well-ordered and tidy mind.

I must admit that when we were first married I was a little surprised at the amount of time she spent looking after our new home, but I thought that this was a phase which most brides passed through, and I looked on it with more than a little amusement.

But now. I am afraid, that amusement is rapidly being trans-

106

formed into anger and bewilderment. After three years of marriage and the birth of our daughter, now aged two, my wife spends even longer cleaning, washing, dusting and tidying. If she sees me smoking she almost follows me around with an ashtray in her hand, and our poor little girl is washed and changed goodness knows how many times a day. Consequently it is almost impossible to relax in my own home.

Perhaps even this situation would be tolerable, but my wife has allowed her mania for cleanliness to enter our sex lives. As I have mentioned, at one time I found it attractive that she should want to bathe and beautify herself before coming to bed. This was all very well, but now I too am forced to have a bath every time I want to make love, or else she refuses me. Also, as soon as we have made love she leaps out of bed and into a bath herself, despite the fact that I have asked her not to do this.

Sometimes my anger and resentment is such that I feel like getting grease and dirt all over me just to spite my wife. That I should have such thoughts is worrying me, and I fear that unless my wife can be made to see that her behavior is extremist to the point of being ludicrous, our marriage will gradually fall to pieces. I have tried talking to her about this but she insists that I am making excuses to cover up my own laziness. While I am aware of the fact that dirt and foul odors can take much of the pleasure out of sex, the reverse can also be true.

R.T.

THE MUD BATH

As a keen transvestite, when business took me away from home for a period last summer I packed a complete set of undies, nylons, slip and panties, suspender belt and bra, together with a plaid micro-mini skirt and white nylon blouse.

Having explored my new surroundings in the first couple of evenings and found no other followers of the cult, I decided on the third evening to find a secluded spot somewhere in the countryside. I waited till 10:30 in the evening and placing my case in the rear of the car drove out of town. It was still quite warm and it took me half an hour before I found a likely locality, a little lane running alongside a wood. Having found space to park my car I collected my undies and wandered into the confines of the wood. I could still see quite easily and soon stumbled out in a sizable clearing with a carpet of lush grass sloping down to a small slowly flowing river.

Quickly I disrobed and donned my suspender belt and bra, drew on each nylon carefully and after securing them to my suspenders followed with my white nylon panties and mini skirt. Standing up and feeling the pull of my tightly suspendered nylons reawoke that sexy feeling and taking a few steps down toward the river's edge without my shoes on told me that a heavy dew had already begun to settle. Somehow the wet, soft ground did something to me for I wanted to feel the same virgin dampness soaking into my panties. Quickly I sat down, hoisting my mini skirt, and slid slowly down the slope so that the moisture quickly penetrated the nylon. Then the thought crossed my mind. 'If the dew has this effect, what would it be like to wade into the river until the water reaches and covers my panties?' And I waded in immediately, searching for a cavity in the river bed, which I soon found. Although the water was almost ice cold, I didn't mind, and let it rise over my knees and to the tops of my nylons. A further step and it was lapping against my crotch. Still moving forward, I felt first the lacy edging of my panties make contact and then they were completely submerged and hugging my form. Then I noticed about 20 yards along the bank what appeared to be a miniature sand bank. As I got nearer I realized it was a piece of ground which had earlier been flooded but which was now slightly above the level of the river and was a pool of soft mud.

Suddenly I wanted to wallow in the muddy ooze and completely foul my lovely white panties. Carefully I removed my mini skirt, trying not to get it more wet than I could help, and flung it out to the bank. I now stood in just my underwear. My foot sank into the mud, and I felt the soft mass sliding up past my calf. Holding on to a tree root, I let my legs sink in and experienced an utterly new sensation as the mud held me gently in its all-embracing caress. Slowly I moved my weight from one foot to the other, with each reversal sinking lower and lower, until, when the mud had almost reached my crotch, I came to the solid bed of the river. I now sat back and felt the beautiful soft brown mud oozing up over my genitals until the whole of my once lovely white panties was engulfed in the mire. Any movement now produced an electrifying thrill through my whole body and I was constantly having to break off just prior to the point of no return. I now had a full erection and to ease the situation I hauled it to freedom via the leg of my panties. As I moved up and down I felt sensations such as I had never dreamed possible, until finally, I flung myself forward and put my whole weight behind one long thrust into the soft, muddy depths, reaching an overpowering orgasm.

It was an experience I shall always remember. Sexual pleasure can come from almost any source.

S.T.

NEVER-ENDING DESIRE

A few years ago, when I met the one and only man in my life, I was a virgin. It took weeks of the art of gentle seduction before I finally gave him my body.

Now I find in fact we both enjoy our love games and love-making very much. Yet this man tells me I am a nymph, but at the same time would tell you I am neither lesbian nor bisexual. He also knows that I would not give myself to just any man to get satisfaction.

Sometimes I feel an overwhelming feeling and a need to have sex, but then again, unless it's my man I'm near, the feeling is just not there.

I will admit however, that if I get this feeling and he does not, all I have to do is slowly strip in front of him and things begin to happen. Another thing I will admit is that I do have a never-ending desire for sex, but only with this one man. It is a joke between us; he feels sure, or so he says, that I could lay on my back having violent love made to me for twenty-four hours and still want more.

Personally I see nothing wrong with enjoying plenty of sex. Do I sound like a nymphomaniac to you?

Miss J.F.

Nymphomania in its true form is a rare condition, and although it has many elements in common with promiscuity, the two states have quite different causes and effects. What is often termed nymphomania is usually promiscuity, relatively well controlled, probably highly selective and of a nature that would be considered relatively normal if found in the average male.

Nymphomania is a pathological condition accompanied by an intense and sustained sexual desire which cannot be relieved by intercourse or orgasm. In its true form it is exceptionally rare and, like most anomalies of this type, seems to be caused by unusual conditions of neuromuscular disease. Nymphomania is a compulsive form of sexual behavior and leads to irrational and self-defeating activities. Compulsivity of any type, whether it be in the realm of cleanliness, study, work or sex, is normally an indication of emotional stress.

There is nothing in Miss J.F.'s letter to indicate that she is a nymphomaniac. – F.

HOMOSEXUAL URGES

I am 44, married with one son. Most of the time I lead a normal, average life, but every now and then I feel like having an affair with a man or even a boy. I get a great urge to suck a penis and to have anal intercourse performed on me. I have never experienced this, and don't expect I ever shall, as I am afraid of the consequences for my wife and son if I were found out.

My wife sometimes puts her finger in my anus, which is most pleasant, but not often since she is not very keen. Also she lets me suck her off which I must admit gives me greater satisfaction than actual intercourse.

I should like your views and advice.

B.R.

PERIODIC YEARNINGS

I am 37 years of age and married, and find that my feelings in this matter are similar to B.R.'s in that a strong desire for homosexual intercourse arises periodically. This feeling is dominant at the moment and I find myself, for example, seeking out very crowded cars in subways. The sensation of my own thighs and penis pressed hard against the buttocks of another man – or conversely feeling someone behind me pressing against my bottom – produces in me a strange, lightheaded feeling.

My own experience of homosexual intercourse started very badly indeed in that I was raped at the age of 12 by a man of 40, in whose house I lived for some time as a war-time evacuee.

Initially, this man's technique was extremely primitive. I had not been in the house for more than a few days when his wife went out for the evening, leaving us alone. At this time I was not even aware of the existence of sexual intercourse between men, and I had no hesitation when he called me into his bedroom, saying he had something to show me. He certainly had, for when I unsuspectingly entered the bedroom he was already stripped naked and had achieved an erection that looked enormous to me. Without further ado he stripped me naked, threw me face down on the bed, and thrust his penis up inside me to the hilt. Naturally, without prior lubrication, I found this sudden full-scale penetration extremely painful, both at the time and for two or three days afterwards.

However, several days later when we were left alone again, I found that I was involuntarily hoping that he would take me again and, of course, I was not disappointed. On this second occasion, finding that I was quite willing, he lubricated me first, and then inserted his penis very gradually. In complete contrast to the previous occasion, I enjoyed the sensation of his penis thrusting up and down inside me immensely, and afterwards was more than willing to cooperate whenever he wanted intercourse with me.

During my period of about ten months in this house, intercourse occurred at least once a week, usually on the evening when the lady of the house was absent. After several weeks I was also introduced to the pleasures of flagellation. Sometimes I would be beaten before intercourse, but more often than not he would ask me to whip him after intercourse.

Although I am usually oriented toward women, I have had several encounters with other men since this time. The latter have always been older men than I and I have always played the passive role; I have never experienced homosexual intercourse as the active partner.

It is evident, therefore, that I find nothing unusual in B.R.'s periodic yearnings for sex with another man, though I think in my case they arose from my childhood experiences.

J.V.

Homosexuality, like most other human behavior, is not an either-all matter — but a question of degree. For example, among male homosexuals there are the extremely effeminate, lisping, cosmetic-using 'queens' who act as much like an exaggerated woman as possible, as well as the extremely masculine, domineering 'butch' type. (On certain masculinity-femininity tests he scores as more masculine than the average heterosexual male.) In addition, even persons who have never engaged in homosexual activities may have some homosexual feelings, either at a very low level or so strongly that they need to use every method of conscious control to avoid acting on them.

What, then, distinguishes the homosexual from the heterosexual? In my experience the most distinguishing characteristic of the homosexual is his self-image. Some men who engage in occasional homosexual activities never consider themselves homosexual, but when a man decides that he is homosexual, and organizes his perception of himself and his life along those lines, he becomes compulsively homosexual and considers himself incapable of relationships with the opposite sex. These men frequently enter into the homosexual or gay subculture, frequenting certain bars and restaurants, dressing in a particular style, decorating their homes in certain ways. They adopt a host of secondary characteristics in their allegiance to the gay world.

There are, of course, certain advantages to being a member of the gay community. For one, like members of most persecuted minorities, homosexuals have ties to each other. Being a homosexual can give one entree into a variety of social circles which are sometimes closed to anyone who is not part of that group. In some gay bars, for example, one can get lists of gay bars in other parts of the world so that a homosexual arriving in Copenhagen can find himself in a familiar milieu within 15 minutes after his arrival and find a lover within half an hour. Another advantage which many of my homosexual patients have mentioned is the economic one. A man going out with a woman is generally expected to take care of all the expenses for the evening. Homosexuals more frequently share expenses.

The major problem areas in homosexuality do not involve the homosexual who has found his identity, but the heterosexual who is fearful of his homosexuality, or the homosexual who is, in part, adopting the condemnatory attitude of society. Because society's attitude is so harsh, many men feel tremendous shame and embarrassment because they have experimented with homosexual activities, even though only once or twice.

Most men who are predominantly heterosexual occasionally have homosexual fantasies. In my experience I have found that as in other kinds of acting out, many people have been able to substitute fantasy for reality. Those who can embrace and enjoy their homosexual fantasies if they are so inclined, often feel less necessity for carrying them out in the real world.

Since society takes a much less stringent view toward female homosexuality, women are more likely to be able to have an occasional homosexual experience without necessarily condemning themselves in the same way men do. Obviously this relates to our society's attitude about males and females. As long as males are considered the 'superior' group, a man is going to be faced with greater condemnation when he deviates from the masculine role than a woman who deviates by acting like the 'superior' male sex. – H.G.

GENITAL TOUCH

My wife and I have been having an argument about the following point. She says that a man enjoys having his genitals fondled and played with by a woman because a latent enjoyable sexual feeling was aroused in this way by his mother when he was a baby.

Because of his physical formation and for hygienic reasons, a mother has to constantly wash, powder and generally take care of a boy's growing penis and the surrounding area, pulling back the foreskin regularly to make sure everything develops properly.

While all mothers get a thrill out of this, and love to see their sons' genitalia, some get an extra big kick and play with their boys longer than is necessary, some even masturbating their youngsters.

I say this is nonsense. Women love to have their privates fondled as much as men and mothers seldom do this to their daughters. The feeling is always there, in both sexes from birth, and develops towards adolescence.

Which of us is right?

J.G.

Both men and women like to have their genitalia fondled because of the physical sensations induced. Infants of both sexes are washed, powdered and touched in the genital area by their parents, while in the male infant the pulling back of the foreskin involves a slightly higher degree of handling. It's quite likely that these actions stay in a person's mind to some extent,

113

depending on his or her psychological makeup, and that their recall is pleasurable.

To say that all mothers get a thrill out of looking at and handling their sons' genitals and the implication that mothers 'play' with their sons' penises appears to be an assumption based on pure guesswork. Undoubtedly some mothers experience these feelings in the strong terms your wife uses but any sweeping statement beyond that is nothing more than speculation. – F.

ANAL INTERCOURSE

Why go to all the trouble and perhaps side effects of using contraceptives when a perfectly natural and delicious method of contraception is provided by nature. I refer to anal intercourse; not for the whole period of love-making, but for a short time before the male orgasm.

May I describe the method which I consider to be the most comfortable one?

The male should lie on his side across the bed. The female should lift her legs and place them across the male's thighs with her knees bent. It will be found that this position is just right for the insertion of the penis into the vagina. The male places one of his hands under the female's buttocks – a slight lift and a gentle squeeze does help. This way the female can have as many orgasms as she can manage. Some time before the male reaches his climax he introduces a lubricant into the female's anus using his finger. Having prepared the anus, if he is gentle he can insert his penis in the anus and continue his motion. At the same time he can continue to caress the female breasts and clitoris and insert his fingers into the vagina.

After final orgasm most women like to remain close in their lover's arms without withdrawal and the above position is very comfortable.

Many women, I know, will be initially repelled by the idea, but having once tried it most are delighted. I have been assured that the feeling of perfect safety without previous preparation or pills puts the female mind at rest.

This method allows complete flesh to flesh contact throughout and as withdrawal or rather change-over takes place at an early stage, there is no split-second risk of bad timing or of either partner being left in the air. This all contributes toward making the act even better than normal intercourse.

A point to be noted is that after the birth of several children, the female vagina does not grip the penis as tightly and so makes orgasm for both partners more difficult to achieve. Child-birth does not alter the anus to the same extent and the anal muscles are easily exercised during the act. This, in addition to the male caressing of vagina and clitoris can improve lovemaking for those who presently find it unsatisfactory.

J.S.

Re: anal intercourse, Kinsey writes: 'The anus, like the entrance to the vagina is richly supplied with nerves, but the rectum, like the depths of the vagina, is a tube which is poorly supplied with sensory nerves. However, the receiving partner often reports that deep penetration of the rectum may bring satisfaction which is, in many respects, comparable to that which may be obtained from a deep vaginal insertion.

'The anal area is erotically responsive in some individuals. In others it appears to have no particular erotic significance even though it may be highly sensitive to tactile stimulation. As many as half or more of the population may find some degree of erotic satisfaction in anal stimulation, but good incidence data are not available. There are some females and males who may be as aroused erotically by anal stimulation as they are by stimulation of the genitalia, or who may be more intensely aroused.'

In addition to the physiological explanation given by Kinsey, certain psychological factors are involved in the desire for anal intercourse.

Children frequently have the notion that intercourse takes place anally, rather than vaginally. Since their earliest erotic fantasies dealt with anal penetration, they thus tend to find such activity exciting as adults. Also, anal intercourse is still a taboo in the minds of many persons, and breaking the taboo becomes an additional source of sexual excitement.

The fantasy that anal intercourse is painful may intensify the desire for it. However, male homosexuals and women who practice anal intercourse have reported that it need not be painful if a person learns how to relax the sphincter and if a good lubricant is used.

Some authorities feel that there is some danger of infection if

115

the penis or finger is transferred from the anal area to the vagina. They recommend that anal intercourse, if desired, take place after vaginal entrance – not before.

As a birth control measure anal intercourse is not completely effective. There is still a slight possibility that the sperm will travel along the moist area separating the anus from the vagina. Although there is much lower probability of impregnation, there is still a possibility.

It should be noted that in many states any sexual activity other than vaginal intercourse between married partners is legally defined as criminal. Therefore anal intercourse, sometimes referred to as sodomy, is an offense in some states. In this connection Kinsey noted that if the laws were enforced throughout the country, 95% of the male population of the United States would be confined to penal institutions because of their sexual practices. – H.G.

CINDERELLA STORY

I have followed the letters on swapping and group sex and, truly, had been bewildered by it. Even though various writers said they thoroughly enjoyed the experience, I just couldn't understand how any woman could possibly go through with it. So I mentioned it to a girlfriend of mine who amazed me by confessing she and her husband occasionally indulge in group sex.

I was quite shaken by this revelation, but as a result, I have come to understand at least one of the reasons why married couples engage in this practice. My friend has been married for three years, and I knew her before she got married. Hers was a kind of Cinderella story. She originally came to this country as a child's nurse from Sweden. I met her, and we became friendly when she was working for friends of ours. Through them, she met a charming and wealthy boy from a very good family who immediately fell in love with her. She was terribly happy when they became engaged and later married and told me she intended to be a very good wife and make her marriage work, as she had come from a very unhappy background.

To all appearances she has indeed become a very good wife and has been quite accepted by his family and friends. However, she has never been really in love with him or terribly excited by him sexually. She says she is a very sexy girl. Rather than indulge in furtive affairs and endanger her marriage, she gradually introduced the idea of sex parties to her husband who was quite willing to go along. She insists she gets the sex she feels she really needs this way, and it makes her feel more affectionate toward her husband for enjoying it with her. I rather think he enjoys showing off his lovely wife to his friends and, anyway, she is by far the most dominant of the two, and he would be swayed by her in any family decisions, I'm sure. I suppose he gets some comfort from the thought she's not likely to run off with another man because of a sexual attraction, and he obviously really loves her.

In a situation such as theirs I can see how group sex helps their marriage work. It must be remembered she wasn't in love with her husband when she married him. This kind of sexual experience wasn't introduced to alleviate boredom where there was total love and attraction before. It wasn't used to recapture a lost feeling.

Most couples don't want community marriage, just a little sexual variety from time to time. I'm afraid to try it myself, in case seeing my husband make love to another woman unleashes uncontrollable feelings of jealousy and resentment which might interfere with other aspects of our marriage. I suppose that's a result of my suppressions and guilt connected with sex, but even if that were true, these are dangerous emotions to start fooling around with unnecessarily.

Mrs. G.D.

SUPPORTS SWINGERS

One strong point in support of the swingers that will have the backing of many a husband married to a frigid wife is the fact that although pornography does not generally arouse women, observing sexual intimacy in others apparently does. I could imagine many husbands taking their wives to a swinging meeting just to get them 'switched on', then rushing them home before the feeling wears off. This fact seems to have escaped the great Dr. Kinsey as he stated that on observing sexual action there was a very rare response in females. Perhaps things have changed since he wrote those words.

J.W.

I have worked with 'swingers' for many years, and have never found their activities a cure for either frigidity or impotence. A person who has to look at swinging as a form of therapy probably still feels somewhat guilty about the idea.

As in many other kinds of fantasies, acting out the fantasy does not increase its power of erotic stimulation; in fact, it frequently has the opposite effect, and after comparatively few experiences, most couples are surfeited and go back to their previous lifestyles. However, those who look to swinging as a spur to diminished libido unfortunately find it only temporarily helpful and quickly develop a tolerance so that they need wilder and wilder scenes.

I believe that one of the major reasons why men are attracted to 'swinging' and troilism is their difficulty in believing that women, too, have strong sexual urges. Seeing the women they are involved with or seeing other women respond with excitement to the group sex scene helps convince them that women too are sexual beings.

Group sex provides opportunities for exhibitionism and voyeurism – displaying oneself sexually and watching others in the sex acts. Many people subconsciously wish to do these things, but would never do it on their own. In these situations, where all consent, the wish can be fulfilled.

In situations involving two couples, the voyeuristic or watching element is generally most strong. In a way it is the re-enactment of what Freudians call 'primal scene' – the child intruding upon the parents while they are engaged in sexual intercourse. The forbidden nature of this experience, or merely even the thought of invading others' sexual privacy, is taken as a challenge to some people: they feel they must confront what they fear. Instead of giving in to fears and avoiding frightening situations, what is called a reaction formation takes place – they do just the opposite.

Contrary to the popular notion that men who engage in orgies are superpotent, many need this kind of extra stimulation to be potent at all. Orgies are particularly appealing to inhibited men who have a great fear of rejection. They are also appealing to men who are acutely worried about whether they can measure up to other men and deserve female companionship. For some, the group situation even provides an opportunity to act out homosexual urges without guilt.

Whereas the swingers I knew years ago tended to be people

118

outside the mainstream of conventional society, today many highly conventional couples meet weekly with other like-minded couples for group sex, the same as they formerly met to play bridge. I believe that one of the reasons this phenomenon is growing involves the sense of isolation – the feeling of being alienated – which disturbs so many. People find it increasingly difficult to establish close human contact. Group sex may be an effort to establish contact with others. For many, it is an attempt to achieve instant intimacy. – H.G.

EXTRAMARITAL PETTING

We've discussed the pros and cons of having sex with another couple or couples, and have come to the conclusion that we would take the plunge if we happened to meet the right couple and if the right situation happened to present itself. We're aware of the potential dangers that are inherent within such a situation, but we both have enough confidence in and love for one another to enjoy this novel form of erotica.

Lately, we've begun to indulge in 'petting' with other couples at parties – something we would never have dared to do in the past. We both find it rather exciting, and it tends to serve as preliminary loveplay for the eventual coitus which takes place when we get home. We've seen no discussion on marital, or rather extramarital petting. Obviously, it's more acceptable and easier to indulge in than group sex – but somehow I feel it's a more hypocritical and dishonest form of extramarital sex for those couples who indulge in it.

R.T.

Extramarital petting, like premarital petting, is frequently the activity of those who do no want to engage in actual intercourse but enjoy the stimulation. Some couples enjoy extramarital petting because they find their marital sex life consists almost exclusively of coitus, and many of them want more of the simple pleasures of petting. Unfortunately, because they cannot tell each other that they would sometimes enjoy petting rather than intercourse, they have to find others to pet with.

According to the Kinsey investigators, one-sixth of a sample of more than 1,000 females had engaged in extra-marital petting although they had never engaged in extra-marital coitus.

Many women apparently enjoy the excitement of this kind of activity, but prefer not to experience the guilt that would be involved in actual intercourse with someone other than their husbands.

However, as our age becomes more permissive, many of those who would formerly engage only in extramarital petting are moving on to extramarital coitus. – H.G.

SOCIAL SEX

Both my wife and I would like to clarify certain misconceptions about what we refer to as 'social sex' otherwise known as group sex, wife-swapping, etc., which have appeared in various letters.

Our credentials for having some knowledge on the subject are as follows: We've been happily married for over 20 years, and for the past five years have discovered that variations in social sex have helped us immeasurably in keeping our marriage and especially its sexual side, stimulating, and decidedly never dull.

A certain number of your correspondents have stressed the dangers inherent within the playing of this sexual game. Admittedly, those couples who indulge in social sex because they feel it will revive a dying marriage – or who use it because they have lost all feeling for one another – are only kidding themselves. If their marriage is on it last legs, it would be terribly naïve to think that communal sex would remedy the situation. It would only hasten its demise.

I have known married men who have gone into social sex because of their fears of not being able to satisfy their wives sexually and wives who have played the game not because they were particularly interested in doing so but because they knew it was what their husbands wanted. These plus other wrong reasons can do more harm than good to a marital relationship.

Over the past five years, we have met a number of other couples, who like ourselves are happily married and who play, not because they're bored with one another and with marriage, but because it's one of the games that married folk can play in order to keep themselves and their marriage alive and alert and exciting. It's fun when a group of compatible couples are able to shed their clothes, and their inhibitions. How much more sensual and erotic it is to dance in the nude or to go swimming in the nude or to play games in the nude!

There's a bit of voyeurism in all of us which in turn acts as a powerful sexual stimulant. Watching people completely uninhibited, dancing, indulging in loveplay or even in variations of intercourse is a superb stimulant, especially for middle-aged men, who, if they were honest with themselves, would admit to their need for sexual stimulus – no matter how much they love and adore their wives.

A man is not responsible for the way nature created his nervous system. But he is responsible for his actions, and if he would only face the truth and satisfy, instead of frustrating his needs, he would be a much happier man, and a vastly better husband.

We feel that only a small minority of married couples are emotionally and intellectually equipped to play. The majority of married folk are so infected with sexual guilt, repression and fear, the very thought of social sex, or wife-swapping as they call it, fills them with revulsion – or at least, so it would appear on the surface. Deep down, I am certain there are an impressive number of married men whose fantasies while making love with their wives are not too dissimilar from what the titillating Sunday press would refer to as sex orgies. What virile male, indeed, would not be stimulated by a scene in which he is surrounded by nude women writhing in ecstacy of sheer physical pleasure. For most men, trapped in their own fears and ignorance, their only contact with the above will be via their fantasies. For those relatively few liberated men (and women) it will be more reality than fantasy.

The reason for this lengthy letter is not to persuade married people to partake of the joys of communal sex but to caution them against condemning and slandering what we consider to be a delightfully erotic indoor (and sometimes) outdoor sport. As the old saying goes, 'If you haven't tried it ...'

D.G.

RECIPE FOR A HAPPY MARRIAGE

Although I appreciate that some people may require variety in the form of extramarital affairs or spouse-swapping to keep their marriage alive, these are things that I could not accept. If my husband wanted variety, then I would prefer not to know about it officially, although I feel sure I would 'sense' it somehow. No doubt this will prove that I am possessive and selfish, but if my husband was willing to share me, and have me share him, with others, this would be absolute rejection for me.

The easiest way to combat marital boredom is, to my mind, by taking on outside relationships. It isn't very difficult for a man or a woman to find temporary excitement elsewhere. It is much harder to maintain excitement within one's marriage, and still try to raise children, keep house and keep oneself attractive and interesting. It is very easy, and very tempting sometimes when one is inundated with all the 1001 things that belong to wife- and mother-hood, to lose sight of the fact that one is a woman.

It takes extra time – and time which is sometimes at a premium – not to just 'let go'. But when a woman knows that she can still 'turn on,' and be 'turned on' by her husband – that he enjoys the living and loving that make up their marriage, and while she knows that he chose her and is content with her, she is able to put everything of which she is capable into making him happy and showing him that he is still the greatest.

Marriage isn't only good sex . . . it's also all the compromises and sacrifices that help two people live together. It's a wife making sure that her husband has clean shirts, and a good meal – dressing to attract him, spending time listening to him, encouraging him in his ambitions and hopes, and never, never, taking him for granted.

It's a husband being kind, and showing, by his actions, that his wife is important to him beyond any temporary excitement another woman might offer. It's knowing, after many years of living together, that one wouldn't want to be married to anyone else, and it's showing this, by the innumerable little 'acts of love' each partner does for the other.

Mrs. J.C.

UGLY INCLINATION

Most normal men prefer girls who are reasonably good looking, perhaps not in the beauty queen class, but at least having one or two saving features. This is not the case with me. It is quite the opposite. When attempting to procure a girl for the purposes which most men require I find it very stimulating to try to get the most disgusting-looking woman I can lay my eyes on: the uglier the girl the greater the pleasure I receive. I manage to make quite a few conquests, as the ugly girls are very willing to participate in sex play with me because, I should think, they realize that they won't receive many other offers.

When I was last at our local camera club with a friend, we noticed that a new member was in our midst. One could not really miss this girl as she was the most revolting-looking thing I have ever seen – short and extremely fat, with lots of hair on her legs and a good growth of moustache on her top lip. As soon as I saw her I wanted to make love to her, thinking of lots of different things I would like to do with her. When I told my friend what my thoughts were, he was so disgusted he left me and went home.

After a while I managed to persuade this girl to come to my flat after the meeting. As we walked together I was very embarrassed by her because all the men we passed started to laugh and make fun of me.

After having a drink at home I got her to bed easily. After doing things to her that I would not like to write about, I eventually reached a climax. When this happened I seemed to realize how ugly she was (as is always the case) and proceeded to urinate over her. She didn't like this and ran out of my flat screaming. I then felt very disgusted with myself.

Will you please advise me because if I carry on like this for much longer I think I may do something that I will regret?

N.C.

I have known a number of men with preferences similar to N.C.'s. Their choice was determined by a number of factors. Some felt that ugly women would be grateful for the attention shown them, and therefore would be easier conquests; others were fixated on ugly women because of some earlier sexual experience; still others had the idea that sex itself was ugly and therefore required an ugly partner.

Many men in our society apparently separate sexual from affectional desires. They tend to divide women into two classes: good women like mother and sister for affection, and bad (ugly) women for sex. Thus they deliberately seek sexual gratification from women for whom they can experience no affectional response and ones whom they find unattractive in every way.

What seems to disturb N.C. more than his preference for ugly

123

women is the disgust he feels after orgasm, which he then trans-
fers to his sexual partner in sadistic, brutal behavior. I have
found this type of behavior closely tied to a feeling that sex in
general is ugly, violent and brutal. Such belief becomes the core
of the problem. This split between affectional and sexual drives
prevents many men from achieving full satisfaction either in
sexual or in loving relationships. – H.G.

... AND PUPPY DOGS' TAILS

When my boyfriend and I first started making love, I found I
had a keen sexual appetite, and wanted sex on any occasion that
presented itself. We lived together and later married. Since then
my desire for intercourse has declined.

I find that I abhor the idea of the penis. I cannot hold or
caress it and when it becomes moist I cannot bear to be near it
as it repulses me in the same way that worms and slimy snails
do, and always have done for as long as I can recall. My fear of
worms and snails is so great that I think I would faint if I
touched one, and a moist penis resembles these in my mind. I
have tried desperately to overcome this fear but I find myself
loathing it more. I cannot kiss using my tongue as this too
repulses me.

The problem inhibits me and our relationship tremendously.
I am reluctant to try new things, such as different positions, or
fellatio, and I find it difficult to become aroused. I must point
out that our relationship is such that there is no moral inhibition
whatsoever between us so far as talking this over is concerned.
It is just that when the opportunity arises for me to do what I
know I would really like to do, I cannot manage anything.

We would be most grateful if you could enlighten our problem.

Mrs. D.S.

You describe very clearly a phobic anxiety, and also illustrate
an important psychological phenomenon – 'generalization.'

A phobia simply means an unreasonable fear or dread associ-
ated with some object or situation. Some examples of sexually
associated phobias are: ophidiophobia *– fear of snails;* hel-
minthophobia *– fear of worms, and* coitophobia *– fear of*
coitus. There are many more.

In your case the previously established dread of worms has, as you say, become associated with the penis, especially the aspect of 'moisture and slime', qualities which repulse you. In consequence coitus has become abhorrent. This neurotic transfer of fear to the penis exemplifies the principle of generalization which simply states that anxiety, or fear or revulsion etc., which is associated with any object, will tend also to become fixed on other objects which resemble the original in some way.

An early classical illustration of this important psychological law is afforded by the famous case of Albert, a small boy, who in an experiment was made to fear white rats. Albert's phobia, however, generalized to many other animals and even inanimate objects which bore some similarities to white rats. Interestingly, the closer the resemblance to the original fear-producing stimulus (white rats), the greater the anxiety. Thus mice evoked considerably more anxiety in Albert than did balls of white cotton wool, which just made him feel uneasy.

The roots of phobias are usually found in early unpleasant experiences. In your case it is possible that as a child you suffered a 'psychologically traumatic experience' in which worms and/or snails figured prominently. You may or may not be able to recall such an experience, since extremely powerful traumatic events may be repressed from consciousness; these memories, inaccessible to ordinary recall, may only be available through the use of hypnosis or drug-induced abreaction (psychological exploratory) techniques.

Behavior therapy, a recent addition to psychic therapies, may offer a speedy recovery for some phobias. Your case would seem to lend itself to 'hierarchial desensitization', a variety of behaviour therapy by which phobias can often be quickly cured.

Essentially this aims to remove your phobia by teaching you to remain physically and mentally relaxed while being confronted with phobic stimuli (snails, worms, penis) starting with the least, and progressing to the most disturbing, as desensitization proceeds. In practice the commonest method of presenting the noxious stimuli would be to instruct you to imagine them visually. However, photographs, or even real objects could be used. – F,

NIGHT SHIFT

Some ten years ago, when I was 25, I was a nurse in a large London hospital, and masturbation of the younger male patients by us nurses was then at its height.

There were four of us who indulged freely in this practice, although of course we had to be discreet and selected our fortunate victims very carefully for fear of discovery.

I used to get a tremendous thrill, as I still do, from stroking a limp penis to erection, and with the sight and feel of the flowing semen, I experienced a climax which is completely satisfying, not requiring any self-manipulation whatever.

In fact, I was a virgin, and completely untouched intimately by any male, until my wedding night, and yet I had manhandled dozens of penises during my teens and early 20s; my excitement being derived purely from the feel of a penis in my hands, followed by the sight of the seminal fluid.

My own fetish goes even further than I have described in that I found very early on that I definitely preferred the sight and feel of a circumcised penis; the bare, unprotected head looks so vulnerable and somehow helpless that I cannot resist playing with it to watch the ensuing orgasm. My husband, who has seen this letter, is a 'roundhead' and can certainly vouch for this. Also I think the circumcised glans has a nice clean, dry appearance, and I feel much more inclined to suck the penis to ejaculation.

Before I got married, my breasts were a constant source of embarrassment, being almost nonexistent, and barely filling an A cup. However, once married and consuming a far more frequent and regular oral intake of semen, my bust size went from 34 to 37 in 18 months. Of course, I intend to maintain this vital statistic, and many a happy evening is spent with my hubby lying on the sofa, trying, not too successfully, to watch TV while I am lying between his thighs, teasing and playing with fingers and tongue, sometimes for hours at a time.

I hope female readers may benefit from what I know to be a sure-fire formula for keeping both yourself and your man happy.

Mrs. L.R.

SEMEN FETISH

Reading about extra services provided by nurses vividly recalled my own experience some 23 years ago when, at the age of

19, I spent 12 weeks as a private patient in a large hospital. My private room allowed almost unlimited visiting and my family usually visited me in the afternoons and my girlfriend two or three evenings a week.

One of the night nurses was especially friendly and it was fairly late in the evening when this particular girl first stayed to talk at length and said how fed up I must be being parted for so long from such a beautiful young girl. (Although only 16 years of age at the time my girlfriend was indeed stunning and was later to become a familiar name in the entertainment world.) I cannot now recall exactly what led up to it, but before the nurse left me, I had been 'manually seduced' with obviously experienced fingers. This developed into a nightly occurrence whenever she was on duty and I assumed that she was genuinely trying to be helpful. It was all rather clinical but nevertheless enjoyable, although I made no attempt to touch her in any way.

However, after I had been discharged from the hospital I thought it appreciative to take my nurse to dinner, and we later returned to her quarters for a late coffee and what I expected and hoped would be a further demonstration of my thanks! I was not allowed even to kiss her; but within a very short time she was kneeling before me as I sat in a chair and masturbating me in a more erotic and enjoyable way that I have ever experienced either before or since; such was her expertise that I came three times without difficulty. On each occasion she seemed to reach some sort of orgasm herself while I was ejaculating.

Afterwards we talked and she even apologized for her behavior, which she attributed to her experience during night duties in the ward. She found that many patients masturbated after the ward lights had been dimmed and that she got an immense thrill from watching them which reached a climax when she felt they were ejaculating. She also admitted to my surprise that, although a virgin, the buildup of excitement was strong enough to induce a satisfying orgasm when semen made contact with her hand.

I have not noticed any reference to a 'semen fetish' but I wonder whether this is as isolated as I would think or expect. I have known two or three girls since who, having satisfied themselves through intercourse, have preferred to watch a manually produced ejaculation rather than receive the sperm in their vagina – and this has had nothing to do with contraception.

R.S.

127

MILES OF JOY

I don't know how any woman can find an erect penis unpleasant; indeed I regard it as the means by which a woman receives the most glorious and exquisite sensations of her life.

In the four years of my courtship (I should add that I am now married) my fiancé and I had intercourse on an average of 10 times a month or 120 times a year. This meant that during our courtship we had intercourse about five hundred times.

My first thought when I saw my boyfriend's trouser leg showing a bulge was that it was a compliment to me, inasmuch that I meant enough to him to cause him to want me in that way. It gave me a wonderful thrill when I first touched it through the material. The next thrill came when I saw it for the first time in all its glory, hard and upstanding. A little shiver of delight ran down my spine as I touched for the first time what was to give me supreme joy.

As my husband's penis is roughly six inches long in erection, we reckon that allowing for two inches remaining inside on each outward stroke, four inches of it are returned on each stroke he makes forward. We both enjoy a movement of fifty or sixty strokes a minute for at least ten minutes which means I receive four inches, five hundred times or over fifty yards each time we have sex. On that reckoning, during those four years, I have received, with the utmost joy and rapture, more than 12 miles of erect penis!

We girls, if we are honest enough to admit it, are just as drawn to the 'flesh that stands in homage' as the owners of that flesh are 'to enter our shrine'. I openly admit that I am looking forward to 'many more miles' with my husband.

Mrs. K.N.

DIFFERENT STROKES

Mrs. K.N.'s enthusiasm delights me but surely, she has to work a little harder – or is it longer? – for her mileage.

A mirror will show her that she doesn't receive her husband's full six inches with each thrust, so perhaps should reduce her calculations by an inch at a time – variation, according to position would give about this average. (Not a scientific figure but an impression gained from observation.)

Having on occasions played around with a stopwatch myself, I must query '50 or 60 strokes a minute for at least 10 minutes'.

Ten minutes or more – yes! But 50 or 60 strokes every minute – no! Or Mr. K.N. is a better man than I, and many others. Perhaps it is possible in the last minute before climax, but on an average, over 10 minutes, I would suggest about 30 strokes a minute.

I wonder if Mr. and Mrs. K.N. could be persuaded to do a little experimentation and find out what it actually is and not what it feels like, which is what I am sure Mrs. K.N. has noted.

A.D.

NEXT 12 MILES

My wife and I were highly amused and appreciative of the well-developed sense of humor shown by Mrs. K.N. in her letter about receiving, with the utmost joy and rapture, in four years, 'more than 12 miles of her husband's erect penis'.

No one would wish to poke fun at this performance, nor disparage her receptivity in any way, but we do feel strongly that her husband did not appear to be given sufficient praise or recognition. Let us then at least uphold Mr. K.N.'s effort, for we calculate that his penis was traveling at an incredible speed – no mean feat!

Mrs. K.N. informs us that she openly admits to looking forward to many more miles with her husband – presumably over the period of the next four years. Pausing momentarily, only to consider the excessive wear and tear on the stair carpet, we are inclined to wonder whether or not she has ever given any serious thought to rapturously receiving her next 12 miles in one fell swoop, as it were, which we calculate would last for three days, 11 hours, 20 minutes!

In the event that this alternative suggestion, for some obscure reason, is unacceptable, then Gentlemen, let us now all be upstanding in order to wish Mr. and Mrs. K.N. a very Happy and Joyful New Year.

S.S.

RESETTING THE ODOMETER

Mrs. K.N. is being somewhat modest in her 'mileage' claim of over 12 miles for the coital distance 'traveled' by her and her husband! The correct figure, based on the information she quotes, is in fact, 15.15 miles! Her calculation is based on insertion distance only, but the total 'travel' is of course, 30.3 miles, quite a distance, even to walk.

I feel that it would be a bad thing to regard sexual intercourse in terms of mileage especially if one happens to be a motorist!

R.A.

NOT FOR BEGINNERS

My wife and I recently discovered a new and interesting way of heightening our sexual pleasure. Shortly before Christmas, I brought home a very large black plastic garbage container, and left it in the hall. We had had a few drinks, and when my wife suggested that we should get into it and make love, I thought she was joking. However, I cautiously agreed, and to my surprise we found it quite easy to intertwine our limbs inside, although our movements were naturally restricted.

I cannot describe the curious feeling of security which this lent to the occasion, but we both did agree that the feeling of the cold black plastic on our naked bodies provided stimulation never before experienced.

One feels that couples should combine to explore new ways of keeping their sexual practices exciting.

T.R.

TYPICAL OR AN EXCEPTION?

My wife and I enjoy sex, but although I would like to experiment and try other positions, she insists I make love to her in the old uninspiring way of 'man on top position'.

My wife has a lovely body and knows how to use it to please. I have bought her scanty pants, G-strings, tiny bras and many other exciting clothes, but she refuses to wear them. However, I have purchased several items for sexual pleasure which give her wonderful sensations and deep satisfaction. Among these is a large rubber dildo, which, although she requires a little persuasion, she enjoys to the full.

I personally would also enjoy meeting other couples and trying group sex. She talked about it, but in the end dismissed the subject out of hand. When I am making love to her and she is reaching the point of no return, she likes me to talk to her in

130

gutter language, pretending she is about to be fucked by a stranger with the penis and balls of a stallion. I know I would enjoy watching her being made love to by such a well-built man, and she would also enjoy it, but she constantly refuses to cooperate.

She will watch blue films and look at photographs of the sex act and laughingly comment on them. Yet will not stroke my penis without me placing her hand upon it, nor will she perform fellatio upon me, and yet she and I enjoy cunnilingus.

Are these contradictions typical, or is my wife an exception?

K.O.

Certainly in sex many people feel free about some activities, inhibited about others. Your wife is no exception.

We frequently regard inconsistency of behavior as a problem when we do not get the response we want. If the inconsistency meets our own needs, then it becomes compatibility. – R.G.

CRUCIFORM POSITION

With advancing years, the joints become less supple. The following method which I call the 'cruciform position' is worth a trial. I have not seen it described in any of the manuals I have read but it can scarcely be a complete novelty.

The couple lie at right angles to each other with their legs intertwined to bring their genitals into proximity. The woman lies on her back with her left leg stretched out and her right leg partly drawn up. The man lies on his side and passes his left leg under both of the woman's legs and his right leg under her right leg and over her left leg. Her left thigh is thus encircled by the man's thighs and his scrotum and perineum rest against the inner side of her left thigh. The woman's right leg rests on her partner's hip or waist. The penis now points at the woman's vulva and can be rubbed against her clitoris and finally inserted into the vaginal orifice. The man can now move his body to bring it more nearly parallel to that of the woman so that he can reach her hip with his right hand to give himself purchase and can also fondle her breasts or manipulate her clitoris with his fingers.

With a separate pillow for his head, both parties are now lying completely relaxed and comfortable. Pelvic movements by both partners cause keen stimulation and the woman's sensation can be augmented by drawing her partner's right inner thigh onto her clitoris. The man derives his satisfaction from the friction of the sensitive under side of his penis against the side wall of the vagina and also from the contact of his scrotum and perineum with the woman's thighs. The feeling of gripping something soft between one's thighs is an added pleasure.

If the woman is slow to reach orgasm, she is in a good position to apply digital stimulation to her own clitoris. By doing this, she can control the state of her arousal and the man is free to move his penis inside her vagina or lie doggo as he pleases. By stopping all movement at the threshold of orgasm and resting for a minute or two before resuming, the act of coition can be prolonged for as long as desired but eventually the desire for completion becomes irresistible and like all good things, comes to its inevitable culmination.

In our own case, it is generally my wife who first reaches the point of no return but I am always very close behind her and we enjoy a mutual crescendo of sensations. I should think that this position is also one that would be found suitable by lesbian couples for the mutual stimulation of their genitals as practiced in tribadism.

R.V.

VAGINAL vs. CLITORAL ORGASM

A magazine article has sparked off an interesting discussion among my women friends. One afternoon six of them were at my home. One of the girls spotted our copy of Forum and the discussion turned to the subject of female orgasm. Surprisingly our group was split into two camps. There were those, myself included, who maintained that there was a definite difference between a clitoral and a vaginal orgasm, while the others claimed that there was no difference whatsoever either in sensation or intensity.

I maintained that the difference in sensation is due to the fact that in one case the tension is built up in the vagina (internally) and in the second instance it begins in the clitoris (externally). Consequently the vaginal orgasm is slower and more overwhelming than the clitoral orgasm which is extremely sharp and intense. I can best make a descriptive differentiation by using two images; 'stabbing' seems to go with the clitoral orgasm and 'spreading', with the vaginal orgasm. I would not like to say that one is more satisfying than the other, but would maintain that most women enjoy vaginal orgasm most, for obvious psychological reasons.

As mentioned, two of my friends agreed with me while the other three claimed that we were talking nonsense and that an orgasm is an orgasm.

Mrs. J.S.

As a woman, I would like to join the discussion raised by Mrs. J.S. and friends about vaginal vs. clitoral orgasm.

Recent scientific research, particularly by Masters and Johnson, indicates that there is no such thing as a vaginal orgasm without a clitoral orgasm. They observed hundreds of men and women during masturbation and intercourse and noted that all orgasms happen in the same way – in the clitoris. The clitoral and vaginal orgasm form one anatomical entity. The orgasm reaction is generalized to all the pelvic sex organs and is the same regardless of the method or area of stimulation. It may be the result of direct manual or oral stimulation applied to the clitoris, direct pressure resulting from the penis thrusting in the vagina during intercourse, or stimulation of other erogenous zones such as the breasts.

To say that there is no physiological difference is not to say there is no difference in sensation and intensity. Indeed there is. Since each one of us brings our individual reactions to other aspects of living – we respond differently to food, painting, music – the same is true with sex. Orgasm involves not only physiological factors (stimulation) but psychological ones as well – R.G.

WOMEN IN LOVE

Men today have become obsessed with giving a woman sexual pleasure, which they measure only by the number or intensity of orgasms she has during a 'session.' He forgets that a woman does, of course, respond to a good performance in bed and if the man is skillful and his partner has no sexual hang-up she's bound to have her climax eventually. But after it's all over, she may look at him as a total man and think, 'Ugh'.

To me, sex isn't just a good tumble on the bed. It's the feeling that my husband is the center of my existence. He's the man I have in mind when I buy my clothes and wonder, will I appeal to him in my new dress? And I love him more when he notices I've changed my hair or when he says he doesn't enjoy seeing a film without me, than when he tells me he has an erection for me.

Sex is in little private jokes and secret smiles across the table at breakfast, in telling me I'm the prettiest girl at the party and showing me he means it by not flirting in my company. Sex is preparing a special meal together and exchanging innermost thoughts over a bottle of wine, in the gentle kiss at the back of the neck and holding hands watching television. Sex is expressed in bed, in passion, in the warmest, closest caresses and affirmation of love for each other. All love is sex and sex is also, sometimes, orgasm; but for a woman in love it is merely a bonus.

Mrs. R.L.

BONDAGE SHARING

My wife and I are bondage enthusiasts, and in our frequent talks we have tried to analyze the motives which attract us to it.

There is no doubt that the majority of women really enjoy being dominated by the men they love and thoroughly enjoy uninhibited sex with their partners. Being subjected to bondage can add tremendously to their pleasure, especially as they can fantasize freely, even imagining that they are being raped and helpless to prevent it. This my wife has freely admitted to me.

But equally so, since a partnership based on genuine love requires that all pleasures and responsibilities should be shared, it is essential that the male partner accede freely to any demands made on him. Thus, to willingly submit himself to bondage indicates no sense of inferiority on his part. Rather, it is further evidence of his affection for her and his desire to share equally. There are often occasions when a woman likes temporarily to adopt the dominant role, in which she can be free to do anything possible to please and satisfy her male.

During our weekend bondage sessions we take it in turn to accept the dominated role and this most assuredly maintains our ardor and prevents any risk of boredom. And I find that for me to adopt this role is in no way contrary to normal male status. Instead, I am allowing my partner to express her passion and sexuality to the utmost extent, and with complete freedom to let her imagination run riot. I cannot think of anything more exciting than to be trussed up helpless by my wife and to gaze on her naked body as she goes to work on me, fully aware that she is in complete control, so that even though I am in desperate need of an orgasm, I cannot achieve this until she brings it about by one means or another.

The same is equally true when it is her turn to submit to bondage. Every part of her lovely body is at my disposal and she revels in being excited by my caresses almost to the point of screaming. The frequency and intensity of her orgasms are far greater than during normal lovemaking.

The combination of fellatio, cunnilingus and bondage has had fantastic results, and the restricted partner quickly reaches a peak of ecstasy beyond words to describe.

Recently we have acquired several additional items of equipment, notably two vibrators, a dildo, and a leather gag. We have tremendous fun with the vibrators, especially when my wife is trussed up and I can use both of them simultaneously on two highly erogenous zones. The dildo has a variety of uses, and when she has me immobilized she takes a delight in inserting it in my rectum while using her hands to manipulate my penis and scrotum. The gag is most effective, but is used only when severe restriction is imposed, and only for limited periods of time. It certainly adds to one's sense of helplessness, especially when the wearer is made to walk about the house and is unable to make any protests against unexpected attacks.

We are fortunate in that we are both equally interested in bondage – it's not something a husband or wife should force on an unwilling partner – and the stimulation it gives us plays an important role in keeping our love for each other fresh and exciting.

A.L.

A certain amount of playacting enhances sex for many people. In the case of Mr. and Mrs. A.L., the bondage is obviously not treated very seriously and both of them take turns in enacting the role of slave and master.

Many individuals who enjoy acting out bondage sexual fantasies may in every other respect seem to be quite assertive. A friend of mine is a highly successful psychiatrist and director of a large mental hospital. I had seen her frequently at professional meetings where she had no hesitation in speaking assertively and even aggressively and challenging some of the acknowledged authorities in the field.

When she consulted me for therapy, she explained that she was incapable of orgasm during sexual intercourse unless she was first tied and physically abused: 'The most exciting man I ever met was John. I'll never forget the first time I came to his apartment. After some petting he suddenly stood up and sternly commanded me. 'Take your clothes off.' I did and felt myself growing weak in the knees at his brutal attitude. But he did not stop there. 'Go to the closet,' he ordered me, 'and take the whip you deserve.' Obediently I went to the closet and chose a riding crop. I came back and gave it to him. 'Bend over,' he commanded, and he started to beat me across my behind. While he was beating me he entered me anally. I found the pain exquisite and had an enormous orgasm. On other occasions he blacked my eyes or left bruises all over my body. He was a real man.'

This lady had a strict Teutonic father who rarely paid attention to her except to beat her when she misbehaved. She experienced the beating as his interest in and involvement with her. Like so many individuals who enjoy bondage, she had been raised to believe that sex was wrong. In bondage, she could fantasize that sex was forced on her, did not have to take responsibility for her sexual behavior and could thus enjoy it.

Men who enjoy bondage, similarly, are frequently raised by sex-negative parents, where punishment is also symbolically equated with concern.

Another factor contributing to slave-master sex with physical abuse includes identification with the aggressor so that the slave, in fantasy, may actually see himself or herself as the master. My patient explained this gleefully one day when she said that she could get any man to beat her no matter how frightened he was.

Also involved is the relationship of pain to pleasure. Frequently the dividing line is a very fine one so that too much pleasure can lead to pain – and pain to pleasure. Depending on the individual's level of sensitivity, beating becomes a form of tactile stimulation which can be erotically exciting. To be so it must be administered by a person whom the masochist trusts not to exceed certain levels of stimulation.

In general, sadomasochism is more prevalent in cultures

136

where corporal punishment of children is common. In a survey conducted by Dr. Eleanore Luckey and Dr. Gilbert Nass of the University of Connecticut, 8% of U.S. male students and 5% of U.S. female students reported they had been involved in 'whipping and spanking before petting or other intimacy,' compared with 17% English male students and 33% English female students. Vance Packard, who initiated the study, appears to attribute the difference to the English use of rod and whip on pupils guilty of minor infractions. – H.G.

FAMILY LOVE

Sharing a bedroom with my two brothers, I took part in sexplay with them from an early age. I was ten when I first experienced full intercourse with my eldest brother (then 13), and I subsequently became very active with my brothers and their friends, usually in group situations. At puberty I withdrew from this promiscuity, but continued and deepened my intimacy with my brothers.

The time came when we left home and went our separate ways (although I have retained a sexual relationship with them spasmodically), and I eventually met and married my husband. Our love life has been quite satisfactory, and we have a son of 12 and a little girl of five.

My husband is fairly frequently away on business and it was during one of these business trips, a few weeks ago, that when looking in on the children last thing in the evening, I noticed my boy had almost lost his bedclothes. I went to tuck him in – he was sound asleep – and found myself becoming aroused by the sight and feel of his passive naked body with his first soft down of pubic hair.

I was unable to resist kissing and then sucking his penis, and was rewarded by inducing a hard erection. I repeated this practice on several subsequent nights and brought him to a climax each time without awakening him.

On the last occasion my husband was away my boy awoke with a nightmare and to comfort him I took him into my bed. I was awakened later to find that he was against me rubbing his erect penis against my hips. I was able to maneuver myself, while feigning sleep, to enable him to enter my vagina from behind and achieve an ejaculation soon afterward. I now

137

do not know whether to continue my secret (from him?) relationship, or to make open advances.

What is so wrong in complete family love? Incest is only a problem when pregnancies result, and I am safely on the Pill. As far as emotional problems are concerned, I can only cite my own case, where I feel sure I have a more richly satisfying sex life than the majority of 'morally perfect' women.

Mrs. J.P.

Incest is not only a problem when pregnancies result. To assume that would be to disregard all the complex factors that make up a male/female love relationship. Complete family love is one thing, a very positive emotional situation. What you seem to be aiming for is complete family sex, something quite different, with the potential of severely hampering your son's future sex life and, possibly, your own relationship with your husband.

Perhaps you do find your sex life far more satisfying than the majority of what you call 'morally perfect' women. But this is not a moral issue, it is a human issue.

To suppose that your sexual advances toward your son have been undetected by him seems unbelievable. Do you really think that 'while feigning sleep' you can maneuver yourself in a way to enable him to enter you without him guessing your obvious intention?

He is still a child, despite his erections and ejaculations, who needs a mother, not a mistress. His best chance of future sexual happiness lies in making contact with girls his own age, and even this, given the fact that he is only 12, would not normally take place for another four or five years. By continuing this sexual relationship with him you might very well be hindering him from pursuing such exploratory contacts, which in themselves are the building blocks of the more satisfactory, stable and mature love partnerships that most human beings eventually strive for. As a mother you would appreciate the absurdity of feeding gin to a three-month-old baby. What you are doing to your son on a sexual level is not dissimilar.

Apart from possible future reactions there is the present to consider. Your boy is very likely to develop great feelings of hostility, rage, guilt and jealousy toward his father whom he will rightly regard as a sexual rival. Many boys his age experience this feeling as a result of fantasies in which they imagine possessing their mothers. Usually these fantasies pass as they mature and form relationships of their own. In this case, where the situation is real, the growing-out process, if in fact it can still be successfully achieved, is bound to be much more difficult.

You say very little about your husband. However, it is safe to say that most men would react to this situation in a very hostile way. For most men, the last thing they'd want their wives to do is to make love to their sons. – F.

EXTRAMARITAL IMPOTENCE

I am 51 and have been married for 23 years. We have always enjoyed our sex life.

My problem is that when I have sex with my wife everything is fine, I am potent, strong, and virile; but when I go to bed with any other woman I am quite impotent and unable to perform. This has been so all my life and I feel frustrated. I persevered to try and find the cause of my trouble, but it doesn't seem to work.

My present girlfriend is about my age. When we have the opportunity we spend a whole night together. We dine at good restaurants and really enjoy ourselves before going to bed. She is very nice, understanding and patient, but most of the time I have to perform cunnilingus which she enjoys.

Please tell me if this is a complex or if I need psychiatric treatment. I do not know of any psychiatrist and my doctor refuses to help me in this particular case.

J.K.

J.K.'s impotence with other women, but not with his wife, is almost certainly psychologically caused. It is the result of guilt feelings which, in his case, seem to be unconscious. If he was brought up to believe that extramarital intercourse is wrong, it is inevitable that he should feel guilty, with the result about which he complains.

A psychiatrist could help, but there might be some difficulty in finding a psychiatrist who would be willing to help him be unfaithful. – F.

MONOTONY OF SEX

Our life expectancy is increasing year by year, people are living longer, and what's more, a greater percentage of younger people are getting married. The inevitable conclusion is, that marriages today are expected to last much longer than they did in the past. Thus, a couple marrying at twenty can still expect to be together at seventy. Fifty years of the same 'diet' is a lot to expect from any married man. Familiarity breeds contempt, variety is the spice of life. We have all heard these expressions and many of us have seen how they have affected our sex lives.

Boredom in the bedroom, and the monotony of sex with the same person, very often causes frustrations and tensions within the marriage. I feel that in this respect, prostitutes serve a very necessary function. Their services do not break up marriages; if anything they help to strengthen the marriage partnership.

I love my wife more than anyone else in this world, but, in all honesty, I must admit that I get bored with our sex life. I'm all for experimenting and adventure in our sex life but my wife is not. We have talked this problem over several times without coming to any satisfactory conclusion. Sexually, she is easily satisfied and content to have coitus in the same place, at the same time, and in the same position, day after day, year after year. Basically, she is not very interested in sex and will not try anything new.

Little wonder that for a change I would like to visit a prostitute and enjoy her services. I am not a sadist, masochist, or transvestite, and I have no tendencies to any forms of fetishism. I'm just a normal, healthy, passionate bloke who, to avoid the frustrations and tensions which are slowly creeping into our marital relations, would like to satisfy my sexual appetite by occasionally utilizing the services of a prostitute. Surely this is a much better solution than becoming involved with another woman as so many married men do these days. This can only result in heartbreak, mental, and emotional anguish for all concerned. This is not the answer.

A prostitute has a very necessary social service to offer. She is the real answer to the problem of marital sexual boredom if one happens to be married to an uncooperative, unimaginative or inhibited wife.

D.F.

APPETITE ENHANCER

I have discovered a most delicious technique of satisfying my husband's physical and sexual appetites at the same time, and believe me, it's made our marriage more exciting than ever. My husband is one of those men who has a sweet tooth and insists on a dessert after his meals. One night, suddenly 'inspired', I hit upon the idea of serving him his dessert (strawberries) in a most unique manner – instead of a bowl, I substituted my vagina, and if he wanted his dessert, which he did, there was only one way to get it.

Fortunately, my husband is a good sport and he soon got into the spirit of things. Not only did he eat every strawberry, but being quite worked up, he brought me to orgasm cunnilingually (is that the word?) followed by a terrific session in bed.

Since then, he's enjoyed every conceivable type of dessert by means of what he calls the 'cuntainer' – cheese-cake, chocolate mousse, eclairs, apple pie, jelly and his favorite, a chocolate sundae with nuts. Cold ice cream on the vagina can be pretty excruciating, but by the time my husband licks up the last bit of the sundae, I am anything but cold.

From time to time, I have my dessert on his private parts, and there have been occasions when we both had our desserts at the same time. What a glorious ending to a dinner. Someone told me that *The Sensuous Woman* became a best seller because it described how the author placed whipped cream topped by a cherry on her lover's penis. Frankly, I have found that doughnuts go much better with a man's organ than whipped cream.

There's no doubt in my mind that if a wife uses her imagination, she won't have to worry about her marriage getting stale or her husband fooling around with other women. As long as her husband is not a stick-in-the-mud and has a good appetite, there's no limit to what an imaginative wife can cook up for him.

Mrs. J.S.

ENDLESS VARIATIONS

My wife has very firm views that the female should dominate in all sexual activity, and puts forward strong arguments to enforce this. Her views are based on the fact that it is the female who should decide when anything sexual should take place,

141

since a male is always ready for it but a female prefers to choose her own time.

Ever since we were married this has been put into practice. One of her favorite methods is to take me up into the bedroom and order me to strip off. Then I am spreadeagled over the bed with wrists secured by leather straps which we have had made. We have a low bed and this enables my feet to be flat on the floor. This is very important, since some of the sessions are quite hectic and it is essential to be comfortable. My wife then begins to slowly unfasten her blouse or dress and this is done in a very provocative way. When she has removed it completely she has only to stroke her hands over her bra and this never fails to give me an erection. She has lovely breasts and she emphasizes the fact by wearing some of the sexiest bras one can imagine. Her conversation plays a part in the teasing, together, of course, with her innocent questioning of why I'm so excited.

Her hands stroke and tickle all over my body but never touching my penis. After 20 minutes or so of this, one feels as if one will explode and twists and turns in a vain effort to bring one's penis into contact with the tormenting hand. This, of course, is not permitted and as a consequence, one receives a sharp slap and is told to be patient. At this stage my wife will perhaps remove her bra, and let her breasts by sight and touch and various tantalizing gestures bring me to an even higher pitch of excitement. On many occasions she has massaged me with baby oil and I have begged her to give me some relief. But she's so cruel in a lovely way and I am denied any comfort until her teasing is completed which can last anything up to two hours or even more.

In her own good time she will decide when I've had enough and then give me a few slow strokes on my penis. I explode like a mini atom bomb. After a few moments I am released and we make exhilarating love in the normal way.

Over the six years of married life my wife has tried out endless variations to provide added spice and pleasure to our lives; some have been very good while others have amused, and all have contributed to make a wonderful sex relationship between us.

G.R.

142

HONEYSUCKLE

Always searching for new ways to give my husband extra sexual pleasure, a few weeks ago I bought a jar of honey and smeared some on to my breasts before going to bed. My husband happens to love honey – and couldn't have been more delighted with the sexy dessert I offered him.

Needless to say a couple of jars are now on my weekly shopping list.

Mrs. J.P.

GOOD CLEAN FUN

My wife and I used to make love in the bath with considerable pleasure and I have done it with my mistress (and also with at least three other girls) with a great deal of enjoyment.

The foreplay such as soaping each other's bodies, especially the more intimate parts, has a really sensual and very stimulating effect, and I can assure you that the man will, in only a matter of seconds, have acquired an erection to be proud of. The girl, too, seems to require somewhat less manual stimulation than usual to bring her to a receptive mood. One thing I would advise, though, is that a lubricant such as vaseline be applied to both penis and vagina before intromission, or there will be a feeling of roughness caused by the bath water ruining the natural lubricants which are always normally present. For this reason, the bath water should not be too hot or the vaseline will be lost and one is back to 'square one'.

Under a shower, of course, the couple would have to either stand up or kneel, and these are *not* the most enjoyable positions. In the bath, the man can lie almost flat and the girl adopt a sitting position, lowering herself onto his penis. He can then play with or kiss her breasts while she does most of the work. Very satisfying. But I would only recommend intercourse in the bath as an occasional variation in one's normal sex routine.

Everybody today agrees that sex should be interesting and amusing, and that one should enjoy it to the full. With the *right* partner this will always be the case. My mistress and I have quite a number of little private jokes. She often accuses me of 'pressing points' when I insist on anything – the points being her nipples. When I try to be precise about something, she says, I'm 'splitting hairs' and we both laugh. *'Parting hairs'*

143

might be more precise since we both automatically think of her pubic hair when she says this.

One evening when we were watching a play on television, I remarked on the good figure of a blonde actress. She knows I am fond of blondes, although she has light brown hair. The following evening when I got home, she had 'gone blonde' and asked me how I liked it. I replied that I liked it very much, but that if anyone saw her in her bath they would know immediately it wasn't her natural coloring. She was really amused, and quickly stripped off her panties with a chuckle – yes; she had gone blonde there too! Naturally this led me to stroking it 'to see if it felt the same', and before long we were in bed together again. Such events assist in keeping one's interest in one partner fresh, and the more one becomes involved in such little, private, sexy jokes and pranks, the more one automatically enjoys sex.

J.G.

SEXUAL SOPHISTICATE

My husband is what the doctor would describe as the 'sexual sophisticate'. He feels that as long as he performs well in bed and brings me to a climax I should be perfectly content. He regards himself as the perfect lover. I always feel when we're making love that he's practicing an art on me, not making love to me from desire for me. If it's true that practice makes perfect, then I suppose he could be considered the 'perfect' lover. We've been through every position in the book, and he works on my body like a professional violinist on a fine instrument. I never fail to have an orgasm, sometimes two or three, because he knows just what to do at the right time; but when it's all over I never *feel* I've been made love to.

His attitude afterward always makes me feel he's thinking, 'Well, that was a good job well done.' He is very rarely tender with me when we're alone and is rather offhand with me in company. I feel very sensitive about this when we're with other couples who are very affectionate toward one another. I've talked to him about it and he tells me I'm not a child who needs to be reassured all the time. He's always telling me how lucky I am to have such a virile husband and the letters in Forum about impotency or premature ejaculation he points out to me with great glee,

Lots of sex and orgasms really do not compensate for lack of love and kisses outside the bedroom, not for women, anyway.

Mrs. V.F.

WHAT PRICE SATISFACTION

When I got married I was very inexperienced sexually and so my expectation wasn't very high. This meant that my husband could mold me into his way of lovemaking without me being at all critical of his ways – I had nothing to compare him to! He led and I followed.

By our second year of marriage I was getting a little restless. I felt like an actress in a play that was going into its second tremendous year – tremendous for the audience, that is, not the actress. Sex was becoming boring and repetitious – everything was so predictable.

When I tentatively mentioned what I felt to my husband he said: 'Well you just lie there, why don't you do more?' More of what, I wondered? So I got myself a sex book that showed me a great deal I had never thought of and I decided to put some of those things into practice.

The first time was a disaster. It was the first time I got on top of him and he just couldn't imagine what I was up to. He thought I was just horsing around. When he realized I was trying to stimulate his penis while my arms were pinning down his shoulders he made me stop. *That,* he made clear, wasn't what he meant when he asked me to do more.

Next time I waited until we were well under way. When he was about to enter me I turned on my stomach, pressed my behind up against the lower part of his stomach and kind of stroked him gently downwards with my behind toward his penis. There was dead silence. His heavy breathing stopped and I felt like some kind of idiot animal in a cage. 'What was that for?' he asked in an uncomfortable voice. How stupid! What the hell did he think it was for?

After a few more incidents like this he started giving me little lectures about how unfeminine it is for women to become sexually aggressive. You may think I was stupid, but it took me a while to understand that what he was talking about was me. Aggression? That little bit of sexual variety I tried to introduce? I was really getting somewhat angry now.

The situation was getting worse and our lovemaking was

145

dropping down almost to the point of nonexistence. If I showed any signs of straying from the straight and narrow of our man-above position I was reprimanded for being 'aggressive'. When I asked my husband what he meant when he suggested that I 'do more' he said that he meant for me to move around more often and stroke his back in more interesting ways.

That was six months ago and things haven't gotten any better. Instead of sex being just boring it is now also on the verge of tension and strain – he's just watching to see if I will do anything 'funny' and I get to the point of thinking 'fuck him, I'll try what I like'.

I've felt myself eyeing handsome young men more than usual recently and fantasize a lot as to what it would be like to be with one of them. Right now I don't feel emotionally capable of cheating on my husband, but who knows, in another six months' time the idea of making love with someone else might not seem so impossible. In fact – I'll probably do it.

Mrs. D.B.

Taking a lover may turn out to be enjoyable, but I don't really see how that will help the problem at home.

Many people will openly discuss areas of their lives where they feel inadequate, unsure, uncomfortable. When it comes to sexual activity and sexual pleasure, many people feel too threatened to admit that they are anything less than 'great'. This seems especially true of men trying to live up to society's image of the masculine, virile male. Their complete identity appears vested in the genital area.

Sex is a process involving two people, and it takes time and experimentation to find out what gives each one pleasure. The same people who insist on prescribing how a partner should behave in bed might find it quite absurd if the example were extended to eating. Would they be likely to tell someone they cared for how to enjoy a meal?

R.G.

REAR-ENTRY POSITION

I love to be entered from the rear, so much so in fact, that my husband and I rarely have intercourse in any other way, and we have come to consider that this is much more natural than the so-called normal face-to-face position.

146

Perhaps my liking for penetration from behind was the result of my early experiences of sex, and I feel that it may be of interest to readers if I explain how it came about. Between the ages of 17 and 20, I had sex with various boyfriends, and always in the missionary position. Whether or not it was because they were young, like myself, and relatively inexperienced and awkward in lovemaking, I cannot say. The fact is, I never really enjoyed sex, and I never had an orgasm.

When I was 20, I met an older man who was married and obviously had more sex experience. After several dates I invited him to my room one evening. We had had a few drinks and I was feeling rather merry and a bit abandoned, and very soon we were lying together on my bed, naked. After some mutual caressing and loveplay, my boyfriend rolled me over onto my stomach, and began stroking my bottom and genital area from the rear. I can recall to this day how excited I became. I was soon at fever pitch, which was a new experience for me. After a few minutes he placed a doubled-up pillow under my stomach so that it raised my bottom into the air, and then he continued caressing me for a short while. Then, when I had just about reached my very first orgasm, he knelt on the bed between my legs, lay down on top of me, and entered me from behind. During our lovemaking, which lasted about five minutes, I had three orgasms before he reached his. I almost exploded with desire and love at this first really satisfying sex experience.

The next occasion was a few weeks later. This time, after our usual caressing, my lover got me to kneel on the bed with my feet at the edge, and my head resting on my arms low on the bed. He then sat on the floor beside the bed, and stroked and kissed my bottom, my thighs, and eventually began to perform cunnilingus on me. I very soon reached orgasm, and was about to collapse on the bed, when my lover stood upright, held me in the kneeling position, and again penetrated me from the rear. In the next ten minutes or so, I had at least three orgasms, until he came too.

From that day on, I was absolutely sold on rear-entry lovemaking, and very rarely did I achieve on orgasm face-to-face. Some of my subsequent boyfriends found it rather surprising that I should prefer sex that way, but I usually managed to persuade them to enter from behind.

On our honeymoon, my husband, who was then without much experience of sex, was somewhat startled to find me repeatedly turning my back on him during our caresses in bed, but he finally took the hint, and now after many years of marriage, he agrees with me that rear-entry is much more natural, exciting, and often more comfortable than face-to-face love-making.

As to 'being used' in rear-entry positions, I might agree if the woman received no enjoyment from intercourse, but if she achieves orgasms satisfactorily, and enjoys herself this way, there is no question at all of her 'being used' as a submissive, passive partner. On reflection, I can hardly think of a more comfortable position than when a woman lies on her side with her knees drawn up, and the man lies down on his side behind her. There is no pressing weight problem, no awkward angles for penetration, no strain on any part of her body, and it is possible to continue intercourse for a very long time indeed in this position, even to the extent of falling asleep still united after lovemaking.

I can sincerely say that on such occasions I am in heaven, and I treasure these moments long after they have passed. I can also assure any female readers who may have inhibitions about rear-entry sex, that there is nothing to be ashamed of, or afraid of, in taking up such a position in bed. First experiences are certain to dispel any misgivings.

Finally, may I mention a topic which obviously has close connections with rear-entry, that is sexual intercourse in the female anus. Some years ago, before I married, one of my boyfriends, on discovering my liking for rear-entry, immediately assumed that this meant anal coitus, and acted accordingly. I permitted it on this occasion more out of curiosity than anything else, but I soon regretted it as I found it painful, awkward, and frankly embarrassing afterwards. However, some time later my married lover, whom I mentioned earlier, asked me if I would allow it, and to please him I did. Due to his considerate use of adequate lubricant, he entered me and had anal intercourse without much difficulty or discomfort, and I must say that I quite enjoyed it. Since then I have had a sneaking desire for my husband to try it, but I hesitate to ask him, as I feel sure he would disapprove, and I am certain the idea has never crossed his mind.

Mrs. E.H.

Speaking from the man's point of view I entirely agree with

Mrs. E.H. that rear-entry coupling is one of the most satisfying of all methods. I think that the man's increased pleasure may be due to two factors: (1) that the roof of the vagina may be more corrugated than the floor and (2) that penetration is really very deep, and equaled only by the penetration in the woman-above squatting position.

With regards to (1), in any of the face-to-face positions the nerves in the frenum of the penis – which contribute probably more than 80% to the man's orgasmic sensations – are in contact with the vagina floor. In the rear-entry positions, these nerves are in contact with what would be the roof of the vagina if she were lying on her back, and I suggest that the usually much more intense sensations derive from the frenum-nerves being more stimulated by the roof than the floor.

I also favor rear-entry because it gives the man much more freedom of movement than most of the other positions and enables him to stimulate the clitoris, nipples or breasts, to caress the back of the neck with his mouth, or lightly massage the back with both hands, while the woman can reach between her legs and lightly caress his testicles, which most men find wildly exciting. Rear-entry also provides a wide variation of position.

Nevertheless, it is absolutely true, as I can vouch for from my counselling experiences, that very many women indeed object to rear-entry. Their objections – and they are honestly based – are psychological: rear-entry is the normal method used by animals, and these women feel they are being degraded to animals. (As a rule, women who feel strongly against rear-entry, also object to any position other than the face-to-face-man-above.) Writers of sex manuals in the past have also tended to strengthen this view, because, though they describe rear-entry, they almost invariably add, 'One great disadvantage of rear-entry is that the couple are unable to see each other's faces, and so feel that the ultimate intimacy is impossible,' or something like that. In fact, the great majority of women, and quite a large number of men, couple with their eyes closed, and closing the eyes is almost a reflex action when approaching and during climax. – F.

APPLIED APPLIANCES
Various correspondents have brought up the subject of stimulation of women when horse-riding. However, I am

surprised that no one has mentioned the excitement generated by common everyday occurrences. After all, only a minority of the population are lucky enough to indulge in horse-riding.

I personally find considerable satisfaction in perching astride my spin-drier when it is in motion and enjoy the ecstatic vibrations. Another favorite is to rub up against the side of the cooker when the oven is on, and feel the hot smooth edge pressing on my clitoris. I have never attempted to reach orgasm with these stimuli, but certainly the satisfaction due to vibrations and heat is very great.

I understand that many men gain great erotic thrills or even ejaculate, when sitting astride a pulsing motor-bike, and I wonder how many other women are excited by simple household appliances in the way that I am.

Mrs. G.M.

A VOTE FOR HOOVER

Mine is a somewhat unusual, no, seen objectively, a humorous case. I am sexually attracted by our vacuum cleaner.

I can clearly remember the event which made me this way. Until I married and left home, my parents were very careful to avoid all mention of sex or of sexual feelings. However, when I was 12 and a half, my mother and I were playing a game of tag as she was doing the housework. She would tag me 'it' with the end of the vacuum cleaner tube as it extended her reach. Inadvertently she made contact with my genitals and the combination of the suction and the probing gave me an immediate erection – my first 'real' erection. I broke off the game at once and went to my room to try and figure out the meaning of this new feeling by myself (as I have said, asking my mother for an explanation would be unthinkable). Thereafter, I regarded the vacuum cleaner with ambivalence, but my sexual fantasies always involved beautiful girls violating me with a vacuum cleaner hose. Finally Mother got a new vacuum cleaner and the whole affair was put out of my mind for a few years.

A month or so after my marriage, however, I was passing a second-hand electrical shop which had on display in the window the same model and color vacuum cleaner that my mother had. My reaction was immediate and profound – a full erection and a tremendous erotic feeling. I went inside and purchased it and brought it home to my wife as a late 'flat warming' present.

In the intervening six years I have managed to work the vacuum cleaner into our foreplay. We caress each other with various attachments – the most effective being the dusting brush. Once my wife even consented to put the hose (the cleaner was turned on at the time) over my erect penis. All of this, however, was introduced gradually, and my wife does not suspect the extent of my real intentions regarding the vacuum cleaner. Often, when she is out of the house, I masturbate using the vacuum cleaner hose with the cleaner turned on.

This could probably go on for quite some time, except that during the past six years I have moved up financially and now my wife is beginning to pressure me for a newer model.

This brings me to my problem – I am not sure whether I am strong enough emotionally to part company with 'old faithful', and I know that only a vacuum cleaner of that type (the old cylinder type) can satisfy me. I cannot hold out against my wife's requests much longer as I am running out of excuses.

T.W.

T.W. is a lucky man to find such a devoted machine. Wives are easy to find – but such a machine – wow. – R.G.

If I bring our vacuum cleaner over to meet yours, can we watch? – H.G.

SMALL BUST

I am 21, five feet four inches tall and weigh 112 pounds. I am fairly attractive and like going out and enjoying myself. My problem is my bust. A 32A bra is even too big for me.

I worry, cry and get very depressed over this. I've tried creams, tablets and exercises but none have helped. I feel very inadequate and have never let a boyfriend fully touch or kiss my breasts, never keeping a boyfriend too long because I do not want them to find out how small I am. To top it all, I have to wear sponges in my bra. I would be a much happier person if someone could help.

Miss J.H.

Your feelings of inadequacy must have deeper roots, possibly coming from an unacknowledged feeling of sexual inadequacy which you express through discontent with your breasts. A boy-friend who genuinely likes you will also like your breasts because they are yours, just like your skin and hair; he will not regard that part of your anatomy as a separate part of your being, suspended on its own, to be judged like a piece of meat. Besides, some men even prefer women who have small breasts.—F.

Despite the fact that many of our leading movie stars are endowed as modestly as Miss J.H., many women think that having small breasts makes them sexually unattractive, and they fear that men will discover the secret that they have no secret treasure.

Actually a man's response to small breasts varies with the individual, depending on a number of factors such as early conditioning, the first woman he knew sexually, or social fashions of his particular group. Many men are quite capable of being excited by women with any size breasts, from the flattest to the most abundant.

In my clinical experience an excessive concern about the size of any part of the body is usually symptomatic of overall fears of inadequacy and an inability to deal with these fears on so generalized a level. — H.G.

UNIMPORTANCE OF SIZE

When I first met my wife 22 years ago it was not her bust, or should I say lack of it, that attracted me to her. First and foremost it was her face and legs, then her voice, finally her personality. Her breasts did not come into it until much later, when we grew to love each other. She hardly needed a brassiere and in fact she often did not wear one and when I fondled her small breasts I would feel her nipples swell and grow hard.

Don't think that I prefer small breasts, but like the male penis, they come in different sizes. A girl could have a lovely pair of big tits and a terrible face or legs like stumps. You can't have it all ways and most girls and women with largish breasts are always so concerned about droop and sag.

My wife has often expressed a wish that her breasts were bigger. She has often wondered, also, why they have not filled out because of the attention I have paid them with both hands and mouth over the years. The quickest way to rouse her is by sucking her nipples.

During loveplay she will often herself bare a breast to me to be sucked. Then, as her passion rises, she takes my hand and guides my fingers into her vagina. During intercourse, as she approaches climax, tonguing her taut nipples will trigger her climax.

Several times she has pulled my hands from her breasts. The first time was when, after a long bus journey, we alighted near home, both wanting to pee urgently. As we walked home it being late and dark, I put my arm around her, my hand under her jacket, and began fondling her breasts. When her nipples became erect I concentrated upon them. To my surprise she pulled my hand away saying 'You'll make me wet my pants.' Always, if her bladder is full, breast fondling makes the urge to urinate even more urgent.

Breast fondling and sucking and kissing alone will not bring her to orgasm but will make her very moist and ready for intercourse without genital stimulation. In fact, there have been many times when she has taken hold of my erect penis and murmured 'I want this' without even so much as me touching her between her thighs. Conversely, breast and genital stimulation have brought her to orgasm as a prelude to intercourse.

So, Miss J.H. should take heart. Mr. Right will come along and when he does she should let him find out for himself just what she has under her blouse. By all means 'pad out'. My wife does at times and gets quite a kick out of viewing her 'bosom' in a mirror, but then we both know exactly what she has and how sensitive they are. After all, there are women with big breasts who just cannot bear to have them touched.

C.L.

PADDING IT OUT

I feel that my experiences may shed some light on the matter of improving breast size by swallowing semen. I have been married for 17 years and am 38 years old. My husband and I have enjoyed a perfect sex life with absolutely no inhibitions.

Until about five years ago my breast measurement was always a constant 33 inches and even having two children failed to increase the size at all. One day in one of the early issues of Forum we read about fellatio and cunnilingus and being fascinated we tried cunnilingus several times and found it truly wonderful. We then graduated to fellatio which again we found

153

very enjoyable although at that time we went very carefully to avoid my husband coming while in my mouth.

About a month later we were playing and found ourselves in the 69 position. My husband penetrated my vagina deeply with his tongue and I took hold of his penis with my mouth taking as much as I could. At this point I could feel myself reaching a climax, the most intense one I have ever had. In the excitement, my husband also came off and, without thinking, I swallowed several mouthfuls of semen which to my surprise I found very pleasant. We both agreed that this was a perfect way of love-making, and afterwards practiced it two or three times a week, always swallowing all the semen.

After about six weeks I discovered while dressing that I was having a job to do up my bra. I got a tape measure and discovered that I measured 35 inches. I was thrilled to bits, and we carried on with fellatio and cunnilingus. As the months went by so did the size of my breasts increase. My measurements are now 40-26-38 and I am very proud of my lovely breasts. To me this is certainly more than mind over matter!

Mrs. E.G.

Despite the prevalence of this belief, there is no scientific evidence that the swallowing of semen increases breast size. This myth arises out of an unfounded belief in the magical powers of semen, which in reality apply only to the ovum. – H.G.

A CONFIRMED MASOCHIST

I have been married for twelve years and am still very much in love with my husband. Even before we were married, I was aware that he had slightly unusual sexual inclinations: to be specific, he liked me to ill-treat him before we made love. At first it didn't amount to much and I was happy to indulge him.

During the last few years, however, my husband's craving for physical maltreatment has become more intense. For some reason he is no longer able to accept any kind of success without wanting to suffer for it by being punished by me. Whenever, for instance, he lands a new contract, he begs me to treat him as cruelly as I can; the greater the success, the more abuse he demands. Although I always went along with his requests as far as I could, I never really enjoyed tying him up, whipping him or subjecting him to any of the other indignities he craves. I only did it because he wanted it so badly.

About two months ago, a few days after landing an important contract he rang me up and told me to get ready for an evening out. We did a show, had a lovely meal and a marvelous time. When we got home, it was very late and my husband began to make a great fuss of me. When we were both aroused, he dropped to his knees and implored me to punish him.

I agreed, but then he produced from his briefcase a horrid little whip with a metal-tipped tail and begged me to beat him with it till I drew blood. I became a bit hysterical and said I could not possibly do what he wanted.

He got angry and accused me of not understanding and loving him, since I was denying him the intense pleasure that such a whipping would give. We went to bed and have never mentioned the subject again. Not only has he stopped asking me to whip him, but he has not made love to me at all since that evening.

A few weeks later, he had another business triumph and came home with an expensive bracelet, the sort of present he has never bought me before (and frankly not the kind of thing I'd ever wear). He said he was giving it to me as an expression of his love. It was all very puzzling, especially as he seemed so contented and relaxed, just as he used to after I punished him.

That evening, I went into the bathroom, and to my horror I saw his back and thighs were a mass of livid welts. He tried to conceal his back by turning away and using the towel and I just hoped I hadn't given myself away by the expression on my face. Someone, presumably a call girl, had given him a terrible whipping, far worse than anything he ever got from me. I suppose he had it on account of his recent business triumph.

When I confided all this to my girlfriend, who is much more mercenary and materialistic than I, she just shrugged and said, indicating the bracelet which I had shown her, 'Well dear, you seem to be doing all right. After all, if he's getting it from a prostitute, it means you can leave that side of it to her.'

At first I was inclined to agree, but after thinking about it, I wonder whether my husband will ever want to make love to me again. He is obviously getting all the satisfaction he needs at the hands of some professional woman. And all this because I find myself incapable of giving him the sort of brutalities he wants these days.

Mrs. S.R.

THREE IS COMPANY

My wife and I have had a very happy life together. Before we married we discovered we were both highly sexed and compatible in our outlook on life. We were quite satisfied with each other.

Ten years ago we were friendly with a group of business associates, and had some very happy times at dances and parties. Our special friends were Don and Pat, who were the most prolific party-givers in the group. We four used to be together a lot.

After five years of this, Don one night came to our house with the news that Pat had left him. He was really shattered, so of course we did our best to cheer him up.

He practically lived at our house for the next month, and slowly returned to his old self, which pleased us as we were very fond of him.

One night after being out to a party the three of us returned to our home. After a couple more drinks Don went up to bed. He slept in the next room to us, and since when my wife and I were indulging ourselves sexually the bed seemed to create more ecstatic sounds than we did, we decided to spend an hour on the couch.

After about an hour of loveplay I mounted. Just as we were reaching our climax my wife moaned to me to look round, keeping up her wild movements. On looking round I saw Don standing there with a massive erection, flushed and breathless. He mumbled something about forgetting his lighter. We were still continuing all this time – I'm afraid we were too near to coming to care who was there. Don moved nearer and my wife, still in ecstasy, reached out and took his penis in her hand and held it until we had finished.

I'd always been a possessive man with my wife sexually, but seeing her slowly caressing Don's penis. I felt a pang of excitement. As I said before, my wife is highly sexed and could carry on for a lot longer than me. Don by this time had his hand between her thighs and I couldn't bring myself to stop him when he mounted her. The sheer eroticism of the occasion apparently was greater than any restraint we would have had under normal conditions. We all got carried away by the increasing excitement.

He must have carried on for about half an hour, at intervals, begging her not to make him come quickly. By this time I had another erection and was eager for him to finish.

We both fucked her twice that night and she finished with a smile on her face like a cat who has just lapped two saucers of cream.

We have carried on our association for five years. Don had to move away for his business, but he comes back as often as he can. I'm sure he loves my wife nearly as much as I do. He always says she will never be left alone if anything happens to me.

E.C.

ANTI-TROILISM

I am only too well aware that my husband desires a third party, or even a fourth, to be present at our love-making. The idea horrifies me and, if he persists, it will, I feel, only result in the breakup of our marriage. There must be many women who only submit to this because they are frightened of losing their husbands – but which is preferable? If one has to resort to this type of behavior in order to keep a man then I would say he is not worth keeping and it is really the thin edge of the wedge. After having partaken in troilism once, the man would then feel justified in saying 'you have had a man, how about me having a woman as a third party?' The oft misquoted phrase 'improving our marriage' is merely a sop to his conscience (although it is open to doubt whether such men have a conscience at all) so that he can have as many women as he likes. The marriage is obviously doomed to failure and this behavior merely hastens the breakup. Such men, whatever their age, should never get married as they are not mature enough to accept all the responsibilities that marriage entails.

It is often stated in your magazine that what two people in love do together is their own business – with this I agree, but once others are brought in there is nothing left. The suggestion that couples can become 'friends' after wife-swapping etc. is ludicrous. There is no friendship, only fear that the other couple will broadcast what has happened to others.

157

I've no doubt that on reading this your readers' reaction will be that I am a very bitter woman. Perhaps I am. Sometime after my marriage I learned that my husband had spent a weekend with another couple only the very week before he asked me to marry him. I know that at that time we weren't married, but how a man can do such a thing saying at the same time that he loves you is beyond me. It was not even something that happened on the spur of the moment but was premeditated. Lies are bad enough but to lie so coldly and calculatingly shows a complete lack of feeling. Since finding this out, every time my husband touches me I cannot help think of it. In the light of what has happened since, I think I was only needed to look after him, clean, wash, cook etc., in addition to going out to work and assisting with money. You wonder why I am bitter?

If you publish this, my only hope is that it will prevent some women from entering into the trap set for them by suggestions of troilism, wife-swapping etc. and that out of my misery some good may come to others.

Principles may be expensive sometimes, but to live without them and self-respect is far more expensive in the the long run.

Mrs. E.F.

What we have here is the clash of two totally opposed forces. For Mrs. E.F. sex and love are unalterably bound together in a tight emotional union, as they are for many women and men. Her husband doesn't perceive love in the same way but this does not necessarily invalidate his claims that he does love his wife. What Mrs. E.F. is saying is 'if you can't feel the way I do then you can't feel at all.' To her the act of seeking out another partner for sex implies finding a replacement for one's spouse and a definite threat to the existing relationship. What her husband probably wants is not a replacement but a supplement.

This is not to suggest that Mrs. E.F. is being unreasonable in not wishing to accede to her husband's wishes. She has every right to reject being pulled into a situation that she finds repugnant. What she might try to understand is that what she finds repugnant is not distasteful for everyone, especially not so for her husband.

If they both want to have a reasonably harmonious relationship then each must come to terms with the other's personality. To accept does not mean to approve.

In either case it would be advisable for her to have a full and frank talk with him to make it clear how she feels and to see how he views the alternatives open to them. – F.

A MATTER OF TASTE

My husband seems to be obsessed with pornography, photos of nude women, and motion pictures showing striptease and even couples making love. He gets angry that I don't have the same enjoyment when it comes to these things. Not only do I not find these photos and books exciting, but I think they make sex vulgar and dirty.

What is there about men that makes them so interested in pornography? Also, am I correct in assuming that most women think as I do and get no sexual stimulation from dirty pictures and books?

Mrs. N.M.

There is a tremendous individual difference in reacting to sex stimulants – visual, tactile, aural, cerebral, etc. There is nothing evil in these stimulants just as there is nothing evil in a knife, a hammer or a gun – only in their use, their employment for good or evil.

The fact that you are not stimulated by what you call pornography, does not make these photos and pictures 'vulgar and dirty'. They might be, of course – but not for the reasons you ascribe to them. There is nothing vulgar and dirty in the naked body – or all art would be that. There is nothing wrong with a man using such photographs or films to stimulate his sexual potency, to make him a better and more effective lover.

If you cannot share your husband's tastes, that is no reason to blame him for them. Perhaps you love tapioca pudding and he hates it. Should he call you 'vulgar' in your culinary tastes because you do? – F.

EROTICA FOR WOMEN?

I believe that the modern female is not only interested in viewing photographs of male nudes but also, in my own experience, enjoys seeing photographs of sexual acts between male and female and also lesbians.

I say 'in my experience' because I have discussed this very subject with some of the women I have been intimately associated with and the greater majority have said, in a round-about way, that they have been aroused by varying degrees on seeing 'blue' photos at some time or another.

The most detailed answers given to me on the subject were by a married woman of 30 with whom I had a secret affair two years ago. I used to visit her at home while her husband was away on frequent business trips and during one visit, she openly asked me if I would like to see some 'blue' photos. We had talked about pornography in general during an earlier visit, but I must admit I was surprised when she suddenly disappeared into her bedroom and returned with a collection of photographs and Swedish pictorial magazines. They were her own property, unknown to her husband, and collected from various sources over 18 months.

They illustrated, in color mostly, a wide range of acts including intercourse, fellatio, cunnilingus, lesbian lovemaking including the use of a dildo, and female masturbation. Many of them were detailed close-ups.

She told me that photos of this type stimulated her, often to the point where – when she was alone in the house – she sought relief through masturbation. I told her that I had always understood that women were relatively uninterested in 'blue' photos. She laughed and said that was 'all poppycock!' Many of her female friends, she added, were just as aroused by the photos as she was!

From then on, I extended my inquiries with subsequent girlfriends and most confirmed what I had learned.

Surely this goes to show that despite the Kinsey 'findings', females are just as sexually aware as we males; but more secretive about it, perhaps.

J.H.

WHY RUBBER?

I would offer the following as of interest to persons who find a liking for rubber odd or incomprehensible.

Compared with silk, nylon, leather etc., rubber has a lively softness which is unique. Worn as a cape or other loose garment it has a draping quality which conforms to every movement and while concealing yet conveys or suggests the form beneath. The pronounced swish and the soft coloring also enhance the femininity of the wearer, adding a touch of the eternal 'female mystery', so valuable in married relationships.

Even the wearer gains, as not only does she feel more desirable but the play of the material on the bare skin can in itself be an exciting caress. A shy, yet desiring, woman can easily indicate her feelings by wearing a 'garment', and avoid the embarrassment of more direct approach.

Such garments used in loveplay are also extremely easy to maintain in a fresh and wholesome condition, sponging or a quick rinse being all that is necessary.

I am, frankly, puzzled by the whole negative attitude to such a harmless fancy and for myself would freely admit to it.

E.S.

WARDROBE OF RUBBER

Even before our marriage my husband showed his interest in rubber – he called it 'macking' – and although this was of no interest to me at first I have gradually become used to it. He has bought me a whole wardrobe of rubber clothes as the years have passed and now I dress in rubber much of the time.

The various magazines about this that my husband has bought seem to suggest that wearing such clothes is very uncomfortable. In fact this is not so, unless the wearer is very hot or very cold, for much of the time I'm not even aware of them.

I always wear a rubber corset or corselette, rubber panties, a rubber bra if I'm wearing a short corset, and a rubber underslip. Only in prolonged hot weather, or after strenuous housework, do I find perspiration troublesome, and then I just strip off and bathe, putting on fresh rubber clothes after powdering.

I always wear normal clothes on top, of course, and if I have on my high-necked rubber leotard I use a polo jumper to cover it up. I have several raincoats in rubber and plastic for outside wear. When alone in the house with my husband, I use a long rubber housecoat which he likes very much. At night I wear a rubber nightdress over long rubber gloves and sometimes tight jeans or stockings.

I believe I have made my husband very contented by satisfying his needs, and our marriage is a very happy one. I still feel a

161

little guilty though and not even my closest friends know of this practice. I have never actually met another woman who does this although judging from the success of the rubberwear firms, there must be a great many. I should like to ask you how common this sort of thing really is?

V.S.

It is difficult to ascertain exactly how widespread rubber fetishism is since no statistics are available and few textbooks deal with this 'deviation' at any length. However, as far as we can tell from letters received by Forum, rubber fetishists are quite numerous in Britain and, no doubt, throughout the western world. In 1968 there were at least eight firms catering to their needs and this indicates a considerable clientele. Also available are a number of publications dealing with the rubber fetish.

One thing seems to be fairly certain: rubber fetishism is a predominantly male phenomenon and the small number of women involved are – apart from prostitutes – wives or girlfriends who have acquired a liking for rubber clothing through their menfolk. The writer appears to be one of them.

There is no suggestion in her letter of the sadomasochistic elements which are frequently present in rubber fetishism, and it may be that her husband simply enjoys the look, sound and feel of rubber rather in the way that other men like their wives to wear leopardskin coats or nylon negligees. You say that your marriage is a happy one, so be happy. You describe yourself as wearing clothes which both you and your husband find pleasant and exciting – only a puritan could find fault with that! – F.

A BIT OF EXHIBITIONISM

About two years ago at my husband's suggestion, I gave up wearing a bra because he said he would prefer the more natural shape of my breasts, which are very firm and well-shaped. He quickly found that other men noticed the lack of this garment mainly because my nipples tended to become erect as a result of rubbing against my clothes. I soon found that I enjoyed the looks I received from appreciative men and this stimulation of my nipples means that I am always aware of my sexuality.

During the last summer, when see-through fashions started

coming in, I bought several semitransparent blouses and a lovely white lace mini-dress. We both had the greatest pleasure from a simple walk through town or going to a club or park like this. The fact that my breasts were naked under my clothes was quite obvious to the experienced voyeur because of the way they sway and bounce when I move and because of the slight darkness of my nipples.

At home and sometimes at parties I leave my panties off for my husband's pleasure (we have both, incidentally, shaved our pubic areas) and I enjoy teasing my husband when he has business colleagues home in the evenings.

Another, and I think more unusual, means of attracting attention to myself is to wear jewelry on my breasts. My husband is a jeweler and has made me several ornaments which I fix over my nipples with adhesive. One pair has little pendant beads which rattle gently with every movement. Another is a converted charm bracelet which I wear suspended between my breasts. Everyone knows how these bracelets jangle on the wrist, so it can be imagined what a sensation it causes when I go to a dance wearing it under a semi-see-through blouse.

A bit of exhibitionism brings great pleasure to all concerned – so here's to more of it.

Mrs. J.T.

SUBWAY STRIP

I am now 'over 45', but still have the same figure I had when I was eighteen, 38-23-36; the same as my twenty-year-old daughter. In fact, we have passed as sisters.

I would like to comment on the letters from young ladies who wear no panties, and particularly those who proudly proclaim that their boyfriends don't mind!

On my eighteenth birthday, I took off my panties for the last time. My first day without them was marvelous. When a man in the tube started the 'mental strip' process, I thrilled to think that he had only to deal with my dress, and there I was!

Only one man has ever known for sure how little I wear – and I would add that he had to marry me before he found my secret.

My husband has always liked the scantiness of my attire. Needless to say, his undressing of me is not mental, and I love it.

163

One thing I would add; over the years I have found growing within me a strong and growing desire to exhibit my body. I tried a nudist camp, but this gave me no satisfaction, because everybody was the same. Still this desire gnaws at me. I would love to walk round the lake in St. James's Park completely nude.

Am I alone in this desire to exhibit my body, or do others have the same longing? Just recently I have read of two girls who have stripped at dances. Did they do this to create a sensation? Or did they do it because they just had to satisfy a longing, like mine, to show themselves to those who would appreciate the sight?

Mrs. M.C.

ALL IS VANITY

We know that the majority of men are voyeurs while the majority of women are exhibitionists. If we weren't all so aware of the facts as they've previously been told us, would the position be reversed? A man knows that if he exhibits his penis in public he is most likely to be arrested; a woman's reaction is nearly always one of shock and great annoyance. So a man grows to believe that the sight of his body repels rather than sexually stimulates women. Conversely, a woman is told that the sight of her body thrills a man; so she exhibits herself to get the desired result or does she do so because of an instinct to show off?

When I was young and had a good figure I used to thoroughly enjoy stripping slowly and deliberately for a lover but now that I'm married and have had children I feel I've lost my good shape and want to hide it under something pretty when we make love. Now that I'm older I find sex far more satisfying and have a greater need for it than I ever did as a young girl, but gone are my exhibitionistic tendencies. Maybe it was just vanity, not sexiness.

Mrs. N.S.

SHOCKING VICTORIANS

I recently heard of some of the most shocking stories concerning the way Victorians frightened their children with horrible threats about the evils of masturbation, promiscuity and other aspects of sexual behavior.

I was told that parents used to lock their children into monstrous contraptions so that they could not masturbate when in bed at night.

The hypocrisy of the Victorians was always known to me but I found it hard to believe that they could have carried their 'morality' this far. Is there any evidence that what I heard is true? If so, then I can well understand the mixed up values that prevail today.

T.D.

The Victorian era saw the emergence of rather incredible appliances which were intended to discourage masturbation and other sexual practices. This is well illustrated in a book by Dr. Alex Comfort, The Anxiety Makers. *The book contains drawings and photographs of the most abominable types of 'restraint apparatus', including spiked penile rings and jagged chastity belts.*

In the 1880s one device on the market was an 'electric alarm'. This contrivance consisted of a penile ring which was attached to an alarm bell. If an erection occurred the bell would go off warning parents of their offspring's activities.

Other methods were used to prevent the 'terrible sin' of self-abuse, such as the conventional straitjacket and cages for both male and female genitals, complete with padlocks and keys.

Psychological means were also called upon. Masturbation was said to result in almost everything from failing school exams to insanity. Dr. Comfort quotes stories of children fearful of touching their own bodies. One woman tells of how as a small girl she was tied to the bed, her hands bound in such a way as to prevent her sliding down and using her heels as instruments for masturbation.

The obsession with the effects of masturbation became so out of proportion that the medical profession invented a non-existent disease, spermatorroel ophthalmia, said to be a consequence of onanism. However, the Victorians, though responsible for much misery and guilt, cannot take all the blame. Their attitude also grew from an inheritance. In his book, Dr. Comfort quotes the following which is attributed to a Dr. Baynard in the late 18th century: 'If we turn our eyes on licentious Masturbators, we shall find them with meagre Jaws,

*and pale Looks, with feeble Hams and legs without Calves,
their generative faculties weakened if not destroyed in the
Prime of their Years; a Jest to others and a Torment to themselves.'*

*As T.D. remarks, in the light of this knowledge it is not
difficult to see why there is so much guilt in today's society.
Social evolution is never a hurried process and one can hardly
expect the backwash of these ridiculous extremes to have
totally disappeared within a few generations. When one realizes
the abundance of literature and the strength of the cry against
sex and sexuality which permeated the length and breadth of
this country less than 60 years ago, it is quite remarkable that
we have already made progress toward enlightened attitudes.—F.*

CHILD'S PLAY

Could you please tell us at what age children begin to masturbate as this question came up in discussion with some
friends?

Also, how is it best to avoid giving our children a guilt complex even if the question of masturbation is not discussed with
them? A good example of this is my own husband. Although he
was never punished for masturbating he still developed a guilt
complex and we wish to avoid this.

Mrs. G.M.

*Masturbation simply means self-stimulation of the genitals,
without the necessity for orgasm in the definition.*

*Thus children start masturbating as soon as they can get hand
to crotch, and this usually starts in a purposeful way from 3 to 6
months. It is important to realize that this early genital play is
masturbation and to allow the child his exploratory activity
quite naturally.*

*Verbal communication is not necessary to transmit a guilt
complex; just the brushing away of a child's eager hands at this
early stage indicates that what they are doing is not nice.*

*Later this can be reinforced at school, again without pun-
ishment, simply by the constant folklore, the last remains of
Victorian onaphobia. Every small boy must wonder if his spine
really will collapse, his penile arteries sclerose and his palms*

sprout hair, for some degree of guilt is still inherent in the society.

Thus, the best way to avoid any guilt is to allow babies' genital play (and acknowledge it so they know that you know) as just another of the child's many pleasurable activities. – F.

ONLY THE 'NORMAL' POSITION

My problem concerns my relations with my wife. I find it virtually impossible to persuade her to adopt any position in intercourse other than the so-called normal position. I, on the other hand, derive my most intense pleasure and penile stimulation from rear-entry copulation. Quite by accident some while ago, I found the sleep into which she fell after taking a sleeping pill followed by a nip of whisky was so deep, I was able to turn her over onto her stomach, elevate her buttocks with pillows, enter her from the rear and reach violent orgasm without rousing her.

I have carried out this practice several times now, but would welcome your opinion as to the advisability of continuing what might be considered an act degrading to my wife.

D.N.

There is nothing at all degrading in this. It is a recurrent theme in erotic literature, and in real life, a woman will feign sleep when she is very much awake and aware of what is happening. You will find a number of such episodes in Henry Miller's books. It also occurs in Fanny Hill, *Casanova's* Memoirs *and dozens of other classics.*

You must not take it amiss if we express grave doubts whether your wife is really asleep during the intercourse which you practice. The sleeping pill and the whisky might, indeed, induce sleep, but hardly deep enough not to react to the stimulus you provide. It is more likely she either pretends to be asleep or subconsciously welcomes in a half-somnolent condition your action.

You might very well try to discover the cause of your wife's opposition to more elaborate and less orthodox techniques in intercourse. Tact and perseverance might provide you with the answer and thereby with the means of changing her attitude. – F.

167

BUM TAILING

I believe anal intercourse, between male and female couples, to be more common than is generally realized, despite its being against the law. This raises an interesting point. What woman who has voluntarily allowed anal penetration is going to turn in her husband or lover, and what woman will testify she has allowed it to happen?

Walter, the English Casanova, referred to it as 'bum tailing', and in his writings, Marcus Van Heller describes this act as sadistic punishment to the woman.

Of my own experiences, I first heard about this act while sitting round at dinner break with other workmen, when a 'gallant' described his latest sexual conquest as 'she'll take it anywhere, in her mouth, under her arms, between her tits and up her arse'. Another account dealt with a pickup in Hyde Park who knelt and closely covered her vagina with her hand and only allowed penetration into her rectum.

My first personal contact was with my young wife soon after marriage. I had been away from home for some time, and I knew on my return she would be having her period.

She agreed to the act, and knelt down across the bed, and after thoroughly lubricating her anal passage and my own penis, I gained complete penetration, and continued joggling until orgasm.

Some time afterwards, she again asked me to repeat the act which became an occasional practice, as a variation. I am not brutal by nature and have always seen to it there is thorough lubrication, and I always stressed, should the act prove painful to her, to immediately desist.

Since then, I have performed the act with other 'ladybirds'. One was a woman who shared my nights during the war when the family was evacuated. I think her request arose from conversations with other women at work.

After an intimate 'courtship', there came the invitation to 'put it up my back passage, you'll find it nice and tight up there.' I complied, and we performed several times afterward. She always had an orgasm and was extremely excited afterward.

I have discovered all women, at a certain stage in the sexual act, are stimulated by fingering the anus, and some, not all, wriggle furiously when a finger is inserted into the rectum.

I am of the opinion whatever two people do sexually in the

168

privacy of their home, as long as they are both agreeable, is no one's business but their own.

G.D.

Certainly there have been extremely few cases of women testifying against their husbands and lovers in any criminal proceedings brought against the latter for anal intercourse. But it has happened when the female partner was deserted or wanted to revenge herself for adultery. Medieval sexual history records a number of executions for this 'offense' based on such testimony.

No moral or ethical considerations have ever prevented experimenting couples from indulging in this form of coition, but obviously there may be physical and psychological disadvantages due to individual tastes, inhibitions and attitudes. One reason why it might have been comparatively more frequent in the nineteenth century and earlier was, of course, the absence of reliable contraceptives and the consequent fear of pregnancy. Coitus interruptus was the only other alternative and many women preferred 'bum tailing' to it.

Today with the Pill and other generally accessible contraceptives, this consideration obviously no longer prevails. – F.

SLEEPING BEAUTY

I just had to write to you about a unique and unexpected way in which my husband brought me to orgasm.

For bed, I wear a short nightie with panties. On the night in question I was dozing off to sleep, lying on my back when my husband put his arm across me, and slowly moved his hand to my belly. Thinking that I was asleep he slowly eased my nightie up as far as he could, then he started to ease my panties down very slowly, trying not to wake me! Bit by bit he eased them down until he could put his hand between my legs. Curious as to the game he was playing, I decided to play along and thus moved in my 'sleep' so that he could pull my panties away from my bottom.

His next move was to start opening my legs with his foot, which with a little aid from me he did. He then started to tickle my clitoris; he is very expert at this and can pull the skin tight with two fingers so that my clitoris stands proud, and is then able to flick it with another finger. I was very much worked up by now, and was not long in reaching a climax, which I tried not to show.

But that was not his objective that night, for he eased himself up to the top of the bed so that he could place his penis on my bare belly. I could hear him straining and was wondering what he was trying to do. I soon found out. He was holding the bedclothes up with one hand and his penis in the other, and then I felt it! Hot urine on my belly, only a short burst, then he looked over me to see where it had gone. Satisfied with himself he gave me the full treatment. He directed his penis upward towards my breasts and proceeded to give sharp bursts of warm urine all down my body. I could feel it running down me, the sides of my belly, and between my legs. It was all so unexpected that I found that it excited me. He then pulled my panties up and inserted his penis up the leg of my panties and started to masturbate on my wet belly. Simultaneously he played with my clitoris.

Within a few moments I reached another climax, as did my husband.

The kinky bit about it all was the fact that my husband left his penis inside my panties and fell asleep. I was able to get away from him without awakening him to bathe myself.

But of one thing I am sure. He knew that I was not asleep because he repeated the same thing several times afterwards, sometimes taking my hand down to my genitals and trying to work me up with my own finger. Of all the sex I have had with my husband I can honestly say that night was one of the best, because I did not have a clue as to what he was up to and what was coming next.

I write this to show that couples should continually experiment with sex so that it never becomes stale or boring.

Mrs. H.H.

DEFORMITY FEAR

I am 19 and am so worried about my vagina that I never allow my relations with men to get to the physical point. The problem is that my vagina is deformed. I've been looking through all the medical textbooks I could get my hands on and I cannot find one illustration of a woman's private parts that looks like my own. The inner part of my genitals hangs down in an extremely ugly way whereas in the textbooks the inner part is always shown as smaller and neater and hidden by the outer lips. Is there anything I can do about this?

Miss V.J.

Just as breasts come in all shapes and sizes so does the vagina.

The female genitals have two large hair-covered lips called the labia majora, one on either side of the vaginal opening. Within the labia majora are two smaller lips of soft tissue called the labia minora. These are hairless and have a wrinkled appearance. Most sketches tend to show the labia minora almost completely hidden by the labia majora, as you saw in the books you looked at. However it is interesting to note that when photographs are used for such purposes as instructing midwives it is more usual for them to show the labia minora extended markedly beyond the outer lips, which appears to be the way you are constructed.

Both formations are normal. – F.

PERFECTLY NORMAL

Like Miss V.J. I have the labia minora extended markedly beyond the outer lips, and like her I suffered agonies of mind. No book, no picture, no work of art depicts the female who is so constructed – except, as your reply said, photographs shown only to midwives etc.

Let me assure Miss V.J. that this physical feature has never in my experience deterred my lovers or husband. Nevertheless I suffer an initial shyness over what I have always thought to be an embarrassing abnormality. What a relief to learn that it is perfectly normal.

Mrs. A.F.

EROTIC SIGHT

I can assure Mrs. A.F. who is worried about men's response to prominent inner lips, that I find the extended labia minora extremely attractive.

My wife is also constructed this way.

Personally speaking, in fact, I find enlarged inner lips more exciting than the small hidden-away type. Instead of just seeing

171

(in an unexcited state) a slit with hair, the hanging lips afford more variety, and in my view make the vulva look always in an excited state, causing the outer lips to appear larger.

Furthermore, I have seen pictures of such genitals in the naturist publications on sale.

Both Miss V.J. and Mrs. A.F. should consider themselves as absolutely normal – and attractive to men.

S.T.

PATRIARCHAL PUTDOWN

How many women are suffering embarrassment and agony of mind in the mistaken belief that they are malformed or in some way abnormal because they have not read the letters from Miss V.J. and Mrs. A.F. who wrote in about their protruding inner labia?

Mrs. A.F.'s comment on not finding in any books, pictures, or works of art any depiction of women's external genitals as they appear in real life, indicates the length to which the patriarchal establishment goes to pursue its policy of subordinating the individuality of women by fostering the illusion that she has no external genitalia, thereby reducing her sexual individuality to nothing by the promotion of the concept of the cunt as no more than an anonymous and uniform crease.

To her question as to whether men find the likes of her attractive. Without a doubt they do, the real men that is; not those whose pretensions to masculinity depend solely on an imagined superiority to women – the patriarchal types.

The reason men are fascinated (and that word is used deliberately) by well-developed labia is that in response to no more than the male presence they will change in color, in size, and stiffness; a comparable fascination to woman's as in response to her presence alone the penis changes from small and limp to large and erect.

More than that: later, when he is in her 'up to the hilt' and he can feel her labia reaching out to clasp his scrotum as it titillates her clitoris, both he and she enjoy the sensation of her having him in her 'balls and all'.

How many women have protruding inner labia? All, except those unfortunates suffering from an atrophy induced by a censorious society, and except those more unfortunate women who have been circumcised. Whether it be by atrophy or by the

172

knife, for these unfortunates the result is the same – a psychological castration.

Miss V.J. and Mrs. A.F. however have broken the ice, so it is hoped that that might encourage others so that eventually the whole subject is brought out in the open to the mutual advantage of both women *and* men. With due acknowledgment to Germaine Greer, the advancement of one sex depends as much on the other sex as on its own.

Mrs. O.A.

REAWAKENING INTEREST

About three years ago, despite almost a decade of happy marriage, ours seemed to enter a phase of staleness. Our tempers suffered and grew short till, one evening after the theater, we had a bitter quarrel on the underground platform and took separate seats at some distance from each other. I became aware of being eyed up and down by a lone wolf trying his luck and giving way to the mood of sheer pique, I smiled in encouragement and hitched my skirt in a come-hither. When my husband noticed and butted in, there was a stormy scene that left the bewildered stranger high and dry; and on reaching the home-stop, I was hustled and half-dragged to the door of our house.

Without even bothering to switch on any lights, my husband began kissing me excitedly, stripping off my clothes as he did so, and pulled me, fiercely resisting, into the lounge where a coal fire still glowed brightly. When I realized he was not really angry and I had nothing to fear, I stopped struggling and gave in to him and he made love with more passionate abandon than since honeymoon days.

Later, he apologized and we talked till the first grey streak of dawn exchanging all sorts of intimacies with a wonderful new sense of freedom. Apparently the stranger's attentions, crude though they were, had sparked off all his old feelings for me and made him freshly aware of my charms. During the weeks that followed we had much talk on ways and means of repeating the experience but instead of relying on chance encounters, we evolved the following plan that has been successful for almost two years now. I am passing it on in the hope it may encourage and help others who have a similar problem of marital staleness.

When the opportunity seems favorable, my husband invites one of his clients unlikely to revisit the neighborhood again in the foreseeable future, to come home for dinner. I get due warning to prepare one of my special meals and tart myself up in one of my most fetching dresses. At an agreed time just as coffee is served, we get a phone call from his 'aunt' along the road, requesting first aid with a blown fuse.

He excuses himself for a few minutes, then puts through another call, full of apologies but saying he'll be at least half an hour as the 'old lady' has fallen in the darkness and he has to settle her in bed with a hot drink and a brandy. In reality, he comes back to his study upstairs where the tape-recorder is tuned in to no less than three hidden microphones in the lounge. By the rules of the game, I have exactly an hour alone with our guest and am free completely to act just according to my mood and the appeal of his charm.

For the first few occasions, I confined it all to a saucy flirtation of harmless petting and kissing; but as time went on, it went further and further till we now have a few red hot tapes with a sound picture of the whole process. And the further it goes, the more excited and amorous we are on replay where I am honour bound to fill in the gaps of silence by answering honestly just what is happening. Any jealousy that threatens is soon driven out by the variety that has developed in our sex-technique. My husband is much more virile and I am bolder and much less inhibited. I used to feel rather foolish dressing up like a tart and wearing such heavy makeup; but the fact that it appeals to these men as well makes it all seem worth while.

In fact, my husband is sometimes so very much 'on' I give him what we call a 'sailor's fuck' before our session of replaying begins. He likes me to wear my nylons and belt and very high heels and lie down on the divan with my head almost touching the floor and my legs splayed out over the side. He gets a great kick not seeing 'me' but just a half-naked woman lying waiting and willing. When I got over the slight feeling of resentment, I found there is nothing quite so overwhelming as this first fierce screw even though by now we know all the delights of fellatio and cunnilingus.

No doubt there is a deep psychological explanation for all this. But it seems to me now quite natural to value only what you feel you may lose or what seems so special or precious to a stranger. We have even discussed extending it all to swapping or

174

having a third party present but so far we are content with present results for it keeps us both on our mettle and our sex life is perpetually exciting again.

Mrs. E.B.

MASQUERADE

As a bachelor, I often fantasize what it would be like in bed with my wife if I were married and how we both would react to sexual deviations.

One deviation which seems set in my mind is to have my wife apply cosmetics to me. Strange? You see I find women who use cosmetics liberally very sexually stimulating! After all, we only have this life so let's make the most of it.

I visualize my wife in panties, bra, long hose and makeup, applying cosmetics to my face: powder, mascara, liner, lipstick, even hair spray, all applied with a soft woman's touch. What a lovely thought! We would then have sex, makeup and all.

Do other readers have the same fantasies?

J.R.

There are many men who apparently can be sexually stimulated by the sight of heavily made-up women. It is likely that this is due to a combination of visual and olfactory (smell) appeal. The importance of sexually attractive odors, long since appreciated by many women, has just been scientifically established by the noted sexologists Masters and Johnson. They were concerned with the use of variously scented handcreams and lotions, and they discovered that certain scents were much more erotic than others to men. Although far from being a true aphrodisiac, many of the males studied by Masters and Johnson felt that they became more roused and performed better when these scents were used by their female partners. Clearly, this is a most exciting prospect, with obvious commercial implications.

The second part of your letter which deals with your sexual fantasies suggests that you get erotic pleasure out of physical sensations associated with wearing make-up.

One of the presumed functions of sexual fantasies is to act as a safety valve, by which a person can 'act out' (in his mind) repressed and/or unfulfilled wishes and needs. Providing fantasies do not take up a disproportionate amount of waking time

or become obsessive in quality, they presumably serve a useful
purpose in maintaining psychological well-being. – F.

FOOT FANCIER
I never see any mention in magazines of the sexiness of feet.

The female naked foot can be very exciting.

To be masturbated by long elegant toes is an out-of-this-world sexual experience.

R.M.

GOOD VIBES
My girlfriend and I have recently purchased a vibrator and are amazed at its effectiveness in producing female orgasm.

Formerly, although we were both fully satisfied with our sex life, my partner did not find orgasm easy to attain. During lovemaking, she would usually have one orgasm, however long I was able to continue thrusting, even with simultaneous clitoral stimulation by hand. Even when she failed to have orgasm, she was however quite relaxed and happy, and we acquired the vibrator in a lighthearted, experimental mood.

We now find that her orgasm capability has increased enormously. On the first trial, she came to full orgasm after I had rubbed her clitoris with the vibrator for about 10 seconds – manual stimulation usually takes her about five to ten minutes to orgasm. Moreover, whereas she is usually 'turned off' after one manual orgasm, she enjoys up to half a dozen within a few minutes with the vibrator.

We have now evolved the following way of combining the use of the vibrator with our usual lovemaking.

She kneels on the bed, with several pillows under her belly, and while I thrust into her from the rear entry position, she masturbates herself with the vibrator. She has two or three orgasms right away, by which time I have to withdraw to avoid coming too soon. On withdrawal I take the vibrator from her, and masturbate her with it from behind, rubbing it on the clitoris and occasionally thrusting it into her. By the time she has come, I can usually enter her again for a while, and when I am about to come, we repeat the process. There is virtually no limit

176

to how long this can continue — a few nights ago we kept it up for several hours, and eventually she seemed to be having just one long orgasm.

As a result of our favorable experience, we would certainly recommend the vibrator to any woman who is having difficulty attaining orgasm.

D.M.

PANTIE FETISH

I get a great delight out of smelling panties — but with one qualification — I only use the panties of girlfriends.

I consider myself to be very experienced sexually, having done nearly everything I have ever read about, with the exception of anal intercourse, and although enjoying the pantie fetish, do not consider it to be my sole sexual outlet.

It began when I was dating a girl who would not let me get anywhere beyond feeling her breasts outside her clothing. Being absolutely mad about her, I used to masturbate almost every time I went home from seeing her.

Well, one night as I was leaving her flat, I went into the bathroom before leaving (I sometimes used to masturbate there as it helped me to bear the frustration of it all) and quite unexpectedly began rummaging through the washbasket. Finding several pairs of her panties of all colors — pink and light blue being my favorites — I began inspecting them closely and decided to take three pairs home with me.

On reaching my own flat, I got completely undressed and began smelling the crotch part of her panties, while wearing one of the other pairs. The erection I got was instantaneous and fit to burst the panties I had on, so I slipped the pair I was sniffing over my head with the crotch tight against my nose and mouth and brought myself off within 20 seconds. It was unbelievably delightful and really had me hooked from that day on.

Obviously I was subconsciously settling for the next best thing to her fanny — the underwear which enclosed it. The delicate intimate aroma that filled my nostrils was beautiful to say the least. This fetish has remained with me to this day, and I have done the same thing with virtually every girlfriend I've had since.

No sooner do I lose interest in the girl than I discard her panties which I have acquired. Significantly enough I have retained those first panties, although I never did get to make love to that girl.

P.C.

Some time ago I was in Monterrey, Mexico, and passed a lingerie shop which had an enormous display of panties of all sizes and colors. I noticed a young man staring intently at the display with obvious excitement. Two hours later returning from lunch I passed the same shop and the same young man was still staring with unabated fascination at the same store window.

Interest in female underwear is one of the most common of the fetishes, as could be expected by the proximity of panties and bras to sexual areas.

Advertising men are obviously quite aware of the great interest in underwear so that attractive models dressed in underthings have been the staple of the industry since the turn of the century. Anyone who has observed men getting into pitched battles for the G-string of the stripper can appreciate the strength of this wish to possess and admire undergarments.

Since the undergarments cover the forbidden erotic parts, possession of them seems to make some men feel that they are in possession of the parts they hide.

The erotic sensations P.C. experiences when smelling his girlfriends' panties are not unusual. Sexual smells can be a strong stimulus to sexual feelings. Some men even claim to have such a highly developed sense of smell that they can tell when a woman has her period, when she is ovulating and when she is pregnant. This is not as impossible as it may seem since hormonal changes do produce slight differences in the odor caused by the body's secretions. – H.G.

PANTIE MAN

I was very interested in P.C.'s letter about how he relieved his frustration by smelling his girlfriends' panties. It would appear to be without their knowledge or permission either. In my case it was slightly different, in that I did it with my girlfriend's cooperation. It is good to know that I am not the only one who indulged in this habit.

This girlfriend, whom I didn't marry in fact, was the only girl

I ever went steady with who wouldn't make love. She was a virgin, and believed in keeping it for the wedding night. This proved to be very frustrating for me as she was an extremely attractive and well-built girl, and I used to do what P.C. did — masturbate in her bathroom using either her soiled panties, or, on a few occasions, her mother's panties which I fetched from the soiled clothes basket.

I knew I would enjoy it more if I was able to take the panties home to bed with me, so with great delicacy I made the suggestion to her that, as she refused to have intercourse or even masturbate me, the least she could do would be to let me enjoy her panties. After a bit of giggling she more or less consented, but was a bit shocked when she found it was her soiled panties I wanted and not clean ones. I had to explain to her as tactfully as possible that there would be no thrill in a fresh laundered pair, that it was the thrilling, intimate smell which made it so exciting. After a few more days of reassuring, I got the OK.

And so began for me the most exciting (sexually) nine months of my life. I masturbated in bed every night of the week. I took her panties, usually three times a week. I soon had her wearing my favorite styles — sheer nylon and as brief and tight as she could wear them. This really became a fetish with a capital F. I do believe that toward the end of our courtship I could have made love to her if I'd really tried — but I didn't want to.

Although this all took place eight years ago, I still have glorious, vivid memories of that little ritual of ours. After I got supper in her home, we would go into the hall to kiss goodnight. She would step back, pull her skirt up to the waist (I used to insist on seeing her wearing the panties before I got them) giving me a quick look. Then she would slip them off and push them into my pocket. This fetish almost ruined me for other girls. After we split up, I found it difficult to adjust to the fact that I was expected to make love to the girl I was with instead of worshipping her panties.

Although I am now happily married, I still sometimes use my wife's panties for masturbating purposes, but unknown to her.

J.H.

SAUCE FOR THE GOOSE

I enjoy Forum but I notice that although so many men write

and say how they enjoy seeing and wearing girls' and women's underwear and using them, women don't.

I will try to balance the scene. I am 25 and I enjoy men's underpants and briefs. I do the laundry for my uncle who is 46 and my boy cousins, aged 17 and 20. I love to hold up their pants and see the outline of their organs indented in the material. I love to put them on and wear them during the day and masturbate myself in them in bed at night. The opening of the Y-front style is very useful for this. I would like to wear a pair and have intercourse with the man going through the side opening, if it could be done.

Miss V.G.

MAKING OF A HOMOSEXUAL

Despite what I would in all honesty call a normal family background my son has become a homosexual. He claims that he has always been like this and that it has nothing to do with what either his father or I 'did'. But I can't help lying awake nights thinking about where we went wrong. Do people ever become homosexual for anything but psychological reasons?

Mrs. L.C.

Although many attempts have been made to prove that homosexuality is a physiologically based disorder, I have seen no satisfactory evidence to date to support this point of view. At one time it was believed, for example, that male homosexuals suffered from a deficiency of testosterone (male hormone). Male homosexuals were given testosterone, with results that should have been anticipated – the group so treated merely became more active homosexuals.

Treating homosexuality with psychological methods has had considerably more success. These methods have included, among others: (1) psychoanalysis and psychotherapy and (2) behavior modification which makes homosexual wishes and experiences unpleasant and rewards heterosexual behavior. The effectiveness of these methods indicates that homosexuality is probably chiefly psychological in origin.

Some of the early childhood conditions which may go into the development of the homosexual include the following:

(1) Many males make the homosexual choice because of their first experience with a female, namely, their mother, who found

*herself more compatible with a woman-like boy. Such mothers
frequently reward their sons' activities in interests – housework,
cooking, dressing up – which we call 'feminine' in our society.
The son is thus encouraged to give up the male role and make
himself into an imitation female.*

*(2) A young boy in our complex society learns how to be a
man through identification and imitation of other males,
usually his father. If he finds no satisfactory male model, however, he may decide to pattern himself after a female like his
mother who is often smotheringly close.*

*It would be impossible to include all of the possible factors
leading to homosexuality – there are almost as many reasons
given as there are homosexuals. I have known a homosexual
whose mother banished him to sleeping with his father. In this
case the mother decided that husband and son should sleep
together while she kept her bedroom inviolate from male entrance. Under those circumstances, the son developed strong
homosexual feelings because the father was the only one who
showed him any physical affection.*

*In my experience, though, if one examines the context in
which a person made the homosexual choice, that choice then
becomes quite understandable. – H.G.*

PREMATURE EJACULATION

I have always suffered from premature ejaculation and now
that I am thinking of getting married this problem is causing me
great anxiety.

I do in fact ejaculate quite easily even when my penis is in a
flaccid state; also on such occasions as when I read a book
about sex. For some reason which I do not understand I have
no control over my ejaculations.

During loveplay, although my penis is limp, I do obtain
much sensation in the glans; however, the slightest friction in
that area causes an ejaculation.

Can you help me?

R.O.

*Premature ejaculation (ejaculate praecox) can be thus
classified:*

(a) The involuntary ejaculation of semen from the fully erect

penis immediately it penetrates the vagina (Ejaculatis post portas.)

(*b*) *Loss of semen with or without erection caused by stimulation, i.e., erotic thoughts, a kiss or a caress.* (Ejaculatis ante portas.)

Cases of the latter type are often difficult to cure. A man who is unable to complete the sexual act soon begins to feel inferior and inadequate. Anxiety follows and the chances of a successful cure are even more remote.

Causes of sexual hypersensitivity in men are twofold, but as so often happens in these matters a vicious circle appears when the original cause aggravates other factors which when awakened, intensify the defect.

The original cause may be either physical or emotional. In the case of the former, the glans penis may be very sensitive to touch, causing orgasm and emission to occur as soon as stimulation commences. In such a case erection is usually present.

If some sexual anxiety is present, it is usually subconscious and not readily appreciated by the patient. Undoubtedly, most men suffering from premature ejaculation would prefer the cause to be physical so as to deny the possibility of an emotional upset or imbalance. Until the patient is prepared to accept that there could be an emotional element, no progress may be made to effect a cure.

In cases of ejaculatis post portas, *anesthetic ointments such as Nupercainal (Ciba) may be useful. A portion of ointment, about the size of a pea, is rubbed carefully over the whole of the glans, prepuce and shaft of the penis 30 minutes before stimulation commences. More or less ointment may be used as results suggest, and the time interval may also be adjusted.*

Another method which may help is desensitization. The partner stimulates the male very slightly. As soon as he feels that ejaculation may occur all stimulation is stopped. When the sensation has disappeared stimulation may begin again. Using this method with constant repetition, patience and care, stimulation can often be stepped up and ejaculation delayed. It is advisable when handling the penis to use a bland cream (as well as the anesthetic cream) as a lubricated skin surface will stimulate the moist vaginal walls. It must be noted that the aforementioned method requires a partner endowed with patience and compassion.

If the patient suffers from ejaculatis ante portas *where the erection is almost entirely absent, the woman can merely indulge in 'sexual closeness', without actual contact, making no attempt to encourage intercourse. As anxiety about the situation is gradually resolved, the male is able to accept a greater degree of closeness, until eventually real desire to fulfill complete union arises and success will follow.*

Naturally, during the initial periods of sexual closeness the feelings of the male will boil over, and ejaculation will follow. When this happens, after a short pause, the process should continue, unless the male feels distinct aversion. Such ejaculation should not be regarded as failure, but merely as being another step, however frustrating, in attaining complete union.

If all such methods fail to alter the situation, then professional psychiatric treatment is required, and unfortunately this can prove a tedious and time-consuming affair.

It is true that many individuals, male and female, have reservations concerning sexual intercourse before marriage and these reservations are very often important factors in this sort of case. However, I would suggest that R.O. seek professional help regarding his problem before he gets married. – F.

A MATTER OF OVERSENSITIVITY

Your discussions on the subject of rapid ejaculation have tended to imply that the complaint is all-or-nothing in character. It is of course a matter of degree, and it seems that few men are satisfied with their 'duration'! Rapid ejaculation is distressing in that it shows 'feedback' and tends to worsen. I have had some success in dealing with the problem (which becomes more acute after sexual abstinence) and others may be interested in the method.

I would suggest that when rapid ejaculation is triggered psychologically, it is because of exposure to certain key stimuli to which the sufferer is oversensitive. Therapy should consist of the frequent repetition of effective stimulation, like pinups (however these are thought of in society) or listening to erotic records, so that the response is reduced and delayed.

Indeed one may wonder if the demand for erotic art, pornographic literature, etc., is not an attempt by man in his artificial environment to equate his sexual response with his sexual appetite. Sadly the establishment in its wisdom (?) tries to hinder what may be beneficial personal therapy.

J.M.

TRANSSEXUAL WIFE

I am a transsexual living the life of a woman. I started dressing up when I was a boy and have been doing it ever since.

I live with a wonderful man who treats me as his wife and I love him as a wife should. Although I am not a homosexual we make love regularly. I do the housekeeping and cooking and my husband gives me the housekeeping money every week and a dress allowance.

I always dress as a woman as I feel physically sick at the sight of men's clothes. We go out together in normal company and even our friends think I am a woman. I am known as Pauline and my husband would never dream of calling me by any other name. I always dress in a mini-skirt as my legs are very good. My genitals and penis are so small I don't need strapping. In the evenings my husband likes me to sit around in my full slip, panties, tights and bra. I have a small bust which I have developed.

We both hope that one day I can have the operation that will make me a woman but every doctor I have seen doesn't seem to know anyone who can help me, which is why I am writing to you. I must have this operation. After all I am a woman in all respects except for my genitals.

R.G.

There is no operation in the world that can make R.G. a woman if he was born a man. It can make him less a man (by surgical castration) and an ersatz woman (by the surgical building of a 'vaginal' cavity and hormone treatment for breast growth and reduction of body hair) but in purely physical terms he would then be 'neuter'. However, these factors do not rule out the possible psychological effect of such an operation. – F.

BITES HUSBAND

My husband and I have enjoyed a full and satisfying sex life for seven years. We have made love in every position it is possible for two people to get into without taking a course in acrobatics.

As you can therefore imagine, we have a very varied and exciting sex life, but my problem is that recently I have developed an almost uncontrollable urge to bite my husband. He thinks that it is getting beyond a joke but I can't stop it. I think my new deviation started from sucking his penis and has gone on from there, but now I bite him all over and derive a great deal of satisfaction from it.

Before jumping to conclusions that I must be some kind of sadist, let me point out that I don't want to hurt him, but I just love to feel my teeth gripping his flesh.

Do tell me if I am in danger of becoming perverted and if there is any reason for my newly acquired habit.

Mrs. M.S.

'You're good enough to eat' is a well known and much used compliment between lovers.

There's an old male joke about sex and marriage which states: 'For the first six months you feel you could eat it (vagina) and for the rest of the time after that you wish you had.' It seems Mrs. M.S. feels he's still good enough to eat after seven years, but that he doesn't reciprocate the feeling ('he thinks it is getting beyond a joke').

In everyday terms, perhaps Mrs. M.S. just wants to goad him into stepping up his performance a little. After all, seven years can slow a man down. – F.

TRANSVESTITE DILEMMA

I am in my late thirties, married and have children, but at times have an overwhelming need to dress as a woman in every detail. I do this while alone and masturbate. Then I am disgusted with myself for a while but the need to be or resemble a woman always comes back.

I suppose it started in childhood when I tried on my sister's panties and gym slip. I had an erection and knew that lingerie was for me.

In the ensuing years before marriage, I overcame it by keeping occupied and dated lots of girls, but shortly after marriage I fell back into my old practice. This seemed to satisfy my sexual needs. Before we married, my wife was very keen on relations with me, but the responsibilities of marriage have, I suppose, made me take life more seriously and now she no longer seems to want to have anything to do with me. The children were produced out of wifely duty and she had an affair which she found very stimulating.

The affair seemed to make the transvestism worse. A few years after this I dressed up in women's clothes and showed myself to my wife, thinking that I was going mad. She offered to help, saying it was all mind over matter. In desperation I recently got in touch with the Albany Trust and went for a short while to receive electrical treatment, shocks administered to me while looking at photographs of myself in female attire.

It was very embarrassing and I thought it had done the trick and I threw away all my clothes. But several months later I bought new dresses and underthings and now permanently wear tights, panties and a girdle.

It's getting worse! I can understand that my wife cannot bear to have anything to do with 'deviations' as she calls them, but I am really beginning to feel that I want to dress as a woman all the time. I'd like her to come to me and humiliate me while dressed as a schoolgirl. Worse, I would like a man friend.

Perhaps what I really need is a woman who would allow and even assist me in my practices because the sex act under these conditions would, I think, be very enjoyable.

K.M.

TRANSVESTITE SOLUTION

We were married about three years ago, and soon after my transvestite leanings made themselves felt. My wife caught me wearing her clothes as she returned from shopping one Saturday, and a most distressing scene followed. However, as we were so much in love (and still are) she was very understanding and eventually allowed me to wear female underwear occasionally when we made love. Not long afterwards we learned that so many other couples were faced with the problem of one partner being bisexual (which I believe I am).

Sometimes my dear wife will insist on me wearing one of her nighties as we go to sleep. I usually agree to this, but sometimes refuse, as I feel that a refusal must strengthen her belief that I am predominantly masculine and definitely not homosexual.

Tonight, my wife is having an evening out with some girls and she knows that while she is out I am wearing her clothes which she selected for me before leaving. When she returns she will be alone because she knows that I will be dressed as I am now, and as we have coffee together the conversation will be quite normal with only complimentary references to the clothing we are both wearing.

Anyway, I know that I can look forward to a long and uninhibited session of beautiful lovemaking which will last well into the early hours.

So, we are both happy with our new sex life, but recently my wife has expressed a desire for me to buy a vibrator and use it on her. I cannot help wondering whether she may grow to prefer the vibrator to me, and I certainly want to retain my masculine privilege of having natural intercourse with her.

R.J.

As for your wife coming to prefer a vibrator to you – can you imagine yourself preferring an artificial vagina to a real woman? Local genital stimulation is only a part of the enjoyment of sex, especially for women. And a vibrator could do as much for you as it will for her. – F.

CROSS-DRESSING

For some years now, I have practiced cross-dressing, and although I am not a genuine transvestite, I do indulge in this practice as a sort of 'stepping stone'.

I am able to acquire definite sexual pleasure through seeing myself attired in the image of an attractive and shapely 'girl next door'. I do not don a glamorous wig and cocktail dress and reach for the stars. I am content to wear plain but sexy, well-fitting separates. I find that I am excited by what I see as well as by what I feel.

The female posterior holds great attraction for me, especially when encased in a well-fitting tight skirt or dress or shown in relief beneath a pleated or flared skirt. I get butterflies in my stomach when the right sort of girl bends over causing her tight skirt to stretch even tighter.

This brings me to the reason for my cross-dressing. By utilizing my fortunately shapely self, I am able to recreate this image. After dressing in my most sexy outfit, I pivot and pose in front of a long mirror and am overcome by a sensation of intimate, pleasurable excitement deep inside me. I am so at peace with the world that I scarcely notice the incessant painful ache emanating from my 'fixed front'. On one or two occasions, I have been very close to orgasm merely through putting on a newly acquired skirt.

Several years ago, I made contact with a genuine transvestite. He visited me under the guise of a writer looking for material. He brought some of his 'items' with him. When he showed me his collection of undies, I experienced immediate distaste and felt dirty and unclean, despite the fact that I wear briefs myself. I then realized that I could only enjoy my transvestism in solitude, which is now my sole pleasure. When I have put on a good face and stand before my mirror, gently smoothing my hand over my hips and to and fro across my plump, soft exquisitely skirted bottom, I know just how heavenly, delightful and above all intimate and personal cross-dressing can be.

S.D.H.

Like most other areas dealing with socio-sexual behavior, a great deal more research is necessary before the factual causes of transvestism are definitely ascertained. Psychologist Daniel G. Brown, writing in the Encyclopaedia of Sexual Behaviour, *makes the valid point that in many instances the basis for the development of transvestism occurs in the early years of childhood.*

According to Dr. Brown, the psychosocial explanation of transvestism is in terms of learning, i.e., transvestism is regarded as an acquired motivational and behavioral pattern, directly traceable to conditioning experiences, usually occurring in childhood. As such, a person's preference for or compelling desire to wear clothes of the other sex is no more the result of inborn constitutional factors than is a vegetarian's strict preference for meatless food. It is true, of course, that just as in other aspects of human behavior, the ease with which conditioning will develop a strong preference can vary from person to person. Wide differences in sensory threshold have been clearly demonstrated and are quite evident. Nevertheless, practically all individuals are conditionable, i.e., have the potentiality for acquiring particular motives, preferences and emotional states of varying degrees of intensity.

Whatever may be the unique combination of childhood experiences and circumstances in a given case of transvestism, one factor almost invariably found to be of prime importance is that in the first two or three years of life, the child was accidentally or intentionally exposed to the experience of wearing and fondling the clothes of the other sex, allowing an imprinting process to occur, in which, for example, the male child's formative sensory experiences may be conditioned to feminine articles of clothing. A frequent related finding in the histories is that the child's hair was kept long and/or in curls like that of a girl.

In addition, the boy is often given extra attention and praise by the parent for wearing feminine clothes and appearing feminine. Interestingly enough, in some instances, a young boy may be punished by being forced to wear feminine clothes, such 'discipline' being referred to as 'pinafore punishment'; nevertheless, such a boy may come to be conditioned to feminine items just as surely as one who is rewarded for wearing them.

It is important to note here that this process involves both conditioning and instrumental or operant forms of learning; that a considerable amount of it is an involuntary learning experience; and that it occurs in the earliest period of life before the child can even verbalize his feelings and preferences. This probably explains the fact that many transvestites report not only that the clothes of the other sex feel 'natural', but also that they 'can't help' feeling the way they do about such clothes. In this connection, it is possible that the much greater incidence of transvestism reported in males compared to females may be based in part on the more frequent occurrence of boys dressed as girls in the first two or three years of life. – F.

AN ORAL PERSON

I would like to ask your experts for some advice. Not that I really have a problem but I would like to know if I am unusual at all.

I think I am highly sexed but definitely not in the least a nymphomaniac, as I am highly selective in my bed partners. But if I am attracted to a man, I can't be bothered with pretending I don't want to go to bed or making him chase me for it; and when we get into bed, the thing I want to do most is go down on him.

I thoroughly enjoy intercourse but rarely have orgasm that way. I love to have the penis in my mouth and masturbate myself at the same time. I come when he comes and love to swallow the semen. This doesn't bother me a bit and I have never met a man who doesn't enjoy it enormously, but I often read of fellatio being classed as a perversion. You tend to include it as a perversion if it replaces intercourse.

The only other thing that does worry me a bit is that I smoke very heavily, 50 cigarettes or more a day; it seems I'm a very oral person in every way. I did try to give up smoking with the help of a hypnotist but became very edgy and nervous and couldn't stop eating. I had to go back to smoking because I started to get so fat. My sexual habits don't worry me at all, but I do wonder why some people get so much more pleasure through the mouth than others.

Mrs. M.T.

Oral sex has been practiced since the beginning of time; there are written records about it going back thousands of years. Animals practice it, too.

The term 'oral person' or 'oral personality' derives from the psychoanalytic theory of stages of development. According to Freud and one of his early followers, Abraham, the individual goes through a number of stages in which his libido or sexual feelings are concentrated in or connected to various parts of the body. The earliest stage is the oral stage where all satisfaction comes from sucking and biting. The second stage is the anal, where the child becomes interested in the waste products of the body and the anus, and the third stage is the genital, where libidinal feelings are concentrated in the genital area.

Also according to psychoanalytic theory, an individual who does not get full satisfaction in any one of these stages remains fixated at that level and thereafter attempts to get all his gratification from that one stage. The orally fixated individual is one who still derives sexual pleasure solely from oral stimulation – fellatio, cunnilingus, excessive eating, chewing gum, smoking. All these actions can be considered forms of oral stimulation.

In their natural development, many individuals retain parts of these earlier stages, but as long as these do not become com-pulsive and the only way they can get satisfaction, there is no serious problem. Thus, while a person may still enjoy oral stimulation, he does not have a problem if he is able to enjoy other forms of sexual activity, including genital. – H.G.

PLEASURE OF SUCKING

Could I inquire if there are many men who, in their pre-liminary loveplay take as much pleasure as I do in suckling the wife's breast? To open my mouth as wide as possible and take in her nipple, and as much of her bosom as possible, gives me a wonderful feeling of anticipation for the lovemaking that nearly always follows.

An even more erotic thrill is experienced when my partner takes my head in her arm and with the other hands slips a breast from her dress and places it in my eagerly awaiting mouth. I enjoy seeing and caressing nice legs and buttocks, but I often wonder if there are other men who prefer fondling the breast to other parts of the female anatomy, lovely as they all can be.

This loveplay need not necessarily always lead up to inter-course; circumstances may not always be favorable. But as a prelude to sex, my wife's initiative in drawing me to her and giving me her breast to suck never fails to arouse me.

A.R.

COMMUNICATION

I have been married nearly two months now and my wife and I each know how to give each other the maximum amount of pleasure.

Although we used to pet a lot when we were courting and had intercourse an average of twice a week, we find that sex is very much more enjoyable now we are married. I know the places on my wife's body which give her pleasure when they are stroked and I know this because she told me on our wedding night, when it was quite dark in our bedroom and there was no fear of embarrassment. She whispered in my ear all the things she wanted me to do to her and I told her my preferences. I believe

191

a lot of couples would do well to tell each other their secret desires in the dark; that way neither would be likely to be embarrassed.

When we became engaged, I discovered my wife's breasts were so sensitive that she could be brought to orgasm by caressing them. I would stroke the underside of her breasts until her nipples became hard, when I would cup each breast in either hand and squeeze and stroke them with my fingers, which very soon gave her a climax.

It was only after we got married that she told me she liked to have her nipples pinched between forefinger and thumb while she had her climax.

In our courting days I used to caress her clitoris frequently and she used to writhe about on my lap, but, again, it was only after our marriage that she told me that the tip of her clitoris was supersensitive and begged me to rotate my forefinger on it. Naturally I granted her wish and made a mental note that this was her favourite caress.

She is now capable of reaching a climax pretty quickly and we find that we are able to achieve what to my mind is the most marvelous thrill imaginable – simultaneous orgasm. I often feel my penis being subjected to a very strong suction and while I am experiencing the wonderful sensations of orgasm, her vagina grips my penis like a vise.

After intercourse we lie clasped in each other's arms, still coupled, and we often talk about the most intimate things including our sex fantasies. For instance, my wife confessed that she has a secret wish to ride on the back of a stallion while he is mating with a mare.

Something we have discovered recently involves me rubbing her clitoris with the underside of my penis, with her actually directing the movement with her hands. We can keep this up for several minutes and have even reached orgasm together doing this.

My wife tells me never to think twice before putting my hand under her skirt. She deliberately wears short dresses and miniskirts and in the evenings, when we are at home, she leaves her panties off.

The point I wish to make is simply this – if there was more frankness and communication in sex, between the partners, there'd be a lot more happy marriages.

                                                              D.R.

COITUS FREQUENCY

My wife and I are both in our early 20s and would like to know what is the average number of times for sex in one week?

B.B.

It is absolutely impossible to lay down any rules about frequency of intercourse, simply because we all have different sexual needs. We respond to what is known as our sex drive, and our sex drive is controlled by the interaction of certain hormones in our bodies. These hormones work at different degrees of intensity not only from individual to individual, but from time to time in the same individual. Thus, one week our sex drive may urge us to want to make love three or four times, and the next week only once or twice.

As a general rule, our hormones work within certain limits. In the great majority of people in their 20s, they provide a sex drive which demands on average, over a year, three or four orgasms a week. To give such people a label – for convenience sake – we say they are average-sexed.

But there are some people whose hormones work at a faster rate than average, and produce a sex drive which requires outlets in orgasm say, once, twice or even more often each day. We call them highly sexed.

At the other end of the scale, there are those whose sex drives require one outlet every ten days or two weeks. They are the low-sexed. After 35, the sex drive gradually slows down.

The main thing is that we should make love when, for one reason or another, we feel we want to. Frequency is personal to each couple. What any other couple does has nothing to do with us. – F.

MUSCULAR CONTROL

I am perhaps one of your more fortunate readers in that I do not really have a 'problem' in my physical life. My previous marriage was superficially quite satisfactory, except for the psychological aspect of our sex life, lacking what I could only have described at the time as a feeling of 'completeness' after intercourse.

In my present marriage I have found what I was looking for

– a person with whom I can experience every kind of physical expression of love without any distaste, incompleteness, or dissatisfaction. We have recently tried anal intercourse for the first time, and although I found it rather difficult, it has not in the least put me off trying again – I would do anything if it would please my husband, and he is patient and willing to do anything to please me.

The one thing I would like to know a little more about is the control of my vaginal muscles. I can use these to a reasonable extent, but my husband has hinted that this could be improved by the odd remark about French night-club performers, and has said it would be nice if I could grip more firmly. I wondered if you could perhaps give me any information on how to improve the control of my vaginal muscles.

Mrs. B.L.

The vaginal 'grip' that Mrs. B.L. refers to is exerted by use of the pubococcygeus, a wide band which forms part of the main muscle of the pelvic diaphragm. It is about an inch and a half inside the body surface and supports the organs of the pelvis as well as the rectal, urinary and vaginal passages. This muscle band can be contracted in isolation since it is surrounded by bone and does not therefore affect other muscles.

Flaws in this muscle were found to result in the involuntary passing of urine during exertion, such as lifting something heavy or coughing. An American doctor, Arnold Kegel, designed exercises for female sufferers to strengthen the muscle and relieve urinary incontinence. But his patients got a bonus – many of them told him that they were reaching full sexual satisfaction for the first time. This happens because although the vaginal passage has no nerve endings in it, the muscles beneath incorporate pressure-sensitive nerve endings and the contraction of these muscles is probably the foremost physical response of the female to penetration. This response is directly related to the muscle tone of the pubococcygeus which can be measured by a doctor with an instrument called a perineometer.

However, women can learn to contract the muscle band by themselves: since it controls the urinary flow, attempts to interrupt the flow will indicate whether or not contractions are taking place. Having located the muscle and discovered how to contract it in this way, exercises increasing to ten or more con-

tractions an hour can be done. After a few months, conscious 'practice' may be discontinued since the muscle remains partially contracted and toned up.

If Mrs. B.L. tries this method, she should soon have a firm grip on her husband – to their mutual satisfaction. – F.

VAGINAL CONTROL

The question of vaginal efficiency and control is, I think, very important, and one in which we are given no instructions. As a single woman of 40, leading, for the most part, a celibate life, I can have only occasional visits from my lover whose married sexual life has been infrequent and unsatisfactory. Perhaps it is because the experience is so rare and 'special' for us that I felt I must read all I could and make up in thoughtfulness and imagination for what I lacked in experience.

There are one or two books of exercises for women which give a page or two on the use of the vaginal and pelvic muscles, and Van De Velde wrote a book on the subject which was mainly for the medical reader engaged in the physical training of women.

I think the main thing to realize is that these muscles mainly lie dormant. Vaginal exercises can be practiced at any time. Lie on your back quite relaxed with knees apart and slightly bent. Slip into the vagina an ordinary candle or similar article. Make a few to-and-fro movements with it, now rotate it to stimulate sensation in the area. Next clench the band of muscle around the outlet of the vagina as if squeezing the object, hold for a count of three and relax. Again – and repeat up to ten times.

Next, imagining the penis filling the upper end of the vagina, try to locate the muscles which will nip it near the rim of the glans. This is more difficult. You may find these muscles almost useless, but I assure you they will come into action with persistent and regular effort, so much so, that without using any artificial aid you can use a few minutes every day, standing at the sink, in the bus queue, anywhere, alternately and together clenching and relaxing these important muscles.

I cannot yet actively 'milk' the penis but my partner would testify to the improvement I have shown in the muscular tone and activity, and I can add that my greater tightness and control make me much more conscious of, and sensitive to, the penile penetration and thrust.

Miss T.H.

SWEET SEX

I am a divorcée aged 42 with no family. I have my own house and do a part-time job in a city office. I have had a few lodgers over the past three years but until Eric came here to live six months ago I had never had any sexual relations with anyone since my divorce. Eric is a very healthy, happy-go-lucky person and we soon got friendly, but I still resisted all his advances and frequently relieved myself by masturbating.

About four months ago I threw caution aside and have never enjoyed sex or had so much pleasure from it before.

It started when I took a cup of coffee to him in his room one night. I'd had a bath and was in my nightdress and dressing gown and I had heard him working in his room. He was in his pajamas writing at a table when I went in. I sat on the edge of the table while he drank his coffee and while moving around on his chair the fly opening of his trousers gaped wide, revealing some of his pubic hair. He didn't realize it was in view so I sat there looking at it. This brought on a sensation within me and an urge to stroke the pubic hair. On an uncontrollable impulse I suddenly leaned over and did so. Obviously, all my pent up desires took control, and the fellatio which ensued seemed to come very naturally.

After his climax, he got up, took me over to his bed and said, 'Now it's your turn'. Taking off my dressing gown and nightdress, he laid me on the edge of the bed while he knelt on the floor and brought me off orally.

Although we masturbated each other both by hand and orally it was still a few days before I would let myself have full intercourse. Since then we have never looked back. We especially enjoy reading about and trying out the new sexual techniques, positions, methods of stimulation, etc., sent in by your readers. Here for instance are two of ours.

Over the last three weeks we have greatly enjoyed ourselves while watching television. At the start of a sports program we undress each other and Eric sits back in an easy chair. I ease myself over his erect penis until it is fully home and I can lean back on him. An exciting football match like the cup final can

196

be quite exhilarating as he is on the move all the time. Show-jumping is also very effective for him, as I tend to go over every jump with the horse, thus making him come about half-way through the program. Our position is very convenient for caressing and fondling each other during less exciting moments and during commercials. If Eric gets too involved with the game and I feel him going a bit limp, a little fondling of his testicles and perineum soon has him back to normal firmness.

The second one arose after I found that Eric had a great liking for a well-known brand of mints. One evening, when he was on the settee reading the paper, I went out to the kitchen. There I softened up a mint and rubbed it all around my vulva. I then put another one inside my vagina so that it was protruding a bit. I went in and sat beside him with the box of mints. We had one each and after a couple of minutes Eric asked for another one. His eyes sparkled as I lifted my skirt, opened my legs and said, 'Help yourself'. He certainly did and the following ten minutes was wonderful as he took his time eating the protruding mint, bringing me to an orgasm in the process. Needless to say this little experiment has since been repeated to our mutual enjoyment.

Mrs. E.M.

COLD COMFORT

Being an unmarried woman of 36, I am writing to you as I consider I am stimulated sexually in a rather unusual way.

In the very coldest of weather, when there is ice and snow around, I get sexually excited by imagining I am being forced to strip naked and to lower myself into a bath of ice-cold water. With these thoughts in mind I fill the bath with cold water and tip a couple of buckets of snow and ice into the bath to make the water very cold.

I keep another bucket of snow beside the bath. Still imagining I am being forced to do it I open the bathroom window wide to let in the cold air. I then slowly strip myself naked, imagining all the time sadistic men forcing me to do it. When I am stark naked I stand in the bath and slowly lower my bottom and private parts into the icy water, then straighten my legs until my thighs are under the water. In a very short time the parts of my body in the water begin a dull ache as the bitter cold bites into them. I then take two handfuls of snow from the bucket beside the bath and press it hard into my breasts. When my breasts begin to ache also and I can stand it no longer I stand up in the bath and open my legs as wide as I can and press more snow against my vagina.

I am by now fantastically aroused sexually and I masturbate in a frenzy, quickly coming in an explosive orgasm. After this I quickly dry myself and dress in nice warm clothes and feel wonderfully relaxed with all tensions gone as if I had had full intercourse.

I wonder if other readers have relieved themselves in this manner, or am I unique?

Miss R.S.

FROSTIE THE SNOWMAN

I am a male, happily married, and owner of a fish shop with a large yard at the rear surrounded by a very high wall. In the yard I keep a full-sized iron bath. When the cold weather is upon us, especially when the snow is about, after closing shop on a Tuesday night I clean the bath out and lay about four inches of ice at the bottom, then fill it three-quarters full with water and cover it to keep the dirt out. Hopefully, it will freeze overnight.

When I close shop on Wednesday at noon (half-day closing), I light a fire in the kitchen and slowly strip naked. I then go out into the yard, remove the cover from the bath, roll about the yard in the snow and then making quite sure that I keep my head and shoulders out of the water I lower myself into it, staying there for about ten minutes until my body starts to turn blue. Then I rush into the kitchen and dry myself in front of the fire, bringing with me a large chunk of ice. When my body is dry I usually have an erection. I place the chunk of ice between the cheeks of my behind and masturbate with the ice melting into water and running down my thighs and legs.

This relaxes me no end and all my tensions are relieved until the following Wednesday.

W.E.

'Icy preferences' are not so bizarre as might superficially appear. In fact they more or less add up to the ingredients of the Scandinavian Sauna Bath, which can be both relaxing and intensely sexually stimulating. However, in your case you do

198

*things in the reverse order. In the traditional sauna the sequence
is for excessive heat to be followed by a naked frolic outside in
snow or icy water. When suitably cooled the body temperature is
rapidly raised again by returning to the steam room. An added
refinement which adds to the overall sensual pleasure is to be
beaten with twigs.*

*The intense bodily stimulation is almost certainly due to the
extreme rapidity of the bodily temperature changes. However,
the process must be nicely tuned, since if the bodily temperature is either too low or too high for too long, pain (even physical damage) instead of pleasure can ensue.*

*Regarding your preference for 'placing a chunk of ice
between the cheeks of your behind, etc.', this again is not all that
unusual as a variant of sexual stimulation. Thus, at least one
manual recommends the use of snow or icy water applied to the
penis and scrotum as being highly stimulative. Once again the
rationale behind this is the rapid change in temperature which
excites the temperature nerve cells in the skin. – F.*

LESBIAN FALLACIES

While working on a book dealing with lesbianism I have been
curious to observe that, while women usually are repelled by
the idea, the majority of men appear to take an eager interest in
the subject. This puzzles me, for one might expect the reverse to
be true: it can only be supposed that the average male psychology harbors the seeds of envy when he realizes the powerful
forces at work between two women engaged in a sexual liaison
– forces of which he has little or no comprehension. Moreover,
since it's a medically recognized fact that very few men are
equipped to deal with the spiritual and emotional needs at the
root of feminine psychology, this envy may be more readily
understood.

Unfortunately he most usually confines his attentions to the
more physical aspects of a lesbian relationship, thus making a
cardinal blunder, for the feminine drives spring from much
deeper and more diffuse motives which a woman herself finds
considerable difficulty in revealing in word or print, for she is
pathologically aware of the hazards surrounding such a course.

Through the ages lesbians have endured ridicule, social ostracism, blackmail, loss of friends, jobs and accommodations,

while in the Middle Ages they suffered mutilation and even burning at the stake. Happily we are today moving slowly towards a more sympathetic approach, yet many years will pass before lesbianism is accepted as an ineradicable feature of society. Only in more enlightened countries, notably Sweden and Denmark, do lesbians enjoy a degree of freedom, and even there lesbianism exists in a limited framework.

Perhaps the lesbian is herself in part to blame for this state of affairs for upon examination we find the overt, strutting, exhibitionist type is invariably the one to hold the limelight; she is largely responsible for the profound damage to her colleagues, since an ignorant and gullible public are only too eager to judge and condemn from what they read in the more sensational press accounts. A recent illustration of this point was seen in a popular Sunday newspaper, where the neighbors of two women who contrived a marriage were stated to have observed: 'We know all about those two – they're so blatant about it . . .'

Unaccountably (and this may surprise some of your male readers) many lesbians are married with children, while a large number are prostitutes. Not a few are in highly regarded professions. Some are writers, actresses, dancers, probation officers, schoolteachers. Thus it will readily be seen why the overwhelming majority of lesbians must at all costs avoid publicity, since position, home and lucrative professions may be at stake.

Briefly, the reasons for many housewives embarking on a homosexual relationship are often found in an unrewarding marriage where, after years of being used as a masturbating receptacle by an unimaginative husband, she is driven by despair and frustration to seek comfort from one of her own sex.

It should be understood, however, that such a course is not willingly taken, nor is the opportunity easily found, but at least there is the consolation that the framework of her security isn't threatened in the same way as it would be were she to commit adultery. Admittedly, at the outset she may not consciously regard it as a homosexual venture, but as the friendship matures she frequently finds herself ensnared by instincts she scarcely understands yet is unable to resist.

From this it must not be taken that the friendship will necessarily culminate in physical love to the point of mutual masturbation, cunnilingus and the use of artificial penis. Nevertheless, the desire toward physical release exists as an undercurrent to many of her considerations, so that in time she may resort to self-masturbation, fantasy and erotic daydreams in an effort to relieve her tensions.

It might be interesting to note that the dildo (that rubber object so beloved of the lurid novel and pornographic photograph) rarely exists in real-life lesbian affairs. Most often she views such objects with distaste, since to her they represent all the coarser features of man – lust, abuse, tyranny and ignorance of her finer instincts.

As regards the prostitute: it is transparently evident why she seeks consolation with her own sex, for her profession almost always brings her into contact with only the worst side of men and in time she may conclude that all men are alike and indeed superfluous to her real happiness.

Only once during my research did I encounter a woman prone to a somewhat unfeminine pursuit. She was 29, tall, slim and dark, in all her gestures quite reminiscent of a young man, though not in an objectionable way. She habitually wore full drag (masculine attire) and contemptuously refused to carry a handbag. One evening at a pub she quite suddenly asked if I would like to see some pornographic pictures. I nodded, and she went to get them from her car. With mixed feelings I discovered them to be entirely of male homosexuals engaged in fellatio, mutual masturbation and anal penetration, while several were devoted to closeups of the sex organ during ejaculation.

On being asked why she carried such things she replied: 'Whenever I look at them I feel glad beyond words that I'm able to bring *real* happiness to a woman.'

Her lover, incidentally, was a strikingly attractive young woman with two children, who had gained a divorce through persistent sexual abuse from her husband. She sincerely endorsed the saying so often found in lesbian classics that 'once you've had a woman you never want another man'.

Within the framework of one letter it's quite impossible to deal exhaustively with such a profound subject. Nevertheless, I sincerely hope these few words will go toward dispelling some of the popular fancies surrounding lesbianism.

R.O.

It is a good idea to dispel some of the fallacies about lesbianism. However, I'm afraid our correspondent has perpetuated some others of his own.

201

Many of the women he describes who have these marital or sexual problems have had a homosexual orientation before marriage which intensified the problems with their husbands. In my own research on prostitution, I found that about 80% had overt homosexual experiences at one time or another. They did not turn to these experiences because of their unfortunate relationships with men but were more frequently homosexual to begin with. In some cases one of the factors which turned them toward prostitution was an effort to disprove their homosexual inclinations.

Women who say that 'once you've had a woman you never want another man' did not want men very much to begin with. – H.G.

OFF-PUTTING NOISES

Although we have been married for nearly eight years we have only just found out how marvelous sex can be through reading about different techniques and positions.

Before the actual climax we try every imaginable position and one of these is for me to sit astride my husband with my back to him. This gives us both tremendous pleasure and my husband can achieve deep penetration. But after moving to another position, as we never stay in one particular position for more than a couple of minutes, I seem to get a vacuum inside my vagina and air rushes out making some awful noises.

This has happened a few times and it is very off-putting for both of us, so much so, in fact, my husband hasn't been able at times to have an orgasm. He says it puts him right off. It is very embarrassing for both of us and I hope you will be able to tell me what is causing this.

Mrs. M.D.

This is quite a common occurrence. It is caused by tiny pockets of air getting into the vagina entrance along with the penis, when the woman is highly roused and her vaginal lips are intensely swollen. It is more likely to happen if, as you are doing, you constantly put the penis into the vagina and take it out again during loveplay. I'm afraid there is nothing you can do to prevent it, except change your loveplay techniques a little. – F.

GOING NATIVE

My wife and I are in our late 40s. Perhaps I am unusual, but the sight of earrings, worn in the lobes, has always excited me when making love. My work over the years has taken us to all parts of the world and I have acquired a large collection of native earrings.

Soon after we were married and living in Malaya, my wife decided to have her ears pierced. The strange thing was that we discovered that this had the result of turning us both on. If it hadn't been for appearances, my wife would have had me wearing rings in my ears.

Her lobes were pierced by our *amah,* a local native woman. Two holes were made in each lobe, as was the local fashion, to enable twin rings or studs to be worn.

On a visit to what was then North Borneo, we first heard about the custom of piercing the glans penis in order to give greater satisfaction and feeling to the female. (We knew of methods used to enlarge the penis by the insertion of various objects but had not connected the two.) This custom (piercing) intrigued us both. We discovered that there were Chinese 'doctors' who carried out the operation, and my wife, who was nursing at the time, actually saw men who had had it and was amazed at the results.

This custom has been practiced in Burma and India for hundreds of years. We learned that the piercing could be painful and that careful post-operative care was required. This was not always observed by the locals, who ended up with rather deformed glans. The incisions are usually made across the breadth of the penis, and when the resulting hole is enlarged and healed, rods with screws on both ends are inserted, which cause extra friction on the walls of the female vagina. The incisions do not interfere with the normal body functions.

I decided that I would have the operation, my wife being the 'surgeon'. She collected various bits and pieces and I took a few days' leave. The piercing caused very little pain and there was no trouble afterwards. I wore a silk cord in the incision and this was increased in thickness until the resulting hole healed. The sight of my pierced penis sent my wife into raptures. The added pleasure for both of us obtained from this device was and always has been intense.

At first I wore a gold rod with two ivory balls on the ends. Later, when we were in India, my wife obtained a gold ring which she used to adorn my penis; we have since tried various attachments, all with very pleasurable results. My wife had her nose pierced in India and since then I have had beads inserted around and behind the loose skin of the penis. This gives a unique sensation to us both; though I imagine the various sheaths with lumps and projections on must give a similar effect. I used to get asked strange questions when having the company's medical checkups, and used to think up wonderful replies!

We may have a fetish with our jewelry and the wearing of rings, etc., in our bodies, and when we get 'dressed up', which is often, we may look like a couple of primitives, but all we hope is that we go on being contented, expensively 'dressed' and adorned savages for many years to come. We don't feel that what is natural in many cultures is necessarily unnatural for us.

J.B.

JUNGLE TRIP

I suspect that many of your correspondents indulge themselves in fantasy, rather than describe factual occurrences. This seems to me a perfectly valid expression of sexual activity, although many of the contributions indicate a disturbing degree of repression. The extent to which the latter inhibits genuine heterosexual contacts is by no means clear from the content of the letters.

Personally speaking, I find little interest in expressions of delight in inflicting and receiving corporal punishment. I appreciate that it might well be stimulating to smack a woman's bottom, particularly when her skirt is pulled up, but this would not involve any satisfaction in actually hurting the recipient.

My own fantasy runs to the vision of a plump young woman being eaten by a crocodile. I find erotic delight in mental images of her naked bottom and wildly thrashing legs, sticking from the scaly jaws of her voracious captor. I also conceive of the crocodile doing unmentionable things to the woman with its tongue. Such imaginings may be unhealthy but I keep them firmly in the realms of fantasy.

The nearest I have come to it, in fact, was to persuade my wife to wriggle her top half into a large drainpipe on a deserted building site. I then lifted her skirt up and pulled her panties down, watching her wriggle as she tried to extricate herself from the pipe. The fantasy crocodile was quickly forgotten as I kneeled behind her, opened her legs and slipped my penis into her. I confess to some further enjoyment in the reverberating squeaks and cries from the deep seclusion of the drainpipe. When she emerged, flushed, annoyed but very well done, I kissed her dignity back and she soon forgave me. I suspect, however, that she knew what I was about when she crawled into the pipe and in that respect she had little to complain about.

We often discuss other fantastic situations as a prelude to lovemaking. The one which seems to be of mutually absorbing interest and most capable of erotic variations is of my wife on safari being captured, raped and eaten by canibals. We dwell in detail on this, my wife wriggling in my arms as I pretend the stature and prowess of a savage.

I cannot conceive of silent coitus; words are an erotic stimulus second only to my wife's naked or partly clothed body.

J.L.

GROUP SEX

Of all the activities revealed by your correspondents, that one which makes me curious and no doubt other readers as well, is group sex, wife-swapping or social sex, call it what you may.

Is it a result of the permissive age or has it been going on for some time, only just emerging to the surface? There have always been orgies between prostitutes and their clients, but I refer specifically to the games married couples play.

One reader says that he has been married a decade, and it started soon after the wedding day. Another reader, recently married, says that it started on their honeymoon; another married up to 20 years says that it started five years ago.

How did group sex start and when? Is it carried on between two couples or more? The age group seems to be 30 to 40, but which social group is involved, and how wide is the practice?

Unfortunately I cannot undertake any practical investigations myself.

R.B.

Group sex is certainly not a modern phenomenon, nor a symptom of the permissive age in which we live. This practice goes back to the Greeks and Romans, *if not before. In* Fanny Hill *there is an episode describing such activity.*

Whether we acknowledge it or not there is in all of us something of the voyeur. Men, particularly, are stimulated sexually by seeing others make love. With women voyeurism is slightly more complicated, because women are much less aroused by visual stimulants than men are. Very few women, for example, are sexually aroused by pictures or statues of naked men, and few find the sight of the actual erect penis stimulating. Men, on the other hand, are strongly stimulated by such representations of women – hence the success of 'girlie' magazines.

There are, however, many women who are responsive to sexual activities, which may be between two couples only, or more than two. When more than two couples form the group, the resulting activities can be much more varied. Nevertheless, the voyeur tendencies are exploited fully when only two couples participate.

The fact that the 30 to 40 age group is principally involved is not surprising. A couple who married in their late twenties, and who have been sexually adventurous between themselves since, by the age of 30 or 40 have reached the point when they may feel they need some extra sexual stimulus, which group sex can provide.

Group sex is different from wife-swapping. In the latter, the couples change partners, and each couple has intercourse in private. In group sex it is essential that all sexual activities should be carried out 'in the sight of all present'. It is this looking-on which provides the new stimulant. – F.

LET THERE BE LIGHT

My wife and I have taught each other and learned a lot during our nine years of marriage, and have progressed well beyond the missionary position, fellatio and cunnilingus. However, it is only recently that my wife has agreed to having the light on when we make love – this was achieved by my obtaining an extremely low wattage bulb, of the type used for indicating that a piece of machinery is switched on, which casts a dim but pleasant glow in the bedroom.

I understand many women do not like to make love except in the dark. They might try our solution.

D.K.

Studies have shown that men are more aroused by visual stimulation than women. Therefore, men prefer to have the light on while having sex, while women, embarrassed about sex and their bodies, tend to prefer darkness. One of the reasons for this is that so much emphasis is put on female attractiveness (much less than on male) that women feel more self-conscious about their bodies and prefer darkness.

Many women too have discovered that the more hidden and covered they keep their bodies, the more excited and more interested in exploring some men become. This secretiveness on women's part, plus the excitement that visual stimuli cause, explains in part the popularity of such activities as strip shows and the live shows of Scandinavia where demonstrations are given by young couples.

As women are becoming increasingly liberated from repressive attitudes, this taboo against the lighted room is also disappearing. – H.G.

PEEPING TOM

I am married, aged 33, and I am a member of the legal profession. I led a secure home life, where sex was never mentioned and I have never seen my parents nude.

My first sexual experience was at the age of ten when my older cousin made me suck his penis, which I found most distasteful, and stopped, despite the 'bully's' threats. My next experience was when some of the boys at school reached puberty and masturbated in the changing-rooms to display their prowess. Shortly after this, to my joy, I achieved my first erection, having unsuccessfully rubbed myself sore on numerous occasions previously in an endeavor to ejaculate.

Later, while 'birds-nesting' in some woods two young men started talking to me about sex, and I told them I could masturbate. They took me deep into the woods and took all my clothes off and theirs and then one of them masturbated me, while the other stood watching me from behind and masturbating himself. I was very frightened and unable to stop this happening. Fortunately, nothing else happened and I have never seen them since. Then I began to come into contact with girls.

I remember one particularly ugly girl, but with huge breasts, the first in fact. I never even kissed her. I shoved my hand awkwardly up her jumper and then down her vest and squeezed. She screamed like hell. So ended my first 'affair'. Next, I took a girl picnicking and retired with her to some bushes to eat our apples. I undid her blouse and fumbled with her bra, only to be asked by my very innocent companion what I was doing. I thought she was supposed to know and promptly gave up. Next came a cinema usherette I met during the school lunch hour. This was more rewarding, and I spent frequent evenings at the back of the cinema fondling her breasts, but no more.

I learned to dance, and had the uncomfortable business of trying to stem an erection which always came when I felt my partner's body close to mine. This I learned to control fairly quickly. Dancing gave me the opportunity to meet more girls, and I found myself not unattractive to the ladies, and commenced a series of conquests, during which I had intercourse on many occasions, but only to my own satisfaction, never considering that they might want something too.

Then came the army days and while away from home I met a woman separated from her husband and spent many happy weekends with her, and she advanced my sex education tremendously, to the extent that I was now able to give satisfaction as well as receive it.

After the army, I continued a very happy round of sleeping with one girl after another, all normal relationships until I met the girl who said 'no', who also happened to match up to my ideas of a wife. I was soon deeply in love with her and we married nine years ago. With tuition from me she soon proved competent in bed and we both enjoy very good sex relations.

However, my desires extended beyond the marital bed, but being faithful I refused early opportunities which arose for sex outside marriage, suppressing my urgent desires with conscience. Instead, in order to find some way of satisfying myself without being 'unfaithful' I started 'Peeping Tom' activities, which I still pursue regularly. I found that there were a number of houses where young women disrobed themselves, leaving the curtains open or ajar, and where one could stand unobserved not too far away.

I get a tremendous kick out of watching these girls undress, and I masturbate as I watch them, endeavoring to reach a climax as the last vestment comes off. I often wish in fantasy that more women would leave their curtains open, to give pleasure to 'unfortunates' like myself. They are innocent of my activities and no harm is done. However, if I were caught, I think I would consider suicide rather than face the indignity of the charges and consequent disgrace and publicity.

My worst moment came when I actually climbed a tree overlooking a maiden's bedroom in order to get a full view. Only a few moments later there was someone under the tree with an Alsatian dog. I remained still, petrified, but was soon relieved to see the gentleman 'taking the dog for a walk' was also there for the same purpose as I. After the girl had finished her undressing, I waited for the man to disappear and left, never returning to that place, and never again climbing trees.

My most exciting moments which I can always picture vividly are when I see something unusual. One night I watched two young girls first disrobe and then suckle each other's immature breasts, and then they each put their faces between each other's legs and gave each other mutual satisfaction.

On another occasion, I watched a married couple playing a delightful game where they first disrobed each other, then he danced around her in the manner of an ape, and finally made love to her in animal fashion, to which she responded tremendously. I have seen other entertaining incidents.

Strangely enough, I do not enjoy strip shows and find them a bore. I think my 'kick' comes from watching unsuspecting ladies, coupled with a fear of getting caught.

Although I love my wife deeply, I now have an increasing urge to widen my sex relations with other women, and possibly group sex. I disclosed this urge to her but she failed to understand or permit such activities. She realizes that she could not stop me if I wanted to, but insists on being told if it happens and threatens divorce if it does happen, and she means it. I must, however, satisfy this craving for perhaps it will cure my 'peeping' activities, but I cannot tell my wife. I have thought about this for 18 months now, during which time, I have met a number of ladies with whom I would love to dally further. However, I am frightened to make any suggestions or hints (a) for fear of causing offense, and (b) for fear of being rejected.

Thus, I dwell in this state of desire, and wait for the right woman to make some advances, but, unfortunately, the rule still applies, 'a woman will not ask to be kissed'. I, on the other hand, will not indicate my desires, so stalemate! I tried a professional lady, but seeing her disrobe and lie on the bed with legs apart with no mutual feeling or interest, the whole thing was just too commercial, so I gave her the money and left. I did not even get any pleasure from watching her undress, I know not why.

How can I find a woman to share the ultimate heights of sexual pleasure? It seems impossible, especially when I also have to have some feeling or liking for the woman. I cannot advertise for fear of being 'blackmailed', once someone has my name and address. So, I must go on 'peeping' until some charitable lady indicates her need of me, as I need her.

S.C.

BODY CONTACT

Not long ago, I read a small item in a magazine which told about the findings of three psychiatrists reporting on bodily contact. They have discovered most women find bodily contact pleasant, and some find it disagreeable and even repugnant, but there are some women who have such a strong desire to be held, touched, cuddled, that this resembles an addiction. The need can be so strong, women of this type can be promiscuous, even resorting to prostitution. They will have intercourse with a man in return for the physical contact; what they most want is to be cuddled.

This sounds so clear-cut, it seems a very simple desire to satisfy. But, believe me, it isn't. I know, because I am one of those women; and there is very much more to this need, and the satisfying of it, than would appear. For me, the pleasure of touching and to be touched is so great I can reserve it only for a man I want very much. To be touched by a man I don't find attractive is, I think, doubly repulsive to me than to a normally sensitive woman. I certainly would not trade a sexual experience with a man for the pleasure of being cuddled: to me it would not be a pleasure if I didn't want that particular man sexually. In fact, if I don't want someone sexually, I will avoid even the physical contact of a handshake if I can. But when someone is appealing to me, I imagine I get as much thrill out of holding his hand or having his arm around my waist as most women get in the act of intercourse. I'm not talking, of course, about having an orgasm. I'm talking of the mental and physical joy of touching and being touched, to be held by someone whose appeal can

210

be intoxicating. Just a few times in my life have I had this need satisfied.

I am now well in my thirties, free (divorced), and if it were all as simple as our psychologist suggests, I could get myself cuddled by filling my bed any night of the week. Instead, I am very much alone. This great need to give and receive affection is sublimated in many, not terribly pleasant ways. This accentuated sense of touch is, I believe, part of the oral type of person's makeup. All senses are more keyed up, as it were. Touching, cuddling, contact with another warm body are all bound up with kissing, taking in pleasure through the mouth; with smoking, eating and drinking. I believe we are called by some psychologists the self-indulgent type.

Early last year, I met a man for whom I immediately felt this great urge for contact. I met him in the company of a fellow I was dating at the time, and it was a few months before I could actually come close to the man of my choice. When we met by accident at a party or in a bar I would try to get close to him. If we touched shoulders or he put his hand on mine while lighting my cigarette, this small contact was more to me than going to bed with someone else.

When we finally had an affair, I fell madly in love with him. During the time we were together, it is strange to reflect that I smoked less, drank less and lost my usual great interest in food. To be near him and make love with him satisfied this central need in me which usually embraces all the wider interests of most other women.

Mrs. C.T.

Experiments with the raising of animals and young children have shown that physical contact during the early years of life is an important requirement for natural development. For example, monkeys raised by mechanical mothers were incapable of mature sexual behavior in adulthood.

Dealing with children it has been found that the infant who is stroked not only grows up to be psychologically sound, but even more intelligent. Apparently tactile skin sensations during infancy help the actual physical development of the brain and nervous system.

It is certainly true, as C.T. reports, that for many people the need for contact is primarily responsible for sexual behavior. I, too, have known people whose contact hunger was so great they were willing to engage in all types of sexual activity, including promiscuity and prostitution, in an effort to fulfill this strong and powerful craving.

One of the fortunate results of the encounter group movement spreading across the country is the encouragement of holding and touching that does not lead to intercourse.

What's good for puppies is even better for children. – H.G.

MAY AND DECEMBER

I am 22 years of age and since I left home four years ago, I have found that the only sex I enjoy is with men much older than myself.

I was brought up in a very strict home and was allowed to have girlfriends only. If I was caught misbehaving my father would punish me by whipping my bare bottom with a cane. Just before I left home I had my first experience of sex with a boy, but did not like it, mainly because he hurt me and made me bleed a lot. In fact it was this incident which resulted in my parents turning me out of the house.

I managed to team up with two other girls of my own age and we took a flat together. I got a job in a large office. My girlfriends both had boyfriends with whom they were having sex. They tried to get me to go with a boy, but it was no good. I simply wasn't interested in boys, particularly when they tried to get inside me.

However, one day one of the department managers at work asked me to help him get some files from the basement where they were kept. He was a man of about 45 and married. To my surprise when I reached up to get a file down from a shelf he put his hand on my breast and then quickly took it away and apologized, saying his hand had slipped. I was quite sure that it was deliberate, but I laughed it off and said it didn't matter.

To my surprise though, I found that it gave me a thrill. A few days later, I was again asked to help him with the files and on the way down to the basement felt myself getting quite excited. When we got to the file room he again said he was sorry for what had happened the previous day and said he hoped he hadn't offended me.

I said that I didn't mind at all, and I suppose I must have looked as if I had quite enjoyed it, as the next thing that hap-

212

pened was that he put his hand inside my blouse and started feeling my breasts and I felt myself having an immediate reaction. Of course we could not go very far as other people might come into the room at any moment. A week later he was moved to another office.

After this I wondered if I should enjoy men of my own age, but after going out with a boy who tried hard to have me, I found that I was not interested.

Some time later I was at a party with people of different ages and I got talking to one of the older men. I again experienced a thrill when I realized that he was interested in me, and after the party accepted an invitation to go back to his flat for a drink. He started to make mild love to me as we sat on the sofa and I again had the same immediate reaction which I had never achieved with younger men.

He very soon discovered that all I had on under my mini-dress was the smallest pair of see-through panties. The next thing I knew, I was naked, eagerly awaiting to feel him inside my body.

Recently I met a married man who lived away from home during the week. I wasn't slow in responding to his invitation to spend a few days with him at his digs, while his landlady was on holiday.

I have heard that some young girls prefer married men so I suppose I may not be too different, but it does worry me a bit as the usual thing is for a girl to marry someone her own age. Isn't it sort of unnatural for a young girl to marry a man who is old enough to be her father?

Miss J.S.

Since father was the first man in every woman's life, it is not surprising that a number of young women find older men attractive and desirable. In childhood, father's attention and affection is an important source of emotional 'nourishment'. Often father also acts as a counter to mother's role as disciplinarian so that many little girls learn to engage father in the battle against mother's restrictiveness. Many also feel that without mother around, they would have been able to get much more attention and love. As one young woman explained, 'She was always there – getting in the way – not letting Dad love me more.' Many young women continue this competition into adult life. They find tremendous excitement and satisfaction in being involved with older men, preferably married ones, thereby repeating, in a symbolic sense, the rivalry with mother now represented by the hated wife. I have known a number of young women involved in such affairs and sometimes it seemed as though defeating the wife was more important than getting the husband.

On another level, young women find older men attractive because they generally have more experience and more resources. An older man can take her to more exciting places, spend more money, make more interesting conversation, teach her more things. He also frequently shows his gratitude for the reassurance she gives him of his continued masculine appeal by giving her more things than her male contemporaries.

A young psychologist I know made the suggestion that as far as experience is concerned, a young woman should have an older man who would teach her for the first five to ten years of her adult life. And then in her later years, she should choose a young man whom she could similarly instruct.

Chaplin was old enough to be Oona O'Neill's father when he married her – and their marriage has turned out to be a very rewarding one for both of them. The great Hungarian composer, Zoltan Kodaly, at the age of 75, proposed to a girl of 23, asking her, 'Would you like to be my widow?' They had a remarkably happy marriage until he died, well into his 80's. There are innumerable examples of young girls falling in love with older men, preferring them to their contemporaries. – H.G.

OCCUPATIONAL HAZARD

I am a 38-year-old schoolteacher, once married but now divorced and living as a bachelor. My wife and I had no children and since separating from her, my life has been very lonely. For most of the seven years of our relationship we were extremely close and only began to draw apart during the final year. Consequently, my life now is in radical contrast to the way it was during most of my marriage, particularly in terms of physical contact. Whereas I had been used to a great deal of touching and being touched, now there is none of that at all, since I am afraid of becoming involved with another woman due to the emotional difficulties which arose out of the splitup with my wife: jealousy and counterjealousy plus a degree of hatred equal in intensity to the love I had previously felt for her and which it now frightens me even to think of.

I'm sure it's largely as a result of all this that I now find myself attracted to several of my pupils. I teach in a comprehensive school and some of the girls there (aged between 13 and 16) seem very beautiful and almost overwhelmingly desirable at times, so much so that the impulse to touch and caress them can only be combatted by my leaving the room abruptly and either going for a fast walk around the corridors or masturbating in the toilet, an activity which makes me so ashamed that I really have to grit my teeth to be able to walk back into the classroom afterward.

I don't know if it's just me thinking wishfully or not, but I'm under the impression that some of the girls I feel most attracted to are aware of my feeling toward them. Two or three of them have taken to seeking me out after school and asking questions about lessons, a new departure for all of them. One of them even suggested I give her extra tuition in my home. It's no exaggeration when I say I nearly fainted at that. The same night I masturbated to fantasies of making love with her and two other girls from her class, arousing myself to unprecedented peaks of excitement. Afterward I felt so guilty and ashamed about it that I couldn't face going to school for two days.

I am now rather desperate and feel myself drawing closer and closer to a state of mind and body which will demand that I act on these fantasies, and yet I know that if I do I shall condemn myself for all eternity, feeling that I have betrayed the trust inherent in my job. However I am not writing to you for advice but simply to get this off my chest – to confess as it were something I have been afraid to talk about to anyone. Perhaps now I'll bring myself to see a psychiatrist or make an all-out effort to relate to someone nearer my own age. I hope I'll be able to do that.

This brings up the point that I don't think I should be teaching while I am like this, although I know I'm a pretty good teacher and have a genuine vocational sense of what teaching is all about. What can I do though? I am afraid, and I think justifiably so, that if I were to tell my superiors the truth about the way I feel they would dismiss me without a moment's hesitation.

Moreover I think there are others in a similar position to

myself – teachers who, for one reason or another, find it hard to contain themselves sexually when they are in an authoritative position over young people. After all, how easy it would be to say yes to the girl who wants extra tuition in the secret hope that she'll say yes as well when the time comes in a private sitting-room rather than a public classroom. How easy to draw the blinds over one's conscience for an hour and to hell with the consequences. But how much more healthy it would be if we could simply be open and direct about our feelings to a supervising body which would understand and sympathize with what is after all an occupational hazard for many teachers.

T.L.

COOPERATION REQUESTED

Most people, when they hear about an indecent assault on a young girl, tend to consider every person who assaults a young girl to be a potential killer. But this is very, very far from the truth.

The predilection for young girls (by 'young' I mean under the age of about 14) is a very common one, but few men who have the urge to assault girls ever do so.

This is, I think, for two reasons – the almost certainty of their being caught and punished for what is regarded as one of the most horrible crimes it is possible to commit, and the harm they might do to that girl.

As one who suffers from – or rather enjoys – this particular kink, I have come into contact with quite a large number of men – even some women – with the same tastes. Almost all of the above are outwardly very respectable people, and include a doctor and teachers. Many, like me, are happily married and have children of their own. That's one of the odd things about people like us – we would no doubt be horrified if our own children were assaulted.

This is not true, however, of all the people with whom I have come into contact. Some actively encourage people to perform sexplay with their daughters, and two of the people I have met – a man and a woman – actually indulged in sexplay with their own daughters!

Although I have met many people with the same tastes as myself, and who have actually indulged these tastes, I have been in contact with many more whose experiences I believe to be pure fantasy. Yet none of the people in either category seem to me to be people who would go so far as to do any harm to any of the girls.

Most people are blind to the fact that in many cases the girls are willing, and even eager, sexual partners. Unless the man has been brutal with the girl, she normally does not tell her parents. Some affairs go on for months or even years without the girl complaining, and in some cases the parents never find out.

The supreme example of the above concerns a girl of 11. The man involved was not a person I knew anything about as I only heard about this incident through a friend who had seen it reported in a newspaper and who sent me the cutting. Their affair had been going on for four years! They were only found out when the girl's parents found money and cosmetics given to the girl by the man. Apparently she had been having similar affairs with a number of other men as well. Yet the man was sent to prison for a period of four years. Is this fair in a case like this?

I personally would like to see the age of consent reduced to the age of 12, as it was years ago when girls were maturing even later than they are today. Or at least lower it to the age of puberty – i.e. once an individual girl reaches puberty she will be deemed to have reached the age of consent.

Coupled with this, I would like to see proper instruction in sex – not just a quick biology lesson on the reproduction of the rabbit, as still happens in many cases. I think sex instruction should cover all aspects of lovemaking as well. Together with this, there should be instruction in birth control, and contraceptives should be freely available from the age of puberty.

I know that many people will be disgusted or horrified at my suggestions, but they are mainly the people who choose to ignore the rise in sexual offenses and the rise in pregnancies of girls under 16. At least if girls are to have sexual contact before the present age of consent, then they should be adequately prepared for it. Many of them do have such contact so they should be ready.

Unfortunately, a lot of sexual offenses take place with girls under the age of puberty. If we also educated them about sex, then perhaps they would not be frightened when assaulted by a man, and would cooperate rather than scream and consequently lessen the risk of being harmed or even killed by a panic-stricken man.

T.C.

A pedophiliac is extremely fearful of establishing a relationship with a mature woman, and therefore turns to a child. With a child, he feels more adequate and in control. However, like many other human behaviors pedophilia involves other factors in addition to fear. Frequently a pedophiliac has had very early sexual experiences, usually with a member of the family – such as a younger sister. Finding that experience highly pleasurable, he remains fixated at that level, particularly if he experiences mature relationships as demanding and difficult. He therefore returns once more to the early pleasurable experience and looks again for a child.

Pedophiliacs invariably try to rationalize their behavior by claiming that either the young child is a willing partner, or that the sexual play is not harmful to the child unless adults interfere and create the trauma by their attitude. While it is true that the results of early sexual adventures with older men may be exacerbated by the anxiety of significant adults in their environment, it is nevertheless quite difficult to accept the rationalization that the child is a willing partner. A child in a situation with a grown man who is able to exert all types of influences does not have free choice.

In my research on prostitution I noted that about 75% of the women studied had an early age (before 12) sexual rewarded experience with an older man. This led them to regard sex as a method of securing things which they wanted. In addition, women who suffer from extreme anxiety about sex or relationships with men in general frequently report that they, too, have been the object of a child-lover's attention. It is therefore most difficult to accept that pedophilia does not lead to unfortunate consequences for the child involved and that it is merely another deviation.

In my experience many child molesters I treated felt little guilt about their behavior and came for treatment only when they got caught. Even in treatment they are often not interested in changing their behavior but search for means of avoiding the unpleasant consequences. However, as they begin to realize that it is almost impossible to avoid punishment, they can be motivated to control these impulses.

There are many individuals who never act on their pedophiliac impulses. For example, while many women may have these impulses, they do not act on them because in our society women generally have better self-control. so, while ped-

ophiliacs, like other sexual deviants, try to insist that they are victims of ungovernable impulses, this is not true. They, like most others, are capable of control, although sometimes psychological help is necessary. – H.G.

ROAD STAND

My fiancée and I have a strong need for exhibitionism. Because of our circumstances, most of our lovemaking takes place in a car which allows ample opportunity. When we are both in a particularly sexy mood, we venture out onto the road in the nude. I should explain that the road is relatively quiet with a car coming past about every quarter-hour on average. My fiancée either bends face down over the hood in which case I make entry from the rear or she sits on the hood, reclining back almost onto the windshield. I stand between her legs and make entry from the front. Of course the risk of a car coming and catching us in its headlights while we are in action is extremely stimulating. Recently when a car came, I decided to stay and be seen, but in the last few seconds, my fiancée protested, and we ducked down behind the car, I must admit to my relief, because my nerve was on the verge of breaking too!

Of course, inside the car we have much greater confidence. My fiancée does not mind exposing her naked breasts and being fondled while revealed by the headlights of a passing car.

Our experiences prompt me to enquire if it is necessary or desirable to turn sexual fantasy into fact? I believe it is not necessary to do so, but if there is not a good reason to refrain, then why not? However, my experience suggests that satisfied fantasy invariably gives way to a new fantasy.

L.W.

You seem to have a 'normal' or 'orthodox' sex life even though its location must be sometimes uncomfortable and risky. Indecent exposure, as the law calls it, is an offense under law. You might very well expose yourself also to blackmail and rape if some motorist, for instance, stimulated by your activities seen in his headlights decided to stop. But all these are considerations which you must have weighed and are not really the basic problem.

Fantasies are an integral part of sex. They form the larger

219

part of the psychological elements of intercourse. They can add to potency or cause temporary or permanent impotence. Many of them are autoerotic and there is hardly an hour or a day going by without a sexually mature man or woman entertaining them, looking at a pretty girl on the bus or catching a glimpse of an erotic picture in a magazine. Because of this integral quality, there can be no question whether they are wrong or not. They just are. – F.

BARING OF BREASTS

I'm just over 40, happily married, with a husband in a good safe position, so there are no financial worries. I have average good looks, I'm tall and well built, but have been blessed, if this is the right word, with large pendulous breasts. Over the past few months I have had a great desire to expose them and this has become an obsession.

Every Saturday morning a young boy helps our milkman and he calls for the week's money. I answer the door dressed only in a dressing gown which I have left fairly open to show a lot of cleavage. I take as long as possible in counting out my money and my heart pounds with excitement as I feel his eyes riveted on my cleavage. When I bend over in front of him to pick up the milk, my dressing gown opens further and my breasts swing out and for a couple of seconds are completely revealed to him.

An hour later the same thing happens when the paper boy calls. Whenever I go shopping and can get anything delivered I do so, so that I can answer my door wearing a thin, skin-tight blouse. Last week I even registered a letter to myself so that I had to sign for it.

I have not told my husband of these pranks and don't think it would be of any use. Is there any explanation to my problem?

Mrs. C.J.

Superficially, one might ask, what is your problem? You have developed strong exhibitionist tendencies and are fulfilling them by exposing your breasts. You don't say that you are unhappy or appalled by what you do, so your letter sounds more like a statement than an actual plea for help.

You want attention. Because you have not placed yourself in

220

everyday circumstances where such attention would be forth-coming to you as a person, *you are seeking this attention* as a body. – *F.*

RAPE

Could I please ask your advice on a problem that has been worrying me for a long time?

I have been married for two years and have never been with any other man but my husband except for the following extra-ordinary incident.

About a year ago, while my husband was at work, an intruder forced his way into my house and raped me. The man was subsequently caught, found guilty and is now serving a prison sentence.

I suffered no physical harm; I gave in to him because of what he threatened to do if I didn't. What has worried me ever since is the fact that I responded to him during his loveplay. Please allow me to explain further. This was not a quick brutal attack, he was with me for almost an hour.

After he had taken all the money that was about the house he pushed me into the lounge and made me take my clothes off (after threats). He then took his own clothes off and made me fondle his penis. It was while I was doing this that I found myself getting sexually aroused. I tried to suppress this feeling by thinking of how I hated this man and how much I loved my husband but it was no good. To make matters worse he made me repeat obscene things about how big his penis was and how much I liked it. He made me fondle it for a while and then made me lie on the table while he performed cunnilingus. While he was doing this I had an orgasm. He then had intercourse with me and I had another violent orgasm.

Please tell me how it is that this can happen with someone you hate and do not want? How was it that try as I might, I could not stop myself from having these orgasms? Does this mean that subconsciously I am promiscuous? Is this man really guilty of rape? Did I not get as much enjoyment as he did?

I have been trying to live with this terrible shame ever since.

S.S.

221

Sexual response to a rapist is not too surprising. Since so many women have been taught that sexual pleasure is 'bad', sexual activity that is forced relieves them of blame and permits them to enjoy it.

In my experience the only women who have handled rapists effectively have been professional prostitutes. In three cases reported to me, the women spoke to the would-be attacker, saying: 'Not here honey. Let's go some place where we can really be comfortable.' Since most rapists are only capable of sexual enjoyment when it is combined with aggression, all three attackers took to their heels.

You could only consider yourself promiscuous if you found yourself being raped continually. – H.G.

WRESTLING URGE

As a little boy I went through a phase when I ate very little and was very thin, so much so that the sight of my scrawny body, glimpsed one day in the mirror after taking a bath, disgusted me so much that I decided that I didn't ever want to look at it again.

At about that time a young woman friend of my mother's, to whom the latter had been confiding her anxieties about my thinness, took me aside and told me I should try and grow into a 'big strong boy', flexing the muscles of her arm as she said it (which she made me feel). The sight and feel of her bare fleshy arm flexed like that gave me a big sexual thrill and an erection.

Also about that time, after tea with some friends, a little girl and I were sent to play in the garden. The girl was bigger than I and I found her very nice and attractive. She wrestled me, threw me and pinned me. She pinned my arms down akimbo by the wrists with her hands, and my shoulders with her knees. I was very conscious of the size and weight of her body and abundant thighs. My feeling was a mixture of horror and shame combined with a delicious sexual thrill. Again I had an erection.

These experiences have been imprinted on my sexual inclinations ever since. Although I am now tall, have a good, slim, figure, and am intelligent and attractive to women, by a strange fantasy I find it very hard to believe in my own size, while women always seem bigger to me than they really are. My fantasy also makes me appear very strong. The only thing that will regularly arouse my sexual feelings is the sight of a tall, strapping, Amazonian type of girl.

Not surprisingly my sexual behavior is purely passive and in sexual intercourse I am impotent in all postures nowadays. In my fantasies, however, they always, after wrestling me, get on top of me and make love astride. In other words I can never take the initiative in real life but am always longing for them to wrestle me instead.

I have a fascination for girl wrestling. Judging from the quantity of pictures advertised in the wrestling magazines, I am very far from being alone in my kink.

I am now 37 and have been having psychotherapy for some years, but despite my strenuous efforts to achieve 'normal' sex it is beginning to dawn on me that my early experiences made so indelible a mark on my sexual nature that I will never eradicate it. Nevertheless I very much want to have some sort of sexual partnership with a woman.

I believe this urge to wrestle is in everyone, male or female, as can be seen from the behavior not only of young children but of young animals of nearly all kinds, for wrestling playfully is one of the first things they instinctively do with each other. I believe it also has close links with sociability and sexuality: witness the similarity of embracing, wrestling, and making love. However, convention and the force of opinion being what it is, it would normally be very difficult for me to invite a girl, whom I didn't know well, to wrestle.

U.L.

This letter illustrates very clearly how adult sexual behavior may be fashioned by early conditioning during childhood and/or adolescence: in the case of U.L., the apparently chance occurrence of a 'big girl' wrestling with him which produced a 'delicious sexual thrill and erection'. The pleasure associated with this early experience was such as to make him seek out repetition. His lucid description of that initial episode indicates clearly that part, if not most, of the pleasure associated with it was due to being physically and mentally dominated by a 'powerful female'.

Although I have stressed the importance of being physically and mentally dominated I am quite sure that the apposition of two bodies, which inevitably occurs during wrestling, must

223

generate a degree of sensual pleasure, which, of course, adds to
the total experience. – F.

SILK FETISHISM

My first recollection of silk exciting me was years ago when I was 12. My mother bought me a new silk shirt. When I put it on I had an erection and masturbated. This was the first time that silk had stimulated me although my mother had bought me shirts of this material. At night I took a silk shirt to bed and put it between my legs and rubbed myself while masturbating. I found that I enjoyed doing this very much.

When I was 13 an elder cousin, who had homosexual tendencies, made a sexual approach to me. He said that he loved my silk shirt and that it had aroused him. My cousin and I masturbated together regularly and frequently had anal intercourse. One day he suggested that I put on his sister's school uniform. I took all my clothes off and he put a brassiere on me and his sister's school blouse of a silk similar to my shirt. I put on nylon suspenders and a gym slip. I lay on top of the bed and my cousin lay on top of me naked, put his penis between my legs and made love.

The feel of girls' clothing against my body excited me. When I was alone in the house I would go into my sister's bedroom, strip naked and put on a lovely satin bridesmaid dress. I would then masturbate in front of the mirror. When I married four years ago my wife knew of my liking for silk. My desire for silk does not dominate me and I can have intercourse with my wife without silk being used as stimulation for long periods.

My wife often wears silk clothes in order to arouse me. She has a bridesmaid dress of pink satin which she sometimes wears when we are making love. She also wears long satin gloves which she uses for stroking my body.

I enjoy anal intercourse and my wife puts on blue satin underwear. She says that she enjoys the feel of my warm semen seeping through her satin and soaking her skin.

Do you think that my liking for silk was due to my mother dressing me in silk shirts? Quite a lot of the homosexuals who did the act with me when I was younger said that my silk shirts stimulated them, made me look effeminate and desirable to them. Do you think that dressing boys in silk makes them attractive to homosexuals? One sees magazines for people who are interested in rubber, but I have never seen any on silk and satin. Am I a part of a small minority?

A.Y.

Silk fetishism is by no means unusual. Silk, alone and in combination with lace, has always been used by fetishists, combining aesthetic and erotic elements. On the other hand there are people who prefer underclothes of the coarsest kind for stimulation. A divorce case was reported where the woman plaintiff said that since their wedding night, her husband had urged her to wear a cotton petticoat. After giving in to her husband's whim, she felt humiliated. 'If at least he had asked me to wear silk underclothing!' she cried angrily. 'But no. His taste was exclusive . . .' – F.

RUBBER RIVAL

I speak of my special desire for rubberized material. I cannot explain the desire, nor do I wish to. I am quite satisfied that it is there and that both the feel and smell of rubber provide me with the most pleasant sensation and an immediate erection.

My first memory of the aphrodisiac effect of this material was at boarding school when I was supplied with a raincoat and obliged to wear it whenever it rained. While wearing this rubber raincoat I was not immediately aware of the connection between it and my physical condition.

I always endeavored to pass the obstacle course, in order to do a rope climb while attired in my raincoat. I found that the physical sensations during such a climb, could produce an orgasm; this then became coupled with the smell of the rubber coat.

This progressed into the use of the rubberized material as a stimulant to masturbation, and finally resulted in the wearing of rubber garments next to my skin and prolonged masturbation.

Various fantasies and side effects were resorted to during the ensuing year, but these require more detailed explanation. Sufficient to say that the most important aspect of my development was introducing my wife to my fetish.

Soon after I started going out with her, one wet night I was delighted to find that she was wearing a raincoat made of rubberized material. I broached the subject that same night as we had already reached the stage of quite ardent petting. I explained gently and asked her to touch me with her raincoat. The effect was electrifying and produced an immediate ejaculation – the first my wife had ever witnessed.

After this I had no further trouble. The mention of rubber was enough for its use to be implemented. A difficult period did arise after our marriage when my wife came to regard rubber as a 'rival'. It was only due to careful explanation that I was able to overcome this.

I would like to point out that the use of rubber does not dominate our sex life and we are both quite capable of normal sexual relations without any stimulants. However, I am certain that when we are both wearing rubberized garments I am more virile and can achieve two orgasms with ease.

A.M.

A PANDORA'S BOX

I have always felt that sex, and especially love 'games', were much better if spontaneous. On occasion I like to try smacking and caning, bondage, leather or rubber gear, and so on, but early in my marriage I found that it could be embarrassing for either of us to initiate and ask for such play, especially since my wife was very shy.

So over the years I have built up a Pandora's box (as we call it) containing a vast collection of some 50 costumes and types of lingerie – G-string bikinis, harem pantaloons, panties, gym slips and navy pants, leather skirts, and rubber raincoats to name but a few. Other accessories for each game are kept with them – for example the gym slip and navy pants are rolled around a strap and cane.

It does not need much imagination, when one of us chooses a garment from the box, for the other to spot what is wanted, and even the most inhibited wish can be made clear without a word spoken.

Though my wife thought some of my ideas a bit kinky when we married, she soon realized that I, too, found some of her ideas not to my liking. So, using the box, we take turns to choose the theme of an evening's sexplay, tossing up if we have forgotten, and the resulting give and take has worked ever since.

J.S.

WISDOM OF THE EAST

We have recently returned from Hong Kong to find that most of our married friends are either divorced or on the verge of getting a divorce, and we have come to the conclusion that there must be something very wrong with the male-female relationship these days. I am well aware of the fact that there have been many significant changes which have taken place these last few years – the Pill, female emancipation, both financially and socially, a more permissive society, etc. However, there is one important aspect in marriage that one very seldom sees discussed, but which I feel might be one of the great underlying causes of so many marital breakups, and that is, the incredible lack of understanding on the part of so many wives when it comes to the primary sexual needs of their husbands.

It's no great secret that most of the women of my generation (I'm 46) were raised in a Victorian-oriented environment. Sex was something to be endured, not enjoyed. 'Nice girls' were never aggressive. Only boys wanted sex. What has always amazed me is that despite this puritanical upbringing, not all women are frigid. Thank goodness for our genetic differences.

For the first 15 years of our marriage, we lived in the United States. Like most marriages, it didn't take too long a spell before the sexual excitement began to wane. Both my husband and I took for granted that this was the norm in marriage. Frequency of intercourse decreased with the years and by the time we left for the Far East, both of us were frankly bored with the physical side of our marriage, and if the truth be known, with each other. Although I wasn't aware of it at the time, my husband was having brief affairs with other women. At the time, I was a bundle of nerves, constantly irritable and really couldn't understand why I felt as I did. I must have spent a fortune on medical fees and pills.

It's absolutely amazing how ignorant most doctors are on a subject as important as this. During the above period, I must have gone to over ten different doctors, and not one of them ever had the courage to ask me about my sexual relations with

227

my husband. However, they all prescribed pills for the nerves and of course, sleeping pills. All the tranquilizers and sleeping pills in the world are useless if a woman does not have a satisfactory sex life, with exhilarating releases and the ensuing tranquility. Extraordinary as it sounds, this fact did not occur to me during that 15-year period of my marriage. And judging from the many wives with whom I have spoken since my return to the United States, this sad fact of life has also not occurred to a lot of other women.

I am convinced that our move to Hong Kong saved our marriage. Getting away from puritanical America and finding myself in an environment where women are completely feminine and love it, it, was the turning point of our marriage. Among our close friends were a couple – she, Eurasian and he, British. Although she was not a psychologist, she should have been. She was a keen observer and had my marriage pegged to a 'T'.

It was because of her counseling that for the first time in my marriage I began to realize how really unfeminine we western women are. The oriental woman is brought up to look upon sex as something to savor and enjoy. There is no antisex brainwashing when she's a child. By the time they are married, they are aware of the many nuances and ways of stimulating and exciting their husbands. The one thing that never occurred to me before our arrival in the Orient was – men must be stimulated in order to make love. The reason why so many of our American marriages deteriorate is because as they become boring and uninspired, the man, without the proper stimulation loses all desire and without the necessary erection, no sexual fulfillment is possible. It is no use arguing which comes first, the chicken or the egg. How can a woman expect to be made love to by a man when she in turn does nothing to arouse him and bring on his erection? No one knows this better than I. For most of our first 15 years of marriage, I was the one who waited for my husband to start the lovemaking. I expected the stimulation to come from him. After all, 'nice wives', like nice girls, just don't do that type of thing! Talk about digging our own graves.

Also during our first 15 years of marriage, my husband and I never really opened up with one another as to our desires, needs, or even fantasies. One of my fantasies, which always excited me terribly, was being made love to by two men, including my husband. Nothing on earth could have made me

228

reveal such a thing to my husband – that is, before we arrived in Hong Kong. And yet, with our 'new life', I told him of this fantasy plus many more, and he, in turn, told me his innermost desires, which he had kept to himself for so many years. This newfound communication between the both of us came about simultaneously with our newfound freedom in sex. It was truly an incredible revelation for the both of us. It is my Eurasian friend to whom I owe so much gratitude in opening my eyes and making me aware of the wondrous joys that can be found in a marriage if only the two people involved can open up and free themselves from the layers of guilt and fear which have taken the joy out of so many marriages.

Today I can truly say that our marriage is fun. There is no such thing as a planned time or place in making love. It could be under the dining room table or in the woods during a week-end hike. I'm completely unpredictable with my husband. He never knows beforehand when I will be undie-less when we go out for an evening or when I meet him at a restaurant in town. At the movies, with coats covering our laps, those sitting next to us are unaware of what our hands are doing to one another – especially during some of the more erotic films being shown these days.

There is nothing that the both of us won't try if it helps make our marriage stronger. We've experimented with group sex, troilism, nudist hotels, nude parties, going away weekends with another like-minded couple, blue films, large mirrors at all angles, nude swimming, erotic games, and every conceivable form of marital lovemaking.

Needless to say, now that we are completely liberated, my husband doesn't have the slightest need to be unfaithful. If it's 'change' that he needs every once in a while, with me accompanying him, it's no problem. Not only does he find it more exciting that way, but it also does away with the deception, lying hypocrisy and guilt which is always there when one of the partners is cheating.

I only wish I had read advice of this sort when I first got married. When I think of all those years we wasted . . .

Mrs. E.H.

UTTERLY DESPERATE

I am writing to you about a problem which I have never disclosed to anyone before.

I am a young man of 20 and have a small penis, $5\frac{1}{2}$ inches long in full erection, and not very thick. It really worries me to think that this problem will completely destroy my chances of sexually satisfying a woman, in marriage or otherwise. I have seduced a few girls and they have never shown signs of real enjoyment.

I have been courting a very nice girl for some months now, and we make love once or twice a week. It is, however, quite clear (although she tries not to let it show) that she would prefer not to, and I know why. It's the size of my penis, because I really get her worked up before I insert.

I wonder in this age of scientific medical research, whether there is any method (drugs, treatment, hormone injections and so forth), of enlarging my penis. In *The Perfumed Garden* I read that Arabs used heat treatment for penis enlarging.

You can realize that I am utterly desperate. I lie awake for hours at night thinking about it: it even brings me to tears sometimes. Please try to help me.

R.W.

The myth that a man's sexual performance is related to the size of his penis was fully exploded by the thorough, painstaking research of Dr. Masters and Mrs. Johnson. Most psychiatrists would agree that the feeling of penile inferiority is a serious problem for substantial numbers of men.

Masters and Johnson report that penile size turned out to have little relationship to a marital partner's satisfaction in sexual intercourse, for the vagina accommodates itself to the size of the male organ.

The size of the vagina also has little effect on mutual satisfaction in most cases; and accommodation can be helped by suitable timing of the entry of the penis. If the husband has a relatively small penis and the wife a relatively large vagina, for example, he can introduce his penis into the vagina earlier in the excitement phase. When this is done, Masters and Johnson report, 'the fully erect smaller penis can and does function as a dilating agent as effectively as a larger penis'. Conversely, a husband with a relatively large penis can help his wife with a small vagina by delaying entry until a more advanced stage of sexual excitement. 'It becomes obvious,' Masters and Johnson conclude, 'that penile size usually is a minor factor in sexual stimulation of the female partner.' – F.

ALLEVIATE ANXIETIES

In my lifetime I have had three lovers. The first, and the last (my present husband) had what I suppose would be termed an average-sized penis (about six inches), but the middle one had an organ of eight inches in length. It may surprise you to learn that I find that a smaller penis is far more satisfying than a large one.

With my first lover, I reached a climax every time we made love (the relationship lasted about six months). With my second lover, however, I found that my vaginal passage seemed to dry up after a couple of minutes, making it very sore for me, and I therefore didn't always attain an orgasm. Eventually I found that it was a rare occasion for me to have an orgasm, although my lover did all he could to stimulate me beforehand. We came to the conclusion that it must be because we were using a condom as a method of contraception. Since then, however, I have come to the conclusion that it was because the friction in my vagina was too great and, as it was a tight fit, the lubricant didn't have a chance to increase.

With my husband (we have been married now for three and a half years), I virtually always reach orgasm, even if we make love three or four times in one night.

I hope this will alleviate some of the anxieties of the men who have written to you because they are afraid their 'inadequate' size will be a disadvantage to them.

Mrs. G.H.

THE VAGINAL CANAL

I remember reading in Forum that the vaginal canal is 6 in. to 6¼ in. long. Is there much difference between the length of the vagina of a tall woman say 5ft. 8in., and a shorter woman? Also, does the penis have to reach the cervix in order to satisfy the woman? What happens if it is shorter than the coital canal?

J.A.

How long is a piece of string? It depends on the distance between its ends! Similarly, any anatomical measurements are fairly meaningless unless the 'ends' of the measurements are accurately defined. Is one to measure the vagina from the vulva, or the origins of the labia minora, or the hymen? The posterior wall is ½ in. to 1 in. longer than the anterior wall. The vagina is a muscular tube, and its size will vary if the muscles are relaxed or contracted.

The length of the vagina has little relationshp to the height of the individual – it is the size of the bony pelvis that counts. Hence, short, squat, wide-hipped persons will be more likely to have longer vaginal tracks than tall, slim, 'willowy' persons. The height of a person depends to a considerable degree on the length of the legs, particularly the thighs.

The cervix is a curiously insensitive part of the body. In ordinary relationships, its contact with the glans penis is slight and momentary and not easily appreciated by either male or female. Violent movements will be transmitted to the deeper pelvic organs by direct contact and may be appreciated as pain or pleasure by the woman, according to her nature.

As the vagina is so distensible, only in the most exceptional circumstances will a 'short' vagina cause discomfort. 'Dispro-portion' ('he is too big for me') is a common complaint, but exists mostly in the minds of the complainer and is very rarely a physical fact. Spasm of the vaginal muscle due to fear, etc., could make the vagina appear too small and this causes difficulty. – F.

WORKING IN THE DARK

Despite the fact that I've been married for over ten years, it appears that I've been in the dark when it comes to lovemaking during all those years. I was never taught anything about sex, and neither was my wife. The extent of our physical relations is the coital position wherein my wife lies on her back and I on top of her.

I've noticed that one of the sexual acts mentioned in Forum was cunnilingus. Although my friend explained to me what it was, I would like to know whether or not it is considered to be a sexual perversion, and also, if its practice is prevalent?

W.S.

Cunnilingus, as a form of stimulation leading to intercourse or as a non-exclusive means of orgasm in its own right, is a normal activity and certainly not a perversion. However, many psy-chiatrists would agree that it forms a perversion only when it completely replaces coitus, but even here, the opinion is not *unanimous. As an example, Drs. Hannah and Abraham Stone have written that there 'is nothing perverse or degrading ... in any sex practice which is undertaken for the purpose of promoting a more harmonious sexual adjustment between a husband and wife in marriage'. However, Dr. Theodoor Van De Velde, who is considered to be an enlightened author of marriage manuals, wrote (in 1947) an eloquent, even lyrical defense of the 'genital kiss' as he called it, but was careful to add that carried to orgasm, this becomes a perversion. Why it should be stopped before orgasm, he does not make clear.*

Scientific literature contains very little on the subject of cunnilingus. Significantly, most of what little has been written deals with the male partner. Magnus Hirschfeld, in Sexual Pathology, suggested that the practice was related to fetishisms. He wrote: 'The majority of clitoris fetishists are adherents of cunnilinction.' However, he made no attempt to demonstrate that the reverse is true – that most adherents of cunnilingus are clitoris fetishists.

Freud, meanwhile, was uncharacteristically mum on the actual practice of cunnilingus, although he asserted that the male practitioner's interest was essentially symbolic – i.e., he really wanted to suck his mother's breast. The neo-Freudians tend to follow this line, and some add that the desire to engage in cunnilingus underlies some nonsexual behavior.

What is the appeal of cunnilingus? As with fellatio, most often the receptive partner derives both physical and psychic satisfaction, while the aggressive partner's gratification is largely psychic. Dr. Yankowski has written: 'The sensations of cunnilingus usually are inferior for the female to the sensations of coitus – owing largely to the comparative lengths of the average tongue and the average penis. However, the abominable lack of coital skill common to many men, to say nothing of such physical matters as the inability to withhold climax, to sustain an erection or even to achieve erection, results often in the acceptance by females of cunnilingus as the "best" and most satisfying form of sexual congress simply because they never have experienced a "better" or more satisfying form to which it might be compared.'

Psychologically, for some women, cunnilingus is tender and loving; it is an act in which the male ministers to her needs and desires, seeking only to satisfy her. Conversely, for these same women, coitus is 'brutal and sadistic'. It is an act in which the *male 'hammers away' at his partner, seeking to subdue her.*

In cases like these, cunnilingus is rarely the sole means of sexual outlet. Usually the partners in the sexual relationship strike something of a 'bargain' and lend themselves to each other's favorite act on a reasonably equal basis. Thus, when the female in a relationship prefers cunnilingus and the male prefers coitus, it is simple enough to precede the act of coitus with an episode of cunnilingus. The female may be brought to orgasm during this preliminary episode; then, in the act which follows, she may bring her partner to orgasm.

There are also some males who prefer cunnilingus to all other sex acts. This is not because they derive physical satisfaction therefrom. Some men gain great psychological gratification from bringing a girl to orgasm in this manner, even though the men do not achieve orgasm themselves.

In the United States, there have been two major studies, which among other things, deal with the subject. They are Kinsey and Yankowski. Both studies place the practice of cunnilingus considerably below the incidence of heterosexual fellatio. The findings of Kinsey (1954) are as follows: 'Among the younger females in the sample who had not had premarital coitus, only three percent had allowed the male to touch their genitalia orally. The figure was still lower – between one and two percent – among the females who were born before 1900. Among those females who had some, though not extensive coital experience, some 20 percent in the younger generations had accepted such oral stimulation; and among those who had had more extensive coital experience, 46 percent had accepted such contacts. There were surprisingly few differences between the older and younger generations in these respects.'

Yankowski reported: 'Among our respondents, 22 percent of all females reported experience of heterosexual cunnilingus sometime between 14 and 35 ... Unlike our male respondents, the females failed to give evidence of a change of attitude toward cunnilingus between adolescence and maturity ...' – F.

INFECTIONS TRANSMITTED

My wife had developed a vaginal infection (staphylococcus aureus) which led to her having a cervical erosion. This is now in the process of being cured with antibiotics.

However, after indulging in cunnilingus with her, I noticed, a day later, that I got mouth sores (ulcers) on my gums. Could I have picked anything up from her?

K.B.

The cervical erosion is usually present first – the infection arises because of it and produces the symptom of vaginal discharge. Some infections such as staphylococcus and thrush are easily transmitted by oral contact, and so such contact should be avoided in the presence of a vaginal discharge for at least one month after apparent cure.

As clinical appearances of the ulcer can be deceptive, a bacteriological examination may be required to establish a diagnosis, and so medical advice should be sought. – F.

TRICK OF THE TRADE

My wife and I enjoy the many delights of fellatio and cunnilingus, and I have recently overcome a problem which was shortening these happy interludes.

While adopting the 69 position, I was having great difficulty in breathing and frequently had to 'come up for air', which lessened the enjoyment for my wife.

After a great deal of thought, I procured a nose snorkel which I made from an ordinary swimmer's snorkel, a dissected Guy Fawkes mask and plenty of sticking tape. Held in place by elastic, it enables us to spend many happy hours at our favorite hobby.

L.K.

Patent pending, we presume? – F.

PRACTICAL SOLUTION

I am 29 years of age and have been married for seven years. I have always tried to please my husband even though sometimes this has meant partaking in acts which initially at least I didn't like. But the point is, in all cases, I subsequently found I enjoyed them.

Two cases spring particularly to mind. The first was having intercourse while on all fours with my husband inserting his penis from behind. My objection to this, rather illogical though it might seem, was that my husband might be pulling funny faces while I was not looking! This problem was overcome by always performing in front of a mirror.

The second, the performance of fellatio, proved more difficult. I have never objected to the idea of having his penis in my mouth but have always felt difficulty in accepting semen in my mouth. At first I thought it must be the idea of swallowing the ejaculate which caused this revulsion but came to the conclusion that the problem was the feel of it on my tongue, as when I spat it out on to a handkerchief I felt worse than when I swallowed it. After much trial and error we hit on a technique which has solved the problem.

First my husband adopts a supine position while I lean over him and take his penis in my mouth. I then perform fellatio on him, rubbing my tongue around the head of his penis, moving my mouth up and down on him and sucking and pumping the head. Sometimes I put a finger in his anus. Then, when he lets me know he is approaching orgasm, I stop what I am doing and adopt a position on all fours with my head thrown back and my mouth wide open. My husband then squats in front of me and slowly and carefully inserts his penis as far into my mouth as he can, rubbing the head of his penis on the back of the mouth. When he comes the semen, due to the position I am in, runs down the throat without any trouble. I have performed this act many times and have never experienced choking.

With experiment and compromise I have always been able to satisfy my husband's desires so far, and I've been rewarded not just with good sex but by his deep appreciation and gratitude. There is no better way for a woman to show her husband how much she loves him than by cooperating with him in bed, and I have written to you in the hope that my experiences will encourage other unadventurous wives (as I was) to try something new. It's really been worth it for me.

Mrs. E.C.

TASTE OF SEMEN

I have read many letters in Forum concerning the taste, or lack of it, of semen.

However, in my experience over the last six years or so, semen has a very bitter taste and is sometimes quite salty.

Should I attempt to swallow it I get a burning sensation in my throat which lasts for some time afterwards.

I must however point out that I have only performed fellatio on one man – my husband – and therefore cannot say that all semen tastes like this.

I must make clear that it is not the act of fellatio that I find unpleasant. On the contrary I find it extremely pleasant and it gives me an immense feeling of satisfaction to get my husband so sexually aroused by it that he can no longer control his coming. It is merely the taste of the semen and the burning sensation it causes that I find so unpleasant that I cannot bring myself to swallow it. I have even tried swallowing it in small quantities, greatly diluted by my saliva, but always with the same result.

Perhaps you could suggest a remedy as I should like very much to be able to swallow semen, as I am sure it must disturb my husband's enjoyment of fellatio to see me forever spitting his semen out.

Mrs S.T.

Because of the nature of things doctors in general tend to pontificate on matters which can only be known from a theoretical aspect. Diseases from which they have never suffered are described in minute detail. Feelings they can never have are analyzed to the nth degree! This latter must apply particularly to sexual matters and, for male doctors, all matters feminine. This point is clearly made in the book The Female Eunuch *by Germaine Greer, which the authoress writes with emotion from the heart, even a bitterness of some intensity, when castigating male gynecologists for their appraisal of the sufferings of the fairer sex! And so it is with due humility that I venture to give my comments here.*

The semen fluid has a characteristic odor and is likely to have a taste, so I don't believe that it is 'tasteless'. The burning sensation in the throat can be analogous to the feeling following a sip of concentrated spirits.

Quantity varies according to age, degree of continence and constitution, ½ cc–7 cc or more. Probably, as far as I know, a race has little part to play in this except that some races grow old very quickly and even prematurely by Western standards.

Taste and smell are such personal factors that I do not feel generalizations will help. Where there is a smell, there must be

237

(theoretically) a taste, although people's ability to appreciate tastes and smells varies tremendously.

In general all body odors become stronger and so more likely to be unpleasant as one grows older. (Compare the 'sweet' smell of clean kitten and the 'sour' smell of an equally clean but old cat.)

Lots of old people complain bitterly of their genital odor — women in particular think they have a vaginal infection when all they notice is their 'natural' odor.

I cannot suggest any medicament which will help here except that tastes are largely acquired and omnia vincit amor — *love overcomes all things. Love is a strange quality. An act which is truly revolting if associated with one person can become inspiring, greatly desired, enlivening, and exalting with one's lover! — F.*

NOURISHING SEX LIFE

I recently met a girl who seemed quite normal until she invited me up to her flat, when she began behaving in such a strange way that I wonder whether I am in danger of becoming perverted!

Having undressed, she produced a packet of a well-known brand of chocolate finger biscuits and suggested I could use one. 'Not like that,' she said after I'd eaten it. 'Like this,' and she showed me how to insert it into her vagina and use it to stimulate her. When it was well oiled, she withdrew it and told me to eat it, which surprisingly I did with enjoyment. Having repeated this several times, she brought out a packet of ring doughnuts and used one on me; a very satisfying experience.

I now find our relationship not only very satisfying, but nourishing as well!

P.M.

HUSBAND LETS ME DOWN

I'm 24 and my husband is 28. We have been married for five years.

My husband is always telling me how abnormal I am for not having an orgasm during intercourse. I always come off when

I rub his penis between my thighs and I enjoy intercourse but don't get any release out of it. I have once or twice, but only if I am really worked up to the point-of-no-return.

My husband always comes off inside me and I get very excited about this when he takes his penis out. I put it between my legs to fulfill myself, being very careful because I know he can be very tender after intercourse. But he goes very cold and puts me off, making me feel very selfish. I've tried having an orgasm before he takes me but as soon as I put his penis anywhere near me he enters me and it's all over within seconds. He does not like foreplay either, only if I'm caressing his body with my lips. I also enjoy this but if I do it for too long he comes before even going anywhere near me and then I get in a right state.

I am begining to get very frustrated as I don't seem to be able to lie back and enjoy only intercourse.

I started masturbating but this just doesn't seem right when I have a husband to help me reach orgasm. Can you please tell me where I'm going wrong and why I don't get orgasms during intercourse?

Mrs. M.T.

There is no 'right' way to achieve orgasm. Mrs. M.T. is struggling with the generally accepted attitude that women are supposed to be passive and just lie back and enjoy it. If they don't respond that way, they feel like failures as sexual partners and are often reinforced in that feeling by their mates.

Marriage counselor Eleanor Hamilton suggests that women can help themselves come to orgasm and that an important first step is learning to masturbate successfully. Many women refuse to do this, explaining as the letter writer does, 'it just doesn't seem right when I have a husband to help me reach orgasm.' So that again the problem becomes one of what is right and wrong in sex. In reality, a woman's willingness to explore and accept her own sexuality may make the difference between her ability to come to orgasm or not.

One masturbatory technique is to rub a moistened finger around and over the clitoris, which is where all female orgasms happen whether by masturbating, intercourse or fantasy. The amount of pressure on the clitoris and the amount of time needed vary with each woman. Another technique is to cross the legs and exert steady and rhythmic pressure on the whole genital area. Some women use a pillow, a stream of water or an

electric vibrator, and some enjoy inserting something into the
vagina while they are masturbating.

Another aid in reaching orgasm is learning how to breathe by
exhaling fully so that there is no muscular tension in the groin,
pelvis or buttocks. Practicing contracting and relaxing the
vagina has also been described as helpful. A great many women
report that sexual fantasy, unrestrained and unfettered, has
been of considerable assistance in reaching a climax.

The unfortunate aspect of this problem is not the inability to
reach orgasm through intercourse, but the result in terms of
feelings of blame, failure and inadequacy. It is my experience
that as long as people believe that orgasm should be achieved in
a prescribed 'right' way and no other, then as the letter writer
describes, blame and 'Where am I going wrong?'
follow. – R.G.

MR. TOSSER

We have been married for almost 26 years and are still very
much in love with each other and are now nearing 50. Throughout our marriage our sex life has been full and completely
free from any silly old-fashioned restrictions or taboos. We have
always sought new means of keeping our sex life fresh and
exciting and until recently had been eminently successful.

However, about 18 months ago my husband began to develop a certain inadequacy in his sexual ablities. Sometimes he
was unable to raise an erection, at other times to maintain one
for any length of time. We believed that this was caused primarily by extra worry in his professional affairs, as he has a
position of great responsibility. Of course I tried all the obvious
'tricks' or blandishments to encourage him in his passion, but
despite all these he was too frequently unable to erect. We discussed this for hours on end trying to seek a way round our
problem which was, I am sure, a simple matter of loss of
confidence but it was all to no avail.

Despite my own misgivings, my husband felt that we should
try one of the sex aids, and he obtained a belt-type penis of
similar size to himself and eventually persuaded me to let him
try it. I must confess that I had considerable doubts about this
practice. Even though it was a most excellent production, it was
not my husband, so my feelings were mainly against it on

240

psychological grounds rather than physical ones. However, my husband persuaded me to persevere, and eventually I grew to accept it without any mental reservation and I really came to like it. What is more, my husband has gradually regained his confidence and we have fewer and fewer failures. It is, we feel, simply because he knows that if 'things go wrong' we can use the dildo.

However, we have now discovered many new uses for this method of lovemaking. Using 'our friend Mr. Tosser', as we now affectionately call our sex aid, we can go on with varying postures and movements which could never be expected from one's husband by the natural method and believe me, we have had some wonderful rainy afternoons when I have been brought to my climaxes as many as eight times this way.

I hope others with similar troubles will be encouraged to try this method, and I wish them every success.

Mrs S.C.

REAL ORGASM?

I met Joan three years ago, at which time Joan had been married for 16 years. She had never experienced orgasm. In the early part of her married life her husband had tried to achieve this but soon gave up and then only satisfied his own needs. As a result she become disinterested and by the time we met, could be described as frigid.

On the other hand I, married ten years, had experience with a number of women, but not with a woman who could not reach an orgasm.

Over these past three years we have become very close and neither realized just how much sex could be enjoyed but here is the problem. About a year ago during loveplay Joan experienced a sensation which caused her to lose water and shortly after, this happened again. It can now be achieved easily and almost continually. It is usually brought about by my inserting two fingers in her vagina and moving them back and forth quickly. It can also happen during normal intercourse but only in one certan position.

We are puzzled as to whether this is a real orgasm? While Joan likes the feeling she gets from this it is not the totally shattering experience she expected, or what I led her to believe it would be.

R.M.

241

R.M.'s problem may be literary. Orgasms are rarely that total shattering experience. One might speculate that some male writers may use these descriptions to attract women, by implying that with them, love and sex would result in such an experience.

For most human beings, having an orgasm is a very pleasant and exciting experience, but not necessarily one in which the earth rocks, rockets explode, and all the other literary pyrotechnics that have been used to describe the orgastic response. If both of you do not object to Joan's reaction, there is no reason why you cannot go on and enjoy it. However, if you both decide that this reaction is not quite good enough, there is a strong possibility that even the pleasure you now experience may diminish. – H.G.

UNINHIBITED COMMUNICATION

Recently my oldest friend in a sudden burst of confidence revealed that for the whole of his 15 years of married life, his wife had consistently and frequently masturbated. He was amazed because he had prided himself in the sexual field, always considering his wife's needs before his own and laboring under the illusion that he understood his wife fully. He admitted the knowledge had had great erotic effect on him and had increased his admiration for and interest in his wife, but he lamented the fact that had his wife not chosen to confess, the thought would never have occurred to him, and he kicked himself for his lack of sensitivity and insight.

His wife was equally amazed to find the effect was so stimulating to her husband and further questioning – always while lovemaking – revealed what appeared to him the salient points. Confession of the act seemed to add to his wife's pleasure as if in recalling the incidents she was reliving the obvious ecstasy she had experienced. This was done with a mixture of blushing confusion, modesty and defiance. He could not extract any information of accompanying fantasy, and the stimulus was in many cases visual: 'I see my breasts in the mirror when I am dressing; I pause to fondle them, they are terribly full and sensitive producing the most lustful feelings' or 'I sit on a low stool in front of the full length mirror. The sight of my hand manipulating my clitoris adds to my pleasure which is further enhanced

242

with my left hand pushing the object, i.e., a bottle or sometimes a candle, slowly in and out of my vagina.'

He did not figure in any sexual role in her activities. In fact, he appeared to be a deterrent. Initially, she half jokingly blamed him for never being around when she became passionate, but it soon became apparent she waited until she was inaccessible to him and then, sure of no fear of intervention, would indulge, saying 'sometimes I can make it last for hours by pausing in between and using only the object. Feeling the clitoris becoming more and more frantic, I get up from the bed or couch and resume my housework, often walking about with the object deeply embedded in my vagina. Then, as my excitement cools, I return to my manipulation until I can bear it no longer. The orgasms then can be blinding!'

At one stage, he suggested that he might observe her masturbate while she was unaware of his presence. Her reply indicated a certain amount of contempt. 'Not a chance,' she said, 'unless you could become a fly on the wall or a crack on the ceiling,' proving at least to him that her sexuality was divided, and she allowed only a part of herself to escape to him.

Nevertheless she did consent to perform providing he hid himself promising to enact the whole procedure as faithfully as possible.

The speed at which orgasm was achieved and the accompanying ecstatic shrieks convinced the husband that sex in this respect was more violent and uninhibited than the so-called normal sex they shared.

As a result, the husband's lovemaking, which previously had been gentle and overly cautious, took a new turn. Seeing how she enjoyed violence, he adopted this in his sex with her, and the result was most gratifying for both. If at the begining there had been open and uninhibited communication between the two, there would not have been 15 years of masturbatory relief on the part of the wife.

E.J.

UNUSUAL FOREPLAY

I am surprised that none of your correspondents have so far confessed, as I do with absolutely no shame, to the predilection for being trodden on by a woman in high-heeled shoes. Although I recognize that this is a mildly deviant form of

243

sexual behavior, it is surely quite harmless, and, if not used as an end in itself, can add a delightful piquancy to erotic foreplay.

Although by no means a rabid fetishist. I have always been strongly excited by women's shoes (which, incidentally, are surely prettier today than ever before) especially shoes with stiletto heels. These have always seemed to embody the quintessence of femininity.

I first asked my wife to use hers on me when we were engaged. With a little coaxing she soon overcame her inhibitions, warmed to the idea and entered into the spirit of the game, which is how we still regard it. For the past ten years, we have invariably used this 'tramping' as a prelude to lovemaking. Although my wife has never purposely hurt me during this ritual, which is really just a symbolic demonstration of our relationship, she admits to enjoying the sight of me squirming at her feet and is always threatening to 'dig her heels in' ... which only excites me more. She has this to add:

My husband, ever since he was a little boy, has always had this 'thing' about girls' shoes. The first time he asked me to use mine on him, I thought it was a bit idiotic. But the idea seemed to excite him so much I agreed to try it. When I saw what a fizz it got him in, I became very excited myself and couldn't wait to be asked again. I had never dreamed how much a pair of what seemed to me ordinary shoes could mean to a man. Now I do. Besides liking the feeling of power over him it gives me, I also welcome the chance to show off my legs to such good advantage. My husband often buys me new shoes; we choose them together, and he is very particular. I also have a variety of naughty little dresses, and slinky undies that he likes me to wear during our 'sessions'. It is a bit naughty, I suppose, but we find it enormously satisfying and I imagine it's a far less painful form of stimulation than the lashings and scourgings described by some of your other correspondents.

Mr & Mrs. A.I.

Sadomasochism sometimes exists on a purely psychic level, in which case an individual takes pleasure not from inflicting or receiving pain, but from asserting dominance over or being dominated by another individual. In many instances a sexual element very definitely is involved: for example, some individuals can engage in coitus only when bound in leather straps

244

or only after being subjected to considerable verbal abuse by the partner.

This psychic sadomasochism, which is sometimes referred to as 'sexual bondage', often appears in conjunction with other non-genital behavior. It appears frequently with foot fetishism as is evidenced in Mr. and Mrs. A.I.'s letter. It appears occasionally with clothing fetishism.

Most clinicians attempt to explain psychic sadomasochism in terms of the Freudian or behaviorist views of physical sadomasochism; indeed, many insist that both psychic and physical varieties are but surface manifestations of the same phenomenon. However, a dissenting vote is cast by Krafft-Ebing, who sees bondage as a separate entity, brought about by the super-imposition of nonsexual roles upon the sexual relationship.

Krafft-Ebing acknowledges that sexual bondage and physical sadomasochism often occur simultaneously; however, he insists that, when such is true, it is a case of the sadomasochism paving the way for the bondage and not a case of both phenomena springing from the same source.

In any event, sexual bondage apart from physical sado-masochistic activity appears harmless enough from a social point of view, and generally responds well to therapy. – F.

PROFESSIONAL TREATMENT

The first time I blushingly whispered my requirements to a professional girl, she replied: 'Many a backside I've skelped, my lad, and I'll soon redden yours.' I thoroughly enjoyed my spells over the lap of this friendly, hearty woman, and much regretted it when she left the city. She was a darling. Warm and cuddle-some.

My present mistress is Raechel. Let me describe a visit to her.

Up the worn tenement stairs. Knock and a well-built woman opens. She welcomes me with a thin smile, leads me to a bed-room which is as scrupulously clean as herself.

'Quickly!' she commands, and I tear off my clothing. She stands holding a leather thong, and if I hesitate for a second or two, or fumble with shoelaces, she waits until my vest is being pulled over my head, and the whip snakes round in a fiery kiss on my rump. Then I must stand contritely by the bed, quite naked, while she sits down, and pats her lap to indicate readiness.

The spanking by hand is prolonged, and a lecture goes with it. She is an enthusiast, and probably a full 40 minutes, including sundry rests, goes by before she lets me up. Go to the mirror, says Raechel, and see if you like the nice crimson color of your hips. But I must not waste my mistress's time, or out comes that thong again. Back to the bed, this time to lie over it. A pillow is below my tummy, elevating the target area. Raechel picks up her leather hand. This is a five-thonged strap shaped like palm and fingers, with the 'wrist' as grip. It can be anything between stimulating and right painful, depending on the mood of my mistress.

In this relationship, the disciplinarian is absolutely in control. When I have undressed for Raechel, it's like jumping into a fast river; one cannot swim against it.

The only time she whipped me mercilessly was when I attempted intercourse with her. This broke the relationship of stern-aunt-and-meek-nephew. She treated it like attempted incest. She gave me an agonizing thrashing that left my hips puffed up with throbbing weals.

Apart from that, the punishment ends with me in control of the tear ducts, and it is worthwhile for what comes next.

Raechel sits on the bed. She strips off her panties, draws up her dress Gently she gathers me in her powerful arms. She opens her legs, but not for the usual purpose. She cradles me like a baby, my bottom resting on the tender flesh of her inner legs.

Raechel plays a concerto on my instrument, to the deep throbbing accompaniment from the well thumped tympani below me. Ten skilled fingers begin a rousing first movement; it almost seems to make one burst with ecstasy as her fingers trill along in soaring cadenzas. She pauses in time, then comes a long, soulful slow movement, prolonged quiet joy. Finally the allegro molto, fast, vibrant, leads into the rumbustious finale that explodes in splendor.

She is an artiste, is Raechel. And, as it all ebbs to quietness and peace, she clasps me to her very ample bosom, murmuring, there, there, now. She unbuttons her dress, slips off bra, cradles my head in womanly tenderness.

While I wash up in the bathroom – including cold-water plunge for the hips – Raechel makes a cup of tea. We sit and chat like old friends which we are. During the conversation I mention any small sins committed. It gives her material for the next lecture given during punishment.

Before I leave, Raechel catches hold of me, slips down my trousers, administers a delicious, stimulating love-spanking. I am sorry for any man who has missed the experience of being love-spanked by an expert. Then, when I am finally buttoned up, she gives me a maternal goodbye kiss.

It should be added that in addition to this I have a perfectly normal sex life with sundry girlfriends. But about twice a month I feel the need for Raechel's stern treatment. It's the most effective therapy there is for men like myself.

I thoroughly recommend any man who has this longing – and many have – to give it a try. But see that the 'girl' is a well-built, maternal woman, preferably in her 40s or 50s, and put yourself absolutely in her hands. The trouble with most men is that they are as afraid of new sensuous experiences as they are of new ideas.

D.A.

AMATEUR TREATMENT

Both my husband and I are University graduates – my husband is a theoretical physicist while I hold a degree in sociology.

I am a big girl, with what you may call a Renoir-like body; my husband was the first man I ever knew, in the biblical sense of the word, and though I was (as I then believed) deeply in love with him, I was quite unable to achieve any kind of sexual satisfaction during the first two years of our marriage. This of course led to all sorts of tension between us born out of frustration: I even went to consult a psychoanalyst, on my doctor's recommendation, but with no other result than an increased self-doubt. I came close to despair, out of an unreasonable fear of losing my husband's affection.

Then, an entirely playful spanking by my husband resulted in an almost immediate orgasm of bewildering intensity. Thoroughly frightened and confused at first, and of course terribly ashamed at the same time, it took me quite some time to come to terms with myself, to understand above all that I needed this kind of stimulus to achieve self-realization and satisfaction.

My father was a minister, kindness itself, and none of us (I have two sisters and a brother) had ever received any form of corporal punishment. It would therefore be idle to talk about masochism, sadism, or any other silly label some people would try to pin on it. My husband is the gentlest of men, who abhors all violence, including corporal punishment, and is anything but sadistically inclined.

I now frankly and unashamedly enjoy being spanked or caned; indeed, I look forward to it. Apart from the obvious physical satisfaction I derive from it, there is also a tremendous feeling in me of belonging entirely to him which, if anything, increases my physical pleasure. I do not think that he derives any direct physical satisfaction from caning me – rather, I feel that he, too, loves me more than ever, sensing perhaps my greater love for him. He is never overbearing, much less masterful – if anything he prefers to give way in arguments. Thus it cannot be a kind of 'seeking a master.'

I am of course quite unable to offer any kind of explanation as to the reasons. Nor could I welcome any other kind of pain. In fact, I am rather a physical coward. The thought of anybody else caning me fills me with revulsion, so that this behavior simply must be linked to my love for my husband. Naturally, the caning my husband gives me is never excessively hard; it always precedes our lovemaking, and consists simply of my husband giving me as many strokes as I want, on my buttocks and thighs, while holding me bent over an easy chair, until I ask him to stop usually after 12 to 18 strokes, sometimes more, sometimes less. In this way, I always achieve complete satisfaction, and at the same time a deep feeling of happiness.

The inquiries I was able to make among my friends (all married women), revealed that a majority of them (seven out of 13) willingly submit to or ask for spanking, caning or similar stimulation. It is of course well known that a certain amount of pain can be erotically stimulating. So, since this is apparently a widespread form of loveplay, why all the fuss? And especially, since it seems that only women capable of very deep love for their man can genuinely enjoy it, why cry 'perversion'?

Mrs. C.B.

AFFECTIONATE SISTER

I'm 24, married, with two young children. My husband is in an organization which takes him out of the country for quite long spells at a time and being a very responsive female there are times when I miss my husband very much. One weekend six weeks ago I was in one of my responsive moods and two of my lady friends and I made arrangements to have a Saturday night out. So I got my young brother who had just turned 14 to babysit for me. He often does this, staying the night.

Returning from my night out, and still feeling very frustrated, I looked in on the children who were soundly asleep. Looking in my brother's room I found him asleep also, but the covers of his bed had fallen to one side, and I could see my brother lying, wearing nothing but an undershirt which was worked up above his waist leaving the rest of his body exposed.

I stood for about 20 minutes just looking at his fairly well-developed penis and testicles. I then put the bedcovers over my brother and went to my room to bed, but I could not sleep for thinking of what I saw. My brother actually possessed more than my husband. I got out of bed and went to my brother's room, removed my night clothes, went into bed with him and snuggled up close, molding my body with his.

I must have dozed off for when I awoke it was four o'clock. My brother had changed his position and was now facing me. He was awake and also sexually excited. Without any warning I forced one leg under him and the other over him, sliding his penis into me. Although I had to help him all the way to his release he completed the act beautifully, and we had sexual intercourse two more times that day.

My brother and I now have sex regularly and I'm teaching him all that I know. I am fully aware of the facts concerning relationships between brother and sister, but is it a commonly known thing and is it harmful to either partner? I make him wear contraceptives so that there is no risk of pregnancy.

Mrs. A.N.

There is no evidence that incest is necessarily biologically harmful, and it appears to be more common than has been generally recognized. The real dangers that arise from incest are the result of general social revulsion to the act, which for some people may produce great feelings of guilt and shame.

Have you considered the number of possible consequences that your affair with your brother may incur – both to him and to your marriage? In my experience men who engage in sex with older sisters frequently end up quite passive sexually, as they expect women to take the initiative. Also it's quite probable that your husband will not look so kindly at this example of brotherly love. – H.G.

FEMALE 'EJACULATION'

I am 30 and have been having orgasms for about nine years. About four years ago, while receiving oral stimulation. I came to an immense climax, and at the same time thought I'd urinated. This was not so. It proved to be a cloudy liquid with a faint feminine odor.

Now it happens on every occasion and it is very copious. A towel placed underneath is no protection at all to bed, furniture, floor or whatever, apart from the fact that my poor lover gets half drowned in certain positions.

I should like to know the reason for this 'ejaculation 'as I cannot become accustomed to it and on odd occasions find myself holding back rather than soak everything. I don't want this to become more frequent and spoil our pleasure.

Miss C.B.

The sexual secretions of the woman arise from certain glands around the vulval orifice, the vaginal walls and the neck of the uterus.

In quantity they vary greatly – from a mere trace to a 'copious volume'.

Nothing can be done to alter these secretions – a general rule is that a person who has a copious discharge on sexual stimulation is usually well motivated sexually.

Occasionally owing to a vaginal infection the secretions are increased – so a gynecological examination is indicated to ascertain this and if an infection is present, appropriate therapy will be given. Usually, however, a vaginal infection will dry up the secretions. – F.

FRUITLESS SEARCH

I am a male in my 50s. Since adolescence I have had a craving to smell and fondle sweaty female feet. A psychiatrist I consulted told me that this resulted from my mother's habit of swinging me on her foot when I was a small child – a process I enjoyed, I am told, sexually as well as physically. My mother's feet used to perspire freely, and in those days, of course, there were no deodorants available.

As a youth I found it increasingly difficult to obtain cooperation in this respect from girls – those whom I liked because of their sweaty feet would not permit me to take their shoes off, while girls who liked me did not attract me because their feet did not perspire!

My first wife, who died young, was an ideal partner who understood and cooperated without reservation, but my second marriage has broken up mainly because of my wife's refusal to go along with my desires. My life now seems to be a fruitless search for someone with naturally perspiring feet (I believe the proportion is very small among women) but, as in adolescence, my prospective ideal partner seems to elude me.

I am able to have normal intercourse without this type of stimulation, but in these circumstances have to resort to fantasy to produce an orgasm. I frequently masturbate to induce sleep.

K.R.

K.R.'s problem seems to me to be his difficulty in finding sexual partners who will help him satisfy his particular desires.

Smell is a powerful stimulus in the experience of a good many people, though for many others it is a repellent. With some the personal scent used by the partner, or the peculiar body-smells which many of us have, no matter how often we bathe, are the stimulators. (I do not mean in regard to this last, the smell emitted by the secretions of the sexual organs, but the delicate yet definite smell that seems to be given off by the whole body, and which is quite distinctive to each individual.) Among people who respond in this way, there are also a number who find the smell of sweat, generally underarm, a very powerful stimulant.

Nearly all men masturbate from time to time to induce sleep. Nothing more relaxes an over-tensed general nervous system – a preventer of sleep – than an orgasm. – F.

DON JUAN COMPLEX

I have a continual craving for sexual relations with women. I am 26 years old, unmarried and have my own flat. I live in London and have no difficulty finding a never-ending supply of bed partners. As it turns out, the anticipation is always better than the actuality.

After reaching orgasm, I completely lose interest in my partner and can't get rid of her quick enough. I keep on hoping that each new girl will be 'different' although I know deep down that they're all the same.

The truth is, I'm never really satisfied. To me, sex is more important than food. Do you think my problem is purely a psychological one or is it possible for a man to be physiologically oversexed?

R.H.

Satyriasis which is also called erotomania or hypereroticism is a fairly rare occurrence. It may very well be due to the hyperactivity of the genital glands but this is seldom prolonged. Nor should it be confused with the disease called priapism which consists of a permanent and painful erection of the penis, due to a nervous disease. – F.

R.H.'s problem, however, appears to be of psychological origin. It is often referred to as a Don Juan complex after the legendary lover of song and story.

Generally such men are attempting to use sex to satisfy other than purely sexual or affectional desires. There can be many reasons for such behavior, including an essential feeling of loneliness; doubts about one's masculinity which may result in a constant need to prove it through continual seductions; feelings of emptiness; the search for the perfect partner, or the search for the perfect orgasm.

In my experience, I have found that the most frequent problem associated with male and frequently female promiscuity is an inability to establish intimate, loving relationships, or the fear of doing so. The promiscuous individual finds safety in numbers because then he need not be close to any one person. This is dramatically illustrated in R.H.'s sudden loss of interest when sex is over, whereas others frequently find this a time of closeness and enjoy a warm relaxed feeling for the partner.

In my practice, as the men and women developed the ability

252

to first accept and then enjoy closeness, compulsive promiscuity usually disappeared. – H.G.

FOREPLAY EXTOLLED

I would like to suggest that the pleasures of physical contact are a very important, although rather neglected, part of sexual technique. I know, of course, this is treated in all the manuals on sex, but it is usually described as 'foreplay', and one easily gets the impression it is secondary. I suspect quite a number of people have not realized its full possibilities, and I would like to suggest some lines on which to experiment.

My wife's interest and mine was triggered off by reading about a type of erotic stimulation practiced by Singapore girls. Four of them take part. One stimulates the man by all-over massage with oil. The second stimulates by body kissing. The third is the tease. After about an hour of this, the man is more than ready for the fourth who actually engages in intercourse.

I believe these techniques must have been well known to harem girls, because it was traditional the man did nothing, he just lay back. It was the girl's task to stimulate him to the point of orgasm, and this she would often do by manual manipulation. I presume this was more subtle than the practice of European prostitutes which is often crude in the extreme.

As applied in a modern day context, this technique need not be so onesided, but anyway, let me describe it from the man's point of view.

The man lies down, and the woman runs her fingers along his body from the toes to the armpits, in a tickling or rubbing motion, lightly at first, emphasizing the more erogenous zones usually between the legs, the armpits and the spine. This motion gradually becomes more pronounced, with more pressure. As her hand travels up the inside of his legs, she goes under his testicles, then passes her fingers over them lightly. A particularly sensitive spot is the area behind the testicles, what the Indians call the 'yoni'. She can graduate her pressure in various spots according to her partner's reaction.

By this time, if she knows her job well, he should have a good erection, and she can pass her fingers lightly along his penis, and also try kissing and licking his body in the most sensitive parts.

253

If he is getting near to bursting point, she can transfer her attention to another sensitive part of his body giving it gentle massage. In this way a skillful partner can keep him simmering for as long as she likes.

Toward the end, it is very stimulating for her to lay her hand quite heavily on his lower abdominal region, and move it up and down, slowly at first, then getting quicker. The penis can be made to swing, and this is very stimulating, possibly too much so! After a little of this, he should be ready for finishing off in any way they prefer.

The longer the buildup the better. This technique makes it possible to graduate the stimulus, to build up a number of sub-crises, followed by a period of relaxation and gentle stimulus. It is possible for the man to stimulate the woman at the same time, or they can work it in turns.

It is not essential to proceed to orgasm, and a great deal of pleasure can be obtained even if the man is tired. One would not normally recommend postponing orgasm continually as it may be harmful, but delaying it by skillfully transferring attention to less sensitive parts of the body is definitely very pleasurable, and leads to an intense, almost mystical feeling of communion. The exact reaction will no doubt depend very much on the two partners involved. Also a couple who becomes used to this technique, might be able to derive sexual pleasure even if the man's virility were to decline. Are we not too guilty of linking sex solely to the act of intercourse? Variations can also be tried, such as tickling with a feather on sensitive zones.

Since great pleasure can be obtained without orgasm, some people might consider this sort of activity more 'moral' than intercourse during extramarital contacts. Body contact of this sort can be much more satisfying than conversation. I would say you can grade the stimulus from 'general' to 'intense', though it may be difficult to resist the temptation to escalate!

D.M.

A HIGHLY SKILLED ART

Until about a week ago (I'm still in my teens) I was a virgin but only just, as I had come close to intercourse on five or six occasions. During these times I became extremely excited but was in a way glad that intercourse did not occur. Since the age of 13 I have considered myself very uninhibited, and have always discussed sex openly with my mother and sister and friends and consider it an essential part of a rewarding relationship.

When I finally lost my virginity, it was a terrific comedown. The boy was very sweet and kind, and we had only met a few hours before. He is now my regular boyfriend and since then we have had intercourse about five times – each time a disappointment. I discovered that I was much more inhibited than I had imagined.

Finally we talked about it and he was very concerned about me, especially when I admitted to not having come anywhere near an orgasm (which I have never experienced). If my response does not increase, I am afraid that our relationship will break down, even though my boyfriend, who is highly sexed, tries hard to be understanding. I greatly enjoy kissing and fondling even though I find I am not responsive in the vaginal area, but when it comes to intercourse I just close up, although I try to grin and bear it for his sake.

To my horror, I read somewhere that very few young girls achieve orgasm during sex for the first few years. Is this true?

Miss J.D.

Miss J.D.'s experience is not unusual. Although no general rule applies to age requirements before a person achieves sexual satisfaction, Kinsey, et al. found that almost 100% of the males in their study had achieved orgasm by the age of 17 but only 30% of the females had achieved orgasm before marriage. They also reported that the maximum orgasmic response in the female was not reached until the age of 35.

I can sympathize with J.D.'s disappointment that it was a terrific comedown, but the important factor here is that she has expressed her feeling about not being ready for intercourse. If she has sex just for her partner's sake, there is a good possibility that it will take much longer to get pleasure from intercourse. For many people, and especially women, sexual pleasure takes some learning in terms of time, practice and experience. – H.G.

EARLY MORNING ERECTION

I have a problem and I am hoping you can help me. I have

spoken to a close friend about it and he just laughed at me and I can't ask my family doctor because there's nothing wrong with me. At least I don't think there is.

I have a very full sex life without any real desire for it. I have been married to my wife for 15 years and I'm afraid I am not very excited by her any more. However, every morning on waking I find I have a very stiff erection and my wife immediately snatches the opportunity for intercourse; she gets coy and sexy or just jumps right on top of me before I'm properly awake. I don't very often have an orgasm and, to be truthful, I would much prefer to wake up gradually, get up and have breakfast. I never have enjoyed sex first thing in the morning. Even when we were first married I found the evening more romantic and felt like making love when we climbed into bed at night. I've tried to explain this to my wife but she makes fun of me and says we have an upside-down relationship, that I am the one with the inhibitions about sex and that she has to be aggressive. She's convinced I want to start each day by making love to her; I don't want to hurt her feelings by refusing her outright. I don't know how to explain these very definite erections, either. Is it possible I have sexy dreams, of which I'm not aware, that produce these reactions?

C.L.

Recent research on sleep and dreams shows that a large percentage of men have full or partial erections while dreaming, even if they have had intercourse only an hour or so previously. A healthy man may have such an erection for a fifth or a quarter of the time he spends asleep.

An early morning erection is a purely physiological phenomenon and has nothing to do with sexual desire. It is associated with a full bladder and the warmth of the bed. Many men who are conscious of their full bladder are quite unable to proceed to intercourse in spite of the erection and even less likely to have an orgasm if their wives insist on continuing the act.

Marriage is a contract between two persons. Where one partner possesses a greater sexual appetite than the other, trouble is inevitable, unless they can meet on common ground and compromise. – F.

NUDISM UNCOVERED

Last summer I visited a nudist colony with my fiancé for the first time. The experience was so enlightening that I feel it worthwhile to describe.

Having paid our admission for the day we were told we could either use the changing rooms or we could change in the car.

We decided on the latter and were soon undressing in the car. I am broadminded, so the thought of undressing before my fiancé did not worry me. Indeed we are quite used to each other's bodies, but it was a new thing to be stripping off bra and finally panties in the car, knowing that people could stroll by while I was doing it.

We were just about to open the doors and get out when we heard another car coming. It turned out to be the milkman and he drew into the clearing. He must have been expected for within the space of a few minutes there was quite a little crowd round him – fully clothed milkman surrounded by a bevy of nudists.

We both sat and watched as women and men mingled together, many times with their bodies in close proximity, but nowhere did we see the slightest sign of any sexual reaction on the part of the men.

Realizing that this was probably because the men were members or possibly residents I glanced down at my fiancé, for although he is fully conversant with me, I thought that seeing a number of girls and women who were strangers and seeing them in the full beauty of their bodies, with all their charms in view, there would inevitably be a stirring of his impulses.

But there was no sign of this whatsoever. After the crowd gradually dispersed, we got out of the car and walked along the path that was sign-posted to the pool. It was a new experience for us. I thrilled to the feel of the sun and the fresh air on my skin and as we met people who called out a cheery greeting to us, I contrasted it with the feeling one has when on the beach in a bikini. There one has to be continually on the alert that the bikini is not inadvertently exposing an inch too much breast or allowing two stray strands to stray from the mound of Venus, while all the time the male population is mentally stripping off the bikini!

We soon came to the pool, and what a revelation it was. There must have been about thirty people in it, although it was early morning. The sight of so many naked people including children enjoying themselves in the water, was something I shall always treasure.

There were also many people stretched out on the grass, sunbathing, on their stomachs and full length on their backs.

That was another thing that I noticed. When a man sunbathes in swimming trunks, if he is on his back he invariably draws one or both legs up so that the 'bulge' is not too obvious, but in the nude he just lies there having no need to feel conscious of such a thing.

Children, too, accept the human body as perfectly natural, taking not the slightest notice of their elders.

During the afternoon we both realized that although we were familiar with each other's bodies, there was a sense of complete freedom to be found in getting back to nature, and that a clean and healthy body bronzed by the sun and air is a thing of beauty, to be admired by all.

Only twice did we see any sign of sexual activity. While strolling, we came across a couple in a secluded corner who were on the grass and were petting heavily. Later on we saw another couple who were taking advantage of the pool for some underwater petting.

I would also add for the benefit of those who may have any doubts, that there is nothing suggestive or obscene in breasts or genitals swinging freely as swing they must in any kind of exercise.

Later in the afternoon we had tea outside on the huge lawn. We sat with two more couples and chatted for a long time. They had been visiting the camp for over two years and in the whole of that time had never seen or heard of any unpleasant incident taking place, which supports my theory that nudity camps do not breed sexual adventures or orgies. I certainly admired the suntanned bodies of our two male companions while my fiancé enjoyed the company of two well developed girls, but again, although in very close proximity to them, there was not the slightest sign of genital erection.

To anyone who has a day to spare, I say, forget what the fuddy duddys and Mother Grundys have to say. Visit a nudist colony, throw off your clothes and really live.

Miss K.B.

ERECTION REACTION

I readily endorse most of the observations made by Miss K.B. concerning her visit to a naturist club. However, I really must protest about her inclusion of genital erection in the category of 'unpleasant' incidents.

During my 12 years as a member of one of Britain's premier clubs I have noticed several of these natural physical reactions, which are caused by visual stimulation.

One year we had a farewell gala, which included a 'best shaped legs' contest for the ladies. About a dozen competitors were lined up behind a screen which hid only their top half down as far as their midriffs; the rest was left on show for the benefit of the judges. It was then that I noticed that several of the men were either fully or partially aroused by this display of 'central' beauty.

However, I didn't notice any of the ladies raising a protest about this being an unpleasant incident. In fact, I guess that they were thinking the opposite and indeed saw one or two covertly allowing their gaze to wander from the competing girls to the displays of male virility.

Most of the people who attend these delightful hideouts are sufficiently sophisticated and broadminded to realize that a number of men who are easily stimulated by so much feminine shapeliness, are sometimes unable to repress the irresistible natural physical manifestation of their thoughts

I have related this happening merely to show Miss K.B. how very natural the 'nudists' really are, and also to emphasize how sensible and indulgent the normal onlookers may often be.

F.C.

LOVELY SIGHT

All men should be circumcised at birth. Surely there is no more beautiful sight than the flaccid, circumcised penis with its exposed glans of coral pink.

My husband was circumcised shortly after our marriage, over 20 years ago. I have never regretted the removal of his foreskin. I love to see him step naked from his bath – just the sight of his glans and balls (how I detest that clinical word 'testicles') hanging low in his scrotum, excites me like nothing else. I feel that circumcision makes the penis appear longer.

Mrs. M.T.

DISGUSTING MUTILATION

I myself am totally opposed to circumcision. Why in the name of humanity (and sanity) can't our sexual equipment be left the way nature intended it to be? Without a foreskin it is quite impossible to experience the lovely delight of maximum tactile contact with one's partner in coitus which gives rise to such profound sensual stimulation. Why oh why must men be so brutally deprived of this wonderful birthright?

Surely men who are quite determined to be circumcised, must be totally unaware what an asset the foreskin is in providing an extra stimulus in coupling and climax. For without it the glans rapidly becomes coarsened and dry, thereby losing much of its potential response to frictional stimulation and depriving the owner of well over half his normal pleasure during coitus – to say nothing of the increased difficulty in achieving orgasm by masturbating.

Only the unlucky victims of this disgusting mutilation, too, can really know the actual feeling of pain round the corona of the knob which is an inevitable result and which becomes a cause of impotence by virtue of the loss of erection brought about by the 'touchiness' of this prominent ridge. There must be literally tens of thousands of circumcised men who suffer from this distressing handicap. In short, what utter rubbish it is when the authorities (so-called) tell us that circumcision makes no difference to intercourse. What blasphemous audacity to infer that they know better than God how baby boys should be made. Such butchery of such an important part of the sexual equipment is not much short of criminal assault without consent of the patient.

F.C.

F.C.'s reaction is rather unusual. I know of no evidence to substantiate his belief that circumcision contributes to impotence.

Jews and Muslims believe they are following God's command to circumcise their organs. Also there are no reports of cancer of the penis in circumcised males, and a much smaller danger of cancer of the cervic for the wife of a circumcised man. – H.G.

EUREKA!

Lying in the bath one day enjoying a pleasant half hour, I gazed at the various soaps and scents that surrounded me and then let my gaze wander to a well-known brand of toothpaste.

Did not that girl in the TV advertisement state that it was 'Tingly, zingly'? Yes, it was refreshing to the mouth but was that all? Nothing ventured, nothing won – and very soon I was applying a small amount (just in case I had made a big mistake) to my glans and the surrounding area. Very soon I felt that cool, tingly sensation which ended in a warm and sensuous glow that would have made any male passionate and ready to make love. I felt like Archimedes after my discovery and wondered whether it was right for me to run through the streets naked shouting 'Eureka!', but decided that this was A.D. 1971 and not 271 B.C. and that people might not understand.

Needless to say I did not keep my secret to myself and very soon found that a little applied to the clitoris certainly made the passion rise in the female as well as the male.

Ground ginger applied to the warm moist organ also has a very heating effect, but do not overdo it or you will be left with a very inflamed organ.

The beauty of trying these articles is that they can be found in any home and used at any time at little or no cost.

J.W.

NEEDS PORNOGRAPHY

I am 65 years old, and, as one might expect, my sex drive is considerably less than it was ten years ago.

Since my wife went through the menopause and was freed from the anxiety of pregnancy, she has become more sexually demanding and wants to make love at least twice a week. I find that I have to resort to an outside stimulus, namely pornography, to meet her demands. She is not aware that I read pornographic literature or that I have a collection of pictures for this purpose and would be terribly shocked if she ever found out. The truth is I feel guilty about my attraction to pornography, even though I fully comprehend its usefulness.

Is there a case for pornography? Do you agree that in situations such as mine, pornography, far from being a corrupting influence, is in fact beneficial? What tends to make me feel terribly guilty is the fact that I am not particularly stimulated by 'classic erotic literature', but by out-and-out pornography which has no literary merit whatsoever.

N.K.

Whether it is classic erotic literature or out-and-out pornography that stimulates you, there is no need to feel 'terribly guilty'. If this stimulation enables you to continue a harmonious and satisfactory sex life, distinction hardly matters. Sexual stimulation is, in any case, a most individual matter. Some catch fire at a slight touch, others need prolonged and intimate caresses.

Many of the experts who have testified in legal processes regarding pornography have defined 'redeeming social value' of pornography to mean that it has uses like the one described in N.K.'s letter. Many men with waning sexual interest in their own wives find they can maintain satisfactory relationships with the judicious use of pornography. Therefore, the experts have stated that it has a redeeming social value because it may keep a couple together with some sexual happiness.

As our age becomes more permissive, more women are also reporting that they find pornography stimulating.

Some men who fear that they cannot match their wives' late-blooming desires hide pornographic material from them, not necessarily because they feel guilty, but because they fear their wives might become even more sexually demanding. Other men prefer to keep pornography secret because they find it more exciting that way. However, in this as in most other aspects of marriage, many people have found that mutual sharing is preferable to secretive indulgence.

Are you, by the way, sure that your wife would be 'shocked' if she found out? Women are often far more responsive than their husbands believe. – H.G.

AIM TO PLEASE

Our 'game' began a few years ago when we arrived home from an excellent evening out, both desperate to relieve our bladders and making for the toilet together. I stood aside to allow my wife to go first, but she, seeing that my need was great also, sat as far back on the seat as possible with her legs wide apart so that I could aim between them. However, after a second or two, she suddenly grabbed hold of my penis and directed the jet to the region of her clitoris. When I'd finished relieving myself I noticed that she was sitting rigid, eyes closed, almost as if having a fit. After a few moans, she relaxed and smiled. She had had a terrific orgasm without any part of her actually being touched! The evening was completed with normal sexual intercourse.

Since then, we have experimented from time to time with different methods of stimulating each other through urination, and both get a terrific kick out of it. We don't make it a regular feature of our intercourse, just occasionally for variety. Sometimes my wife holds me while I pee, trying not to get me too sexy as this stops the flow completely, or I part her lips while she pees in varying positions – squatting, sitting, standing, or bending over. Another variation is to perform together. I sit down and my wife sits astride me, facing forward. Sometimes I kiss her nipples. My penis rests against her abdomen, or else I hold it along her vulva. We both get very wet, and usually finish up with a grand climax each.

We have noticed lately that during intercourse, especially if my wife is on top, she 'leaks', particularly when nearing orgasm. As she pushes in with her muscles of the vagina and abdomen, little jets of hot water squirt out along my stomach. This only increases our excitement, but does it mean that my wife's muscles or even her bladder have been weakened? They are certainly all right at other times.

Another point is, if male urine gets into the vagina, can it do any harm?

In general, do you think this practice is abnormal and could damage any part of either of us?

Mr. and Mrs. J.M.

Urolagnia is the term used when sexual libido is increased by witnessing the act of urinating.

To have interest in seeing one of the opposite sex urinate is very common. It has been mentioned in the literature for centuries, e.g. Brantome, in the 16th century, states that French nobles frequented places where they could see through cracks in the paneling, noble women urinating.

With this evidence before us it would appear that this is a widely practiced stimulant of sexual desire, is appreciated by

*many men and women and can be accepted as within the limits
of normality.*

*No harm can come of urine getting anywhere on the body or
in the vagina or rectum, unless of course there is any disease
present in the person who is urinating. However, if there is an
infection in the urine he or she will usually not be fit enough to
indulge in such activities anyway. – F.*

MASTURBATION AND ORGASM

My problem is an inability to reach orgasm during intercourse.

I am 19 and have had a number of sexual partners during a
period of three years. I was living with a man for six months
until we parted two months ago, and as I am not having intercourse with anyone at present I am hoping to use this opportunity to clarify my feelings about sexual morality, to cope with
my frustration, and to prepare myself physically and morally in
an attempt to make future relationships more satisfactory.

Until I met my last boyfriend I was masturbating to the point
of orgasm every night (over a period of two years) and am
wondering if this might be the cause of my problem. My clitoral orgasms have recently become less intense, and I no
longer masturbate compulsively. I have noticed that my ability
to obtain orgasm through masturbation decreases not only
when I masturbate excessively but occasionally also when I
have not masturbated for over a week.

Could you advise me as to whether it would help me to
obtain an orgasm if I stopped masturbating altogether (I now
have the willpower to do this) or whether this would decrease
my ability to be stimulated prior to intercourse?

Miss M.C.

*When you have come to terms with yourself about the morality
of your sexual activities, I feel sure your present difficulties will
disappear. May I assure you that as far as masturbation goes
there is nothing sinful or shameful in practicing it. On the contrary, it can be physically and mentally beneficial. What you
decide about premarital intercourse is a matter between you
and your conscience. – F.*

LANGUAGE OF MASTURBATION

A fuller discussion of masturbation might throw light on the large number of new words and phrases, not in general use, which are used in talking of masturbation. The hand that does the work has been called 'the five fingered widow'. Viewing the penis as a mutton bone, there are the phrases 'flogging your mutton' and 'tickling your mutton dagger'. Imagining the penis as a man wearing a hat, we have the up and down movement of the fingers described as 'trying to knock off the soldier's hat' or 'bashing your bishop'!

The spurting of semen has been referred to as 'galloping your maggot' or 'pulling your pudding' (rice pudding I presume). The throbbing of the penis I have heard referred to as 'clocky', 'ticky' or 'benny' (obvious references to the ticking of a clock).

I do hope we can improve on these in our discussion and manage to put the whole question of masturbation on a different plane, so that it is not sniggered at in dark corners but becomes recognized as a normal and almost universal practice and a means of enjoyment in its own right.

J.W.

ADDICTIVE VICE

I had to wait until I was over twenty before I found a girl who was prepared to masturbate herself in front of me. I hadn't realized until then just how much a girl can dote on the feelings she gives herself and just how abandoned she can get when she really lets herself go.

Since then, about half the girls I have made love to have consented to do it for me, and half of those were embarrassed to a degree which somehow made the spectacle all the more intriguing. There is no doubt that watching a girl giving herself an orgasm is a highly addictive vice. I thought at one time that it was a more or less personal perversion, but I notice that the simulacrum of self-abuse is introduced into almost every act of every strip show which suggests that in fact it is a fairly common form of masculine titillation. As an adjunct to a normal sex life in marriage it is a powerful aphrodisiac.

J.N.

GUILTY MASTURBATION

I am very troubled about my excessive masturbation. I am 40 and feel that somehow this is just not normal. I have a good idea that my colleagues at work know of it as I just can't help making it look obvious. Every chance I have I am off to the toilet with various magazines.

I am married, with daughters, and I feel that this is affecting my home life as I'm sure that they know about it. Could you please tell me whether this is normal for a man of my age?

O.A.

Your feeling that both your daughters and your workmates know about your masturbatory activities is the classical psychological response of the person engaged in something that he feels is basically wrong and shameful; this is doubly so if strong feelings of guilt are in evidence as is obvious in your case. You do not go into details, but I would have thought that unless you are very careless or flagrantly open about your habit it is unlikely that anybody knows. However, clearly you run some risk of detection if you are disappearing every 30 minutes or so to the toilet. Even the most unsuspecting of workmates might get curious enough to investigate.

The problem with many sexual activities is not the activity itself, such as masturbation, but the shame and guilt it engenders. Although our society is more permissive now than formerly, many psychiatrists still regard masturbation as childish and immature. Therefore, the grown man who engages in it feels shame. In addition, an adult who indulges in masturbation in preference to sexual intercourse may be disguising hostility toward the woman whom he thus deprives of his affectionate attention. The guilt may then come from the feeling of hostility rather than from the act itself.

Masturbation is a self-limiting activity and thus practically impossible to overdo. A Viennese humorist is reported to have said, 'Sexual intercourse is a poor ersatz for masturbation.' – H.G.

SCHOOL DAYS

I prefer manual sexual excitement after experiencing it with my brother for over 17 years, although I also enjoy intercourse.

Sex meant nothing to us until my brother (14 months older than myself) moved from the private day school we had both been attending to the local grammar school. He was there exposed to the usual tortures and initiations and practiced them on me when we were in bed. I knew what to expect when I too moved to the school.

Meanwhile, we still practiced the tortures on each other in bed wearing only our pajama tops and our tight, white cotton briefs. Our mother was puzzled by this attire but our father agreed with us that it was common practice among men and boys not to wear complete pajama sets.

We carried on in this way until after my 12th birthday when, while returning from school, my brother told me he had been 'raped' during the breaktime. He kept repeating this all the way home, but would reveal nothing else. That night we got to bed as usual but suddenly he pinioned my arms above my head. In the struggle the bedclothes went flying and I ended up tied, spreadeagled on the bed. Almost at once I became tense and excited at being trussed up this way. My brother began to 'rape' me, caressing me intimately until I wet my briefs and he had a second orgasm. When he released me, I had enjoyed it so much we carried on caressing intimately for more than half the night, during which my brother had two more orgasms.

From that time on, we enjoyed sex almost every night and soon after I had my first full orgasm. Sometimes taking it in turns to be tied up we would, also, on occasions, give each other a sound spanking on our naked bottoms with a gym slipper or the hand. It was not very long before the boys at school discovered I could wet my briefs and one breaktime, I was hustled into the toilet by several boys and held firm while my trousers were taken down. I was brought to a climax after being exposed to view. Like my brother this happened to me more than once. On several occasions we both witnessed each other being brought to a climax by the boys.

Now that I am married I find my wife also prefers sex manually. This is because when she went to boarding school other girls would take down her pajamas and sexually excite her or strip her naked in the dormitory at night and bring her to a climax. As she grew older, several of the girls began to sleep together. My wife said that if a girl refused to sleep with another – as she did at first – they would be wakened during the night, stripped naked, spreadeagled on the bed and a candle would be used. This, she said, could be very painful. So the girl would usually cooperate.

On occasions I try to give my wife some pleasure by using the candle in a gentle manner which I find excites her. The only way my wife really enjoys intercourse is by 'rape'. So I take her by force, strip her naked and make love to her while she struggles. In return, she sometimes ties me up and strips me to my briefs and then makes me have an orgasm after first torturing me by squeezing and pulling my genitals, the old schoolboy torture. She has once or twice enjoyed forcing me to have intercourse while I have been tied up.

I, of course, still remember being tied up by my brother and also being held down at school and made to have an orgasm. This gives one the feeling of helplessness against overwhelming odds and therefore one can do nothing but let it happen and enjoy it.

B.T.

SATISFACTION FOR PURISTS

I am 24 and have been married for nearly three years, and although my husband is always boasting about his wide experience with girls he certainly has no knowledge of the female anatomy, especially the clitoris. Sex to him is about three to four minutes grunting and gasping on top and that's it. He does not seem to realize that I have needs as well.

I certainly cannot tell him what I would like him to do – it would be like saying 'this is how I managed before we were married': if he only knew! That is how I get some satisfaction now. I would never tell anyone I knew that I had ever masturbated. Certainly not my husband.

I am not a lesbian, although I have had some sexual experience with other girls, when I was at school, and more recently with a very close friend. I really believe that women make better lovers than men. Women get pleasure from giving as well as receiving, and they know that the journey is just as pleasurable as reaching the destination.

A woman does not want to be rushed, even though women can come off as quickly as men. I could bring myself off in two minutes if I wanted to, but who wants to?

My friend and I have often played with each other, either rubbing ourselves together or masturbating, by hand. I must admit that I found it enjoyable and I got as much pleasure from watching her as I did when she did it for me. I have actually come off once or twice when she did, merely by pressing my thighs together.

That's what I can't understand. Does the male ego require that a woman only has an orgasm during intercourse itself? I am sure if men teased their wives manually more often they would find as I did that watching their reactions can be very stimulating. If I, as a woman, can get excited about it, how much more pleasurable would it be to them?

Let's break this idea that a woman must have an orgasm only during intercourse and if she wants it any other way it is dirty. To satisfy the purists, the penis could be inserted just before orgasm to ensure the desired end result.

Mrs. P.R.

After such liberal comments, Mrs. P.R. still feels the need 'to satisfy' the purists. True liberation is very hard to attain. – R.G.

ADOLESCENT FEARS

I am 18. I reached puberty when I was 14 and soon started to masturbate. By the time I was 17 I was doing it about five times a week, sometimes twice on Saturdays and Sundays. This was too much, but I could not stop. I always felt tired and weak, and I looked terrible. My face was always yellow and dirty looking with a fresh acne spot every day. My school work was awful and I was terrible at games. After masturbating I would feel so depressed, dissatisfied and frustrated I used to start crying.

At Easter when I was home from school I told my brother all about this, and he said my body was ready for a woman. I am sure I'm not ready as I find the sight of a picture of a nude woman with bulbous breasts and pubic hair most repulsive. Some boys at school put up pictures of nudes and stand in front of them and masturbate, but I cannot get an erection when I try.

When I got back to school I decided to have homosexual relations with a boy. I knew a nice boy my age who enjoyed it with other boys as the passive one. He got me ready and instructed me, and I enjoyed it very much.

Now I go to him every weekend and sometimes in the middle of the week. I have stopped masturbating altogether. I feel ever so much better since I have been going with this boy. I look much better. I feel much stronger and my work and games have improved enormously. Only one thing worries me. Shall I ever be able to function with a woman? I certainly want to be married one day. I always see myself married with three children, two boys and one girl. How shall I know when I am ready for sexual intercourse with a woman?

D.C.

Your problem is not unusual, particularly in boarding schools. The main difference between you and thousands of other boys is that you have been able to find someone who is keen to provide what you wish. This homosexual relationship obviously meets a genuine need in you in that it solves your masturbation problems, and leaves you well and happy. I must point out, though, that since you are a minor it is illegal.

Your remaining anxiety is the question of future marriage. You must understand that this is not ruled out by the fact that you are at present aroused by other males. Most human beings are bisexual in varying degrees, and many married men have had homosexual experiences either before or after marriage.

Unfortunately you were plagued by guilt about masturbation in early adolescence. As a result, you falsely believe that masturbation produces pimples, lethargy, and physical debility. Such fears are totally without foundation. If you can accept your activities, there is no reason why you should not later on have heterosexual intercourse, marriage, and the children you desire, as well as enjoy your present experiences to the full.

Nude pin-ups may excite some of your school friends, but they are certainly not as good as the real thing. As for your final question, you will be 'ready for a woman' as soon as you desire one emotionally and physically instead of merely in the abstract. – F.

FLAT-CHESTED COMPLAINT

As a married woman of 34 I know only too well the agonies

of being flat-chested. I have an awful inferiority complex about it. My marriage has never been very satisfactory sexually because I was too ashamed to be seen naked, and if my husband ever tried to caress my nonexistent breasts, I immediately froze and was unable to make love. This caused my husband to feel unwanted and to become semi-impotent.

This eventually led to my having a complete nervous breakdown. After a few weeks of treatment for nerves, I finally plucked up the courage to tell my doctor the real reason for my trouble. He sent me to a psychiatrist who was very understanding. After several sessions he referred me to a plastic surgeon who made it very clear I would have a long wait for an operation to enlarge my breasts. (I have waited two years now!) He wondered whether it was worthwhile as I had lived with it for 32 years – why couldn't I carry on living with it? Little did he know what 'living with it' meant. During adolescence when I was being laughed at by boys and girls of my own age I was letting mature men have intercourse with me, which resulted in two children before I was married. I have also contemplated suicide more times than I can count in fits of deep depression and despair, attempting it once with almost fatal results. Is this what he calls living? Is this how he wants me to carry on"?

Why should I and others like me be flat-chested, when men can be made to develop breasts (how?) and are even changed into women. Surely we are more important (and our husbands) or doesn't anyone know the misery, torment and frustration that we suffer *all* our lives?

I first visited a doctor about my condition when I was 18. He told me that to be flat-chested was perfectly natural – could I tell him of any animal that had breasts when they were not suckling young? I could not, but what about *all the other women* who had breasts? Well, he said, when I'd been married a few years and had two or three children I would then have breasts. Now, 12 years of marriage and three children later, I'm still as flat-chested as a boy. The only time I have had breasts was while I was either pregnant or nursing.

What can I do?

Mrs. S.D.

Hormones taken orally, providing the correct dosage is taken, do help glandular development to a small extent. Large breasts consist mostly of fat and are poor milk producers. They are often sexually insensitive despite their erotic appeal. Certainly, the frequent side effects of hormones render their indiscriminate use undesirable. Hormones rubbed into the breasts in the form of ointment are unlikely to do much harm but are equally unlikely to produce results.

Attempts have been made to increase the size of the breast through placing plastic or metal inserts beneath the wall of the chest and the breast. It is difficult to obtain uniformity and a good cosmetic result. Also, with this kind of surgery later complications are frequent.

It was at first thought that liquid silicones, which are quite inert and set to a flesh consistency, injected into the breast, were the answer. Unfortunately, it was found that this material has a marked tendency to slide downward and could produce ugly deformities. It is extremely difficult to remove the silicone once it has been administered and, in general, it is not a procedure to be recommended.

Counterirritants, that is substances designed to produce an inflammatory swelling of the breasts have been in use throughout history.

The most popular and least harmful of these substances were ordinary stinging nettles which were swished over the breasts. Given good nettles the resultant swelling would be marked but nevertheless transitory. – F.

It is unfortunate that so many of us women judge our personal attractiveness, even our ultimate worth as a human being, by the standards of society. In my growing-up period, I was quite distressed for the opposite reason – R.G.

A LITTLE DEMON

Funnily enough, I am not one of those men who grumble that their wives are not the girls they married. My grouch is the reverse. My wife hasn't changed one noticeable bit except for a few lines on her face and a little extra weight, in 19 years of marriage. She is still as sweet, naïve and enthusiastic over little pleasures as she was during our courtship days. I wish to goodness she'd grow up a bit and broaden her outlook on life. What is becoming to a 20-year-old girl appears like silliness in a woman approaching 40. I've changed, not only mentally but in my social position, during this time, so though I still love her there are so many things I'm forced to exclude from her.

Sexually she still appeals to me; she's so affectionate and seems to want me as much today as on our honeymoon. Sweet, rather romantic lovemaking, cuddling up in bed, and she's perfectly happy with this. So how do I tell her that I have developed a taste for the somewhat unusual? What could happen to a woman like my wife if I suddenly confronted her with the knowledge that it would excite me to see her dressed in an exotic rubber outfit, with breasts and buttocks exposed, and that I'd love to see her parade in front of me for my pleasure, to have her play with her nipples and clitoris and work herself into a frenzy until she would get down on her knees and beg me to satisfy her.

Nearly ten years ago I had a mistress who taught me these wonderful things. She was married and had no intention of breaking up her marriage over her pleasures, so we stopped seeing each other. To this day I still visualize our terrific sessions, but I don't think I would dream of admitting this to my wife, knowing her innocence. Or is it possible that some little demon exists inside every woman and can be brought to light when the time is right? Wouldn't it be strange if she had some similar secret desire she is afraid to tell me about?

W.H.

It is impossible to generalize about human beings beyond giving a few guidelines. Whether the 'little demon' exists within your wife or whether it exists with all women can hardly be answered by a straightforward 'yes' or 'no'.

Obviously your wife has a different conception of sex from yours and as you have kept your fantasies and desires from her, you can hardly expect her to respond to them clairvoyantly. Nor is this likely if you spring all this upon her suddenly without proper preparation. For 19 years you have shown no sign that you are dissatisfied with her lovemaking and you cannot suddenly disclose your frustrations and demands. – F.

THE OLDER WOMAN

Recently I read a magazine article that dealt in a most negative fashion with relationships between older women and teenage boys. Frankly, I do not think that schoolboys will come to any harm by being seduced by a married woman of 37. I didn't.

Perhaps the circumstances were different in that my seducer was a woman in her early 40s and also a widow whom I'd known for nearly ten years before we made love together.

It was during the war. She was the mother of a school pal of mine. He was a year older than I and had been called into service at 17. He had an older sister who was married and several younger sisters who were evacuated to the country. His mother was left alone and I often visited her. She was a very attractive woman with shapely legs and full breasts; breasts that I had seen years before when she was breast-feeding her youngest daughter!

We often went to the cinema together, to the music hall and to the pub. When we parted we nearly always kissed goodnight, but one night the kiss became two, then three and she took hold of my hand and pressed it to her breast. Through her blouse I could feel the sharp point of her nipple and I began to tremble with excitement; Within minutes her blouse was open, her full breast was in my hand and I had a sexual climax. She realized what had happened to me and in a motherly sort of way she soothed me and suggested that I clean myself up. I was only too pleased to do so and somehow I found that I was letting her help me clean up my underclothing in her bedroom. Then, wearing just my shirt, I was sitting on the edge of her bed and once more we were kissing and now we were fondling each other and she guided my hand under her skirt, and up between her thighs, making me rub her. She began to breathe heavily, and kiss me even more passionately. Ultimately, we ended up in bed.

Naturally that incident subsequently led to intercourse on successive meetings. She let me satisfy my curiosity by examining her naked body, offered me her breasts to kiss and suck, and asked me to put my fingers into her vagina. She performed fellatio on me when she was menstruating and one evening shocked me by masturbating herself as she did so. It was the first time that I realized how strong the female sexual urge was, and she told me that for years she had satisfied herself in this way. She pointed out that if it was good enough for me to masturbate, then why not her. I had never spoken to her of my masturbation which I had practiced for years.

274

We were lovers for over three years and when we could we slept together, bathed together, urinated together. We made love in doorways, in air raid shelters.

Sad to say I was subsequently called up and sent overseas rather quickly. I lost touch with her during the remaining war years and her son was killed in action. Perhaps she found another lover in my absence, but she will always remain in my memory.

D.H.

Many older women find young men sexually attractive but are still inhibited about acting on such feelings and are still held back by society's attitude. When an older man becomes involved with a young woman, he is frequently envied, sometimes congratulated, and at worst may be subjected to mild derision. The general reaction to an older woman-younger man combination has been and still continues to be much harsher. I have known women who were involved with younger men who broke off the relationship because they felt so strongly that it was 'inappropriate', even though the relationship was quite important to them.

This attitude generally persists despite research findings that marriages in which the woman is 10 years older than her partner are generally more stable than those where the age is about the same or the man slightly older. – R.G.

ANAL STIMULATION

I had reached the age when I thought I knew everything about stimulation in petting. However, a certain young lady in her early teens decided she knew a trick or two, and I was initiated into rectal stimulation by her.

We were attracted to each other because of a mutual liking for the rear entry coital position. She also loved to be spanked prior to sex. After the usual kissing and loveplay I would say, 'Come, bend over, naughty girl,' and she would quickly slip her panties down, and unbend her shapely bum for me to slap, usually quite hard; in fact I could not hurt her bottom with slapping – judging by how she would keep saying 'harder' until it really tingled.

However, one day, as I was fondling the bare cheeks of her

275

bottom, reddened with slapping, my fingers happened to stray between the clefts, passing once or twice over the anus, which made her wriggle and nip her bum, as if trying to hold my fingers in between. Seeing she was enjoying it, I decided to experiment further. I vaselined my finger and inserted it up the anal passage. It slid up and down quite easily, which brought her quickly to a climax.

Frankly I was not keen at first to do this, thinking it was pretty 'dirty', really, and when I remarked how surprising it was for a nice, clean girl to actually enjoy such a thing, she blamed me for what had transpired, and of course she was right.

It appeared that when we had sex at that time (usually in the rear entry position), I, when on the point of climax, would use the withdrawal method (the pill had not yet been invented). Knowing that girls like the feel of the penis within them, what else was there for me to do but pull my penis out very quickly, and bury the tip, as it were, spurting the semen right between her bare bottom? As it turned out, she found this experience very pleasurable.

Today, I no longer consider anal stimulation 'dirty'. In fact, I consider it an exciting aspect of erotic loveplay, leading to more powerful climaxes and feel that the law making it illegal between husband and wife is pretty ridiculous. What business does anyone have telling a married couple what they can and what they can't do in the privacy of their bedroom, so long as both partners agree on what they want?

J.S.

ANILINCTUS

Having practiced cunnilingus for some time and derived a great deal of pleasure from it, I would like to tell other exponents of this art of a new variation we have discovered.

One evening after a session of anal intercourse my wife was lying on her stomach on the bed and I noticed my seminal fluid seeping from her back passage. My curiosity was aroused and I began to lick it. The sensation I received from this came as a complete surprise, and I was further excited when my tongue ventured right up to her back passage. This aroused her and she began to respond to my advances. I then inserted my tongue fully. I became very agitated and achieved an erection without further stimulation, and after exploring with my tongue for a few moments I ejaculated and the sensation was greater than I have ever known.

Since that initial session of 'anal cunnilingus' we have practiced it at regular intervals, and it seems to arouse both of us to greater pleasures both on its own and as a prelude to intercourse.

F.M.

THE ARISTOCRATS

Anilinctus is a sexual variation as old as the hills. Used most by the French aristocracy, those old indulgents however would only approach anilinctus after having scrupulously prepared themselves, in the hygienic sense as well as the erotic. Thus one would not catch the average French girl in the regrettable condition I just recently found in an English girl. To all intents and purposes she looked as clean as a new pin, but this could hardly be said of a certain part of her anatomy, as I discovered later. This, after an extended and very enjoyable period of foreplay, put me off completely, as you can probably imagine.

Surely mothers could make a more thorough job of instructing their daughters in matters of personal hygiene. Sexually speaking, the anal area of the body is rich in sensation, and I am sure members of both sexes would be more willing to exploit this if only prejudices could be overcome, and cleanliness paid more attention to. The French have successfully used bidets for years, which possibly explains why sex appears to be much more pleasurable over there than here!

J.S.

LOVE VERSUS ORGASM

Eighteen months ago I fell in love with an exceptional girl. After some three months of idyllic romance, my girlfriend began to take the Pill, and we had intercourse for our first time. Unfortunately, although I was 25, I was a rather inexperienced lovemaker and very anxious to please her. She soon learned I was no expert, for our first night of lovemaking was a farce. I rammed my penis inside her and then only managed about an inch of entry. However, my girl was very sweet and patient, and eventually we became quite expert. This would have been fine, except I measured the success of our relationship by the success of our sex.

I needed to realize other things are more important in making love than just having successful coitus. I was so obsessed by using interesting and varied techniques, I forgot to tell my girl how wonderful she was, and paid little attention to making my love conversation interesting and exciting. I did not tell her she was the only girl in the world for me. She, like many other girls, needed this good old-fashioned romanticism which I, like many other men, failed to provide.

Well, you may have guessed. She has gone now, and despite the fact I have several girlfriends, I miss her very much indeed. She went because she felt she did not make me happy and because I did not tell her how happy she made me. What a sad breakdown in communication. Could it be we men are becoming too obsessed with giving our women orgasms at the expense of satisfying their emotions?

I.D.

SOMETHING ABOUT SAUNAS

May we add our method of making marriage more exciting?

For health reasons, my husband had a sauna installed in our home. Initially, he took his saunas alone. One night, we both decided to take the sauna together. On entering, our thoughts were on anything but sex. But soon we discovered that the intense, dry heat had an aphrodisiac effect on both of us. Making love that night inside the sauna was more exciting than any other night of our ten years of marriage.

We're using the sauna today more than ever. And for small, intimate parties, it couldn't be better.

Mrs. K.P.

HORSE LOVER

When I was a small child we lived by a London main-line station and I spent many hours watching the activities in the goods yards. I can remember, in particular, watching the cart horses which were then widely used and being fascinated by their penises.

As a teenager I found that the sight of a horse with an erec-

278

tion gave me a sexual thrill, and I did jobs in the holidays to be near them, such as helping the groom at the local milk depot stables.

I am now middle-aged and have moved away from London, but thanks to the popularity of riding, there are still many horses around this area, particularly stallions. This sexual thrill still comes over me whenever I see a horse flashing his weapon, and although I feel guilty and try to look away, I usually look as long as decently possible if in public.

When I am safely alone with a gelding or stallion I make a sexual feast of the occasion and handle the animal's penis as much as it will allow.

The other day I was shown some photos of a woman playing with the penis of a big black stallion and tossing him off into a bucket held between her knees. As pornographers know what people want, does it mean that the guilty secret I have confessed to no one before – of looking at and becoming sexually aroused whenever I see a horse's penis – is shared by other men and women?

E.C.

The importance of childhood experience during the early formative years, in the development of adult sexual preferences, is amply illustrated by your letter.

Sexual arousal of varying intensities induced by observing animals copulating and/or witnessing the erect penises of the male is a common enough occurrence during childhood, especially in the case of little boys living in the country. It is probably based on an increasing awareness of the importance of the penis as a sexual organ that happens at this time. Generally the bigger the animal's penis the more impressed the boy is likely to be, and the greater will be the visual stimulatory effect on him.

In most instances he develops, sympathetically, an erection himself; this may lead to immediate masturbation, in the presence of the animal, or later in private, usually accompanied by sexual fantasies of 'enormous animal penises' (stallions or bulls are the commonest) or actual animal intercourse. In a minority of cases the sight of an animal's erection is so impressive and stimulatory that the boy may be compelled either to handle it or, alternatively, to attempt intercourse. If successful in either of these activities the immediate sexual gratification may

279

be of sufficient intensity to motivate a repeat performance.

In this way, unless inhibitory guilt or punishment following detection follows, a pattern of sexual behaviour consisting of animal masturbation can become established and consolidated during childhood. This primary sexual preference can prevent or at least complicate the development of heterosexual exchanges, which are normal for our culture. Once a pattern of sexual practices is laid down in this way it tends to persist. It is probably only in a very small proportion of individuals that these preferences persist into adulthood.

Your particular predilection for horses and your comments on a pornographic picture showing a female masturbating a stallion into a bucket merely illustrate the prevailing view that the sight of a big penis is more stimulating than a medium or small one. – F.

PHYSICAL FRIGIDITY

' Lack of communication has never been one of the problems between my husband and me. Both of us are most articulate (my husband often says I am too much so) university graduates, and we have no reluctance whatsoever in discussing our most intimate sexual problems. I emphasize this point in order to explain that my so-called frigidity and apparent lack of ability to reach orgasm does not have, to my knowledge, any psychological foundations.

Sexually, we are both quite uninhibited and liberal. We are both in our early thirties and have two children. Although my husband and I are still very much attached to one another, my inability to reach the glorious heights of sexual passion has been the one area of our relationship which has caused both of us considerable grief.

My doctor has been completely unequipped to deal satisfactorily with my problem. Frankly, I think he is embarrassed to discuss in depth the subject of sexual passion and orgasm. He advised me to take hot baths and prescribed tranquilizers, both of which proved ineffective insofar as my problem is concerned.

My husband feels that my frigidity might be due to physical causes.

Mrs. D.G.

In some cases, frigidity is the result of purely physical factors. One of the most common physical causes of frigidity is dysfunction of the vaginal muscles – specifically, the pubococcygeus, a double band of muscles surrounding the urethral, vaginal and rectal openings; it extends from the front of the pelvis to the tip of the spine. If the pubococcygeus is lax and flabby, the female's sensation during coitus may be slight or nonexistent. It has been discovered that strengthening the pubococcygeus almost invariably results in increased sensory perception in the vaginal area. An instrument called the 'perineometer' which is used to exercise the muscle and to measure improvements in muscle tone has been most successful in the treatment of females who experience what is literally as well as metaphorically sexual anesthesia. Consult your gynecologist regarding the above treatment, if after an examination it is found that you have a dysfunction of the vaginal muscles.

Another physical cause of frigidity is hormonal deficiency. Females whose sex hormones are diminished or abolished often suffer partial or total loss of sex drive and/or partial or total loss of the ability to achieve orgasm. When hormones are diminished – especially the androgen, or so-called 'male' hormones – females find sexual arousal and sexual satisfaction considerably less frequent, Interestingly, hormonal balance in some women is so delicate that sexual arousal and the potential for sexual satisfaction vary in relation to the menstrual cycle: some women who may achieve orgasm easily during the progestenic or menstrual phase, may do so only with considerable difficulty at other times during the cycles.

A third physical cause of frigidity is lesions or adhesions in the genital tract. Disorders of this nature may make coitus so painful that it is impossible for the female to achieve satisfaction or they may desensitize her to stimuli as a result of which satisfaction ordinarily would have been brought about. Problems involving a lacerated cervix, an inflamed bladder, infected bartholin glands, a thick hymen, genital warts, inflamed vaginal membranes or other painful lesions and inflammations may make it impossible for the female to relax sufficiently for orgasm to take place.

Another physical cause is neural malfunction. Sexual arousal is the result of stimulation of sense receptors in the erogenous zones. If, because of neural malfunction, the 'messages'

*received by these sense receptors are not transmitted to the brain,
the female will be incapable of experiencing sexual arousal.*

*Finally, a fifth physical cause of frigidity is failure during
coitus to establish friction with erogenously sensitive areas of
the genitals. Certain genital organs – the labia minora, the clitoris, etc. – are generally more receptive to sexual stimulation
than neighboring organs. If, because of bodily position during
coitus or because of anatomical difference between the male
and the female, contact is not made with these or other erogenously sensitive areas, the female may fail to experience
orgasm, no matter how diligently and enthusiastically both
partners may work at it. – F.*

SEX IN THE CITY

As a woman living (if you want to call it that) in New York
City I am surprised that nobody has ever to my knowledge
written an article or even a letter about the effect city life has on
sex. How anyone can have a decent sex life after spending a
day, a week, or a lifetime in one of our urban deathtraps is
something I don't understand.

The pressures of city living make it impossible to look
anyone in the eye let alone permit yourself the kind of contact
and mutual caring necessary for sexual relationships to
flourish. I got through my day in the city with sunglasses on, a
form of blinding myself I think from my environment. I don't
feel like seeing the junkies on the corner or the freaks on the
bus, nor do I feel like looking at the bus driver who more than
likely is going to have something nasty to say about the fact that
I don't have my change ready. I try to get through my day
shutting out as much of the garbage on the streets as possible.
By what magic am I supposed to open my eyes at night and
look into those of a lover?

However, you can't shut everything out and things do seep
through. Most of what you are exposed to in the city just makes
you anxious. The men I know who work here are so filled with
anxiety about keeping their jobs (most of them are white collar
executives) and 'delivering the goods' (whatever that means)
that they forget half the time that they are alive. They're so
conditioned to living with anxiety that they just accept it. It
doesn't happen to me so much when I am with a man because I

282

am single and the men I see regard me as kind of a novelty, but my married friends tell me that half the time when they go to bed with their husbands they feel as if their vaginas are some kind of receptacle for the accumulation of all the frustrations of the day. When a man has to put up with the backbiting that goes on in an office all day, drink his way through lunch and spend the rest of the day 'wheeling and dealing' or 'being creative' how can you expect him to come home feeling like making love. And I shudder to think what people who are taxi drivers, policemen, construction workers or firemen must feel like. They risk their lives in a jungle for very little pay. If they are married with children, chances are their wives have to work too, to supplement the family income. Some of them have to hold extra jobs at night and with their time schedules and the pressure put on them just to survive, what happens, I wonder, to their capacity to feel warm and loving.

Now I know men have always had to struggle in order to survive. It's nothing new. But they haven't always had to struggle under such complex conditions where the whole quality of life is so dehumanized. Just try calling the telephone company to file a complaint. Or if you really want to feel like nothing try sending a letter back to a department store explaining that your bill is wrong. What you're doing is arguing with a computer. Some people spend their days sitting at a typewriter and drinking coffee that they get from a machine. It's a wonder that they remember about making love at all. If they can manage to recall that it's not just a mechanical act, but one that involves touching, smelling and feeling at its most intimate and human level, I don't know how they manage to do it.

I suppose I could go on forever with descriptions of how the human race has systematically destroyed sex with the construction of cities but I think I ought to mention one last thing and that is the lack of privacy in the city. Unless you are very rich you just can't afford to be alone. People live on top of one another. In an apartment building, especially the new modern variety, you are surrounded by neighbors and not very thick walls. You can be sure your neighbors will hear you having an argument as well as making love. If you share an apartment with your children I can tell you that will do plenty to inhibit you. They can hear everything. It's like making love in the middle of a public hallway.

It's no wonder more and more people are dropping out every

day. People have been saying for years that cities are nice places to visit but they wouldn't want to live there. Now they can add they wouldn't want to love there either.

E.S.
New York City

NEVER TOO LATE

I am a woman who has just had her forty-second birthday and I have had such a remarkable experience during the past year that I would like to share it with your readers. Although I was very well educated and graduated from college, even going on to take courses in graduate school in psychology and sociology, these were of no use in terms of my sexual adjustment.

I married a boy I knew while I was in school. Before we were married we did not have intercourse although we fondled each others' genitals and became very sexually aroused. Whenever I felt myself on the brink of orgasm through clitoral stimulation I stopped myself from coming because all the sexual literature I had read assured me that this was abnormal. The only normal way for a woman to come was through penile penetration. I assumed that once we were married and had intercourse regularly I would have vaginal orgasms through this method.

After marriage, although my husband stimulated me to the point of orgasm, I stopped myself from coming, holding back until he had entered me at which point I hoped to have the promised vaginal orgasm. However, since with his penis inside me the clitoral stimulation decreased rather than increased, I was never able to achieve satisfaction. This caused me much anxiety and distress.

I had read in Freud that women who were unable to have vaginal orgasms were immature, resentful of men and envious of their penises. I imagined all these things to be true of me and I felt a failure. I was too ashamed to discuss this with my husband or with the analyst we visited, not wanting them to discover my failing as a woman. Although I had always been highly sexed, masturbating often and easily sexually aroused by my husband, I began to avoid having sex with him because of my inability to have a vaginal orgasm. When we did have intercourse, I often faked my orgasm hoping to please him but feeling empty and unfulfilled myself. The only release I had was masturbation, which was usually followed by feelings of guilt.

Our marriage went on like this for many years. We stayed

284

together for companionship and for the sake of the child but our sex life was hopeless. He sensed my reluctance to have intercourse and felt hurt and rejected. Yet, I was just not able to tell him the truth. My few attempts at love affairs brought the same results. I gave up hope and thought I would never be able to have normal orgasm with a man.

Several years ago I read the Masters and Johnson report on their studies in sexuality, which revealed that there was no such thing as a vaginal orgasm – that basically women's orgasms were clitoral in origin – it was a simple biological fact. You can well imagine my relief when I realized that there was nothing wrong with me either biologically or psychologically. Furthermore just knowing that any means a woman uses to achieve orgasm is normal greatly lessened my guilt concerning masturbation.

Gradually I summoned up the courage to show the Masters and Johnson report to my husband and told him the truth about my sex misconceptions.

Although I believed what I had read, I still thought it was too late for us to change our habits. However, my husband suggested that we go back to where we had started many years ago. Instead of taking our clothes off and getting into bed he suggested that we stop having intercourse altogether.

He spent several nights on the sofa in our den. Some nights he didn't come home until quite late. We made dinner dates with each other and I began to look forward to seeing him. When he came home at night we began to kiss and fondle each other and I became sexually aroused. This happened several times and still we did not sleep with each other as he insisted that we continue with the experiment. Finally I became so aroused that I felt as if he was no longer my husband but a new lover. It was as if we had returned to our youth and I was filled with the old sexual longings. When we finally did make love, both of us were pent up and wild with excitement. After a brief period of clitoral love play, I let myself go and had an explosive orgasm. Since then, we've tried everything including cunnilingus. Finally, I was even able to have an orgasm with him inside me if there was adequate clitoral stimulation beforehand.

I am grateful to the new era of sexual liberation. Without the new attitudes I might have gone on for the rest of my life sexually frustrated and repressed, believing always that it was my fault.

However, I must say that I feel angry for all those wasted years. It seems totally illogical to me that Sigmund Freud, a man, as well as all the other male sexologists I read, should be the authorities on the orgasms which only women experience. I can only hope that with this new climate we are living in more and more women will be free to express themselves sexually rather than having such a deep sense of inferiority that they find it necessary to refer to outside sources for the 'right way' to enjoy sex. And speaking of outside sources I suppose I really can't condemn them all because where would I be without a most important one, an inventive husband?

Mrs. J.A.

As a woman and a therapist I am always gratified to read a letter like this. I agree that it is too bad so many of us were convinced for so long that the 'experts' knew more about our sexuality and what we should be enjoying than we did.

In 1967 after the findings of Masters and Johnson were published, a noted psychoanalyst, Alexander Lowen, in his book Love and Orgasm, *continued Freud's speculations of 1910 about female sexuality: 'I do not mean to condemn the practice of clitoral stimulation if a woman finds that this is the way she can obtain a sexual release ... However, I advise my patients against this practice since it focuses feelings on the clitoris and prevents the vaginal response. It is not a fully satisfactory experience and cannot be considered the equivalent of a vaginal response.'*

Unfortunately, myths and misconceptions die hard. – R.G.

NEITHER SERVANT NOR MASTER

Like so many couples we considered the sexual side of a happy married life as satisfactory if not especially exciting. We held the view, despite having read books on the subject, that an awful lot of bunkum was talked about sex and its benefits and pleasures exaggerated, and that those who indulged in strange experiments and weird practices were sick and those who wrote about them even sicker.

Then, after the birth of our child, my wife became ill. For almost five years we had no sex life as she went from hospital to hospital with periods at home. During this long, difficult and worrying period I resorted to masturbation. I indulged in a variety of fantasies to produce an erection, the most usual being young women in black raincoats and boots, and there were many times when I used a piece of black rubber. I think this was something I had done in early adolescence. I cannot say I really enjoyed it – indeed I despised myself for my lack of control – and I was more than glad from every point of view when at last, after an operation, my wife was cured.

We began married life again but had sex only rarely and carefully. Then something happened that changed everything. I took her away for a short fishing holiday to a cottage I had bought in the West Country. On our second night there was a thunderstorm and cattle broke into the garden from the field. Between us we drove them out but as we were putting back the fence, I noticed that for this emergency she had hastily put on over her nightdress a long, black plastic raincoat that belonged to her sister, fishing waders and a souwester. It was hardly a fashionable or sensual outfit, but seeing her in the light from the window produced the most extraordinary sexually stimulating effect on me. She was taken aback at my reaction – especially when I embraced her in the pouring rain. When we got back indoors she realized how eager I was and started to take off the raincoat but I would not let her. What followed surprised us both.

Our normal lovemaking following this became more frequent and more interesting for us both. It was as if we were really set on exploring a world newly opened to us.

A month later we went to the cottage again. We went to a party in the village and returned late and rather pleasantly merry. She wanted me to go straight to bed and made several obvious hints, but I refused, remembering that I needed to leave notes for the people who were coming to rent the cottage. I said I would be with her later. But a few minutes later she suddenly appeared dressed in the same boots, raincoat and souwester and – as she slowly but clearly demonstrated to me – nothing else. Absurd really, but it had, almost immediately, much the same effect as before. I suppose we were both a little drunk and so lost any remaining inhibitions and, when I started making advances, she insisted that, as she was 'dressed', I, too, should undress and then 'dress' the part so I should be dressed the way I was dressed the previous time. A sort of extraordinary charade followed when she helped pull on my waders and raincoat, both of us caressing and kissing and saying the strangest things to each other.

Ridiculous, I get embarrassed thinking about it. Both of us got into a very fevered state. The feel of rubber seemed to produce a much larger erection than I was accustomed to and, to my amazement, she was rubbing her clitoris fiercely on the thick rim at the top of my boots. This was the first time we had made love other than in bed and penetration, when it came, was more like an electric shock. The sensations were quite indescribable. I cannot analyze it – the smell and the feel and the creaking sound of the garments and the boots so inspired me (although 'inspired' is not the word) that I wanted to prolong and savor every minute.

To come together is a most wonderful experience and it was the first time it had really happened to us. It was like a seizure. Both of us were crying at the finish. It was an experience I never ever expected. It had such an effect on me that I keep remembering it. Instead of a 7 a.m. start home the following day it was nearly 4 p.m. when we left, both still bemused, and exhausted but happy. She said, 'I never believed it could be like that.'

Perhaps our experience is commonplace to others but I cannot quite understand why, now we are in our 40s, we are having a rather more violent, passionate and more active sex life than when we were first married. In a strange way I feel guilty about it. My elder brother, in whom I have confided, said we should be tapering off our sex life now, not increasing it, and as for the raincoat and boots – he thinks we are asking for physical and mental trouble.

A close friend, on the other hand, remarked that every man needed two women – a wife and mother and a courtesan who will cater for his sexual fantasies and that I am very fortunate in having both in one woman. My wife's view is that she would, she says, wear a horse blanket if it made me happy and such an exciting lover.

Where do we go from here? Is it going to take us to new heights of pleasure if I buy her a rubber nightdress I saw illustrated in a magazine? We do not want to reduce sex in our marriage to something that relies entirely on artificial stimulants. Are we going to find ourselves indulging in weird experiments like some I have seen described and illustrated in some of the magazines now available on some bookstalls? I would hate

288

to be thought 'kinky' in the way some of the couples are, and some of the practices described horrify us both.

She now has a pair of fashionable, wet-look, over-knee boots and a coat and hat to match which I think makes her look very sexy. So far she has not worn them for lovemaking although I think if I asked her she would. I have bought black rubber raincoats and boots which we now reserve for our purposes and she has also covered a pillow with a black plastic material which she places under her pelvis. This was a suggestion of hers. This has proved to be a marvelous aid which we often just use on its own.

I suppose I must accept (and be grateful) that certain materials have the power of sexual arousal for a man (and perhaps a woman too) but I am puzzled why these particular items? It is all so wildly improbable. My wife treats the matter with a certain quiet humor and I know enjoys seeing the effect she has on me simply by undressing and putting on a pair of boots and a raincoat. Best of all she enjoys making love. Her climax now is often almost frightening in its strength and passion – she cries out and leaves deep nailmarks on my back even through a raincoat – and while this is such a marvelous expression of mutual love, I am a little concerned that these physical desires could start to dominate our marriage. We both feel that sex must always be the servant of love and not its master.

H.C.

Sex doesn't have to be either the servant or master of love – in the ideal situation love and sex are companions, each helping to sustain the other without taking complete charge of the other.

You are both very lucky in having found this new stimulation to your lovemaking. The only slight drawback seems to be your unease about it 'getting out of hand'. Thus you found it necessary to get a certain amount of assurance about your activities from your brother and your friend.

Forget about labeling things and what other people are doing and enjoy yourselves – after all both of you are the only ones affected by your sex life and so the only ones who need approve of it. It will only go as far as you want it to go, there is no third force shaping it for you.

Using your earlier adolescent fantasies has helped to spice up your sex life, just as salt makes steak taste better so that you appreciate it more and want to eat more of it. But I doubt that you would ever fancy giving up the steak and only having salt. I think that your overall attitude to sex is on the level. – F.

GUTLESS LUST

I feel very sorry for people who are sexually hungry, or perhaps, I should say, oversexed. By that I mean people who indulge in intercourse every day of the week or even over three times a week. My wife and I do it about once every 10 days, when and where one never knows. You cannot plan these things, which is what a lot of people seem to do by going upstairs and getting dressed in a lot of claptrap such as rubber boots, raincoats, etc. No wonder some people become bored with sex. Then they think that they are going to find a new life by indulging in group sex or some other animal-like action. To me, these sort of things and watching other people make love is no more than gutless lust. This is not lovemaking in the true sense of the word. In fact, animals have better morals.

I hope these few words convey a little of my thoughts on today's permissive society, and no doubt what you have read up to now will make you think I am about 50. But I am 35 and my wife is 38.

A.D.

LEARN FROM ANIMALS

One often comes across phrases such as 'Such behavior would reduce us to the level of animals' and similar comments. In my nonsexual relations with humans I have frequently found that some of them would vastly benefit by 'acting like animals'. If a dog wags his tail, or growls, one does at least know that his intentions are not the very opposite.

Animals are also honest about their sex, and have no inhibitions, at least in the natural state. Some can even be chivalrous, like the boxer dog I know who always stood back with a wag of his tail, and let the bitch drink first, after mating. I can assure you that he had not been trained to do this.

Then there was the mare who would have nothing whatever to do with the stallion until her foal was brought where she could see it, and knew that it was alright. It certainly wouldn't do us any harm to learn from animals for a change!

E.W.

CONTINENTAL PREFERENCE

It seems strange that on the continent females with shaven pubic hair are considered indecent whereas in this country photographs displaying female pubic hair are considered almost pornographic. From a purely medical point of view what is the function of pubic hair?

D.G.

During the process of evolution much adaptation took place. The features which most aid survival are the ones which have tended to be perpetuated.

Hair on the skull helps to protect the skull from heat, cold and injury. Hair on the pubis does likewise and tends to act as a cushion during the often forceful movements of intercourse. However, it is by no means essential, and many people feel more comfortable without pubic hair, just as some people prefer to shave their heads. Depilation is a matter of habit, custom and personal preference.

Man has a relatively hairless body with localized hair at armpits and pubis. Many mammals are the reverse. A lion, for example, has a great mane, a tough hairy back and fine downy hair around the genitals. – F.

CITY SLICKERS

I have tried without success to sell my wife on the idea of removing her pubic hair. Since we all to some degree take notice of what society considers to be 'normal' my failure could be attributable to a lack of information as to how common the shaving of the pubis is. The lack of correspondence on the subject in Forum could indicate that either the practice is so common that no one bothers to mention it – they just go ahead and do it – or it is so unusual that few know of it. A letter from a doctor sometime ago in a magazine did, however, say that in his experience the shaved pubis was present in some three percent of his patients. I would greatly appreciate any information your medical correspondent can give on the incidence of this practice.

A.W.

Most doctors accept that the removal of pubic hair is quite normal, so much so that they can offer no facts, only impressions. In surgical and gynecological practice the presence or absence of pubic hair goes almost unnoticed. All pubic hair is removed prior to any pelvic surgery. Many women who attend the doctor for an internal examination or examination of the pubic area carry out depilation, but whether this is done to facilitate examination or whether it is the patient's usual custom is a matter for conjecture. The general impression is, however, that depilation is not carried out in the majority of cases – but fashions and fancies change so that depilation which might be quite common among 20–30 year-old girls in a city may be unusual among 30–40 year-old women in a rural area. – F.

NATURAL LOOK

No woman will pretend that pubic hair is either pretty or useful, and many would remove it if they believed it to be practical and, more important, normal.

Roman women, amongst others, considered that total depilation (i.e., plucking) was desirable 2000 years ago and it may be that English women would still consider it normal today, had the Roman occupation lasted longer, particularly now, when effective depilators exist.

It may be laziness on the average woman's part, since to avoid unpleasant 'stubble' she must depilate at least twice a week, and I doubt that any of us are sufficiently brave to approach a firm specializing in electrolytic depilation, to remove the problem for good.

Personally, I agree with both the idea and the practice of depilation, which apart from appearance, simplifies marital hygiene, and apparently provides greater visual stimulation, but until your disclosures, I thought I was exceptional in my views. It is this feeling of abnormality which results in your medical correspondent reporting a very low incidence observed by his colleagues, since I'm sure that other women like myself, have delayed non-essential visits to their G.P.'s until they have grown sufficient covering to look natural.

I'm sure those women who agree with me will thank you most heartily for throwing some light into an area surrounded (if not by hair) by mystery.

Mrs. J.C.

THE SHOW MUST GO ON

I have recently bought a new device for fitting over the battery-operated vaginal stimulator. This consists of a rubber tube large enough for the penis and resembling the vagina. I find this a superb invention and, by continually switching on and off, stimulation can be kept going for 20 minutes without difficulty.

One of my pleasures as a voyeur is to visit strip clubs and masturbate quietly under a coat for the two-hour show, finally ejaculating at the end. One club, in particular, puts on a marvelous show, and the girls show their shaved and unshaved vaginas, sometimes fully open. They also simulate masturbation and, generally, it is obvious that they are partially worked up as shown by their distended labias. It is quite obvious in a room full of men that most of them have erections which plainly make them uncomfortable. I would think at least a quarter of the audience masturbate to ejaculation while watching.

It is strange though that, while it is all right for the naked girl on the stage to stimulate her clitoris, it is not considered right for the men in the audience to masturbate openly, and some of the strippers rather resent a man fondling himself during her performance. In some cases I have known them to stop the show because men were sitting with only one hand visible. (This does not, of course, apply to all the girls, and once a particularly sexy stripper complained that her performance must have gone off as no one was masturbating in the front row!)

During showings of blue films, I have had no hesitation in openly masturbating in front of the assembled audience (usually six) and in every case the others have followed suit.

I suppose we are still suffering from the Victorian idea that masturbation is an unforgivable sin.

S.T.

STIMULATION TECHNIQUE

My wife and I have been happily married for over ten years now, but over the last couple of years or so we found that our sexual interest in each other was waning. We are both in our middle 30s, and although we realized that a certain amount of our passion was bound to cool with time and familiarity, we decided to try to revitalize our relationship.

Oddly enough, we were both a bit shy and inhibited about discussing the situation at first – when I broached the subject to my wife she staunchly maintained that she found sex with me just as exciting as she ever had, though her body told me differently. And, to my surprise, I found myself assuring my wife that I found her just as desirable as ever, although I had fully intended to discuss the falling-off of our mutual sexual interest!

Later, we loosened up a bit and both admitted that we didn't feel as intensely as we once had and had lied to save the other person's feelings. I think that very often in a marriage, people cover up their true feelings and desires (or lack of them) in order not to hurt or shock the other person. This is a great mistake, and can lead to years of frustration and unfulfillment.

For instance, one evening my wife asked me what she could do at that particular moment which would excite me most. I'd had a couple of drinks, and without stopping to think I blurted out the one word, 'masturbate'. 'It's funny you should say that,' my wife replied, 'because at this moment, it's the one thing that would excite *me* most.' We were in our bedroom, and she then proceeded, quite slowly, to take her clothes off, caressing the progressively exposed parts of her body as she did so. By the time she was down to her panties, we were both very keyed up. She took them off (again, very slowly) and began to masturbate. I desperately wanted her at this point, and said so, but she said it would be better and more tantalizing if I stayed where I was, watching. This I did until she reached a climax, then mounted her and swiftly had one of my own, Since then, we have frequently made use of this stimulation technique. Surely, I'm not alone among men in finding the sight of a masturbating woman exciting?

W.L.

Obviously not, since it is such a frequent theme in pornographic films and photos.

Because of the double standard of sexuality men frequently find it difficult to accept that women, too, are sexual beings. Observing a woman in the act of masturbation excited many men because it is a graphic demonstration of the reality that women not only masturbate but derive pleasure from it. – H.G.

UNDERSTANDING WIFE

I am 24, good looking and 5 feet 4 inches tall; I can pass as a female in public.

Some three years ago I advertised in a magazine for a friend to share my interests, and started writing to one man. We just wrote about gowns, lingerie, and so on. I sent him a picture of myself in women's clothes, and he wrote back asking to visit me.

The day he was due, I spent all morning getting ready. It took me three hours to make up my face and get into a low-cut evening gown (over a bust form, waist cincher, and padded girdle). My heart pounded as the time of his arrival approached.

He was amazed when he saw me. 'You're bloody fantastic,' he said.

I passed the evening in a state of grand sexual excitement. After a time, he passed me a parcel and asked me to put on the garments it contained – black nylons, and pink suspender belt, bra, and panties, with a magnificent full length filmy black negligee.

This lovely lingerie had been bought for me by a man! I was so excited by his total acceptance of me that I had an erection. But I was not prepared for what followed – he performed fellatio on me. I realized that he was a homosexual and I was bitterly ashamed at what had happened.

I married a very pretty girl who did not know of my transvestism – until one evening she discovered traces of mascara on my eyelashes. It was impossible to attempt an explanation – I had to tell her the whole story. She was shocked. We left the matter pending until one weekend I asked if I could dress for her. She agreed, and I went upstairs, returning in a low-cut gown, and 4 inch heels, full make-up, and a blond wig.

She never had a bigger shock in her short life!

'Why did you marry me? Wouldn't you prefer a man?' she wanted to know. But the ice was broken when she asked how much I had paid for my gown and inquired about my bust form.

Since then we have agreed that I can dress up about once every four months. She helps me dress and styles my wigs, and has made me several gowns – in fact she often borrows odds and ends from my wardrobe.

Our sex life is only moderate, as I would much prefer to dress as a woman for intercourse. Although she will not allow this, though, she does help me reach a climax by telling me how nice a certain gown looks on me. In short, she goes along to save our marriage.

G.K.

FEMALE TRANSVESTISM

So many men write in about getting sexually excited dressing in women's clothes – but what about girls dressing as men?

I am a lesbian and always wear trousers, as do most of us, but this is just comfortable and natural. However, on other occasions I go further and wear trousers that are very butch and put things down the front of them so it looks as if I have a penis. This excites me terribly and very soon I have to masturbate.

I'm not sexually shy but have never told anyone about this and don't do it very often as I am happy with my girlfriend.

T.L.

Mild forms of female transvestism occur very frequently, but your particular case is rare.

Both hetero- and homosexual women indulge in dressing up in male attire and enjoy the sensation of being treated as a man. This form of transvestism is a natural expression of our bisexual nature in the first place. But it is also a protest against the persisting gender roles attributed to the male and the female by society. We are, at the present time, in a transitory period where gender identity is beginning to be less fixed than before. Because of this, female transvestism has decreased in frequency, compared with 40 or 50 years ago.

If you are very young, you will probably grow out of your compulsion quite naturally. At present you identify with the male to such an extent that you would wish for a penis. This is in fact not only a case of gender but of sex identification with men. – F.

UNISEX IS SHAM

Some months ago a magazine ran an article on transvestism and a hefty batch of letters came pouring in. Some men spoke highly of understanding wives who let them 'dress up' in their undies and stockings in the privacy of their homes. Others were pompous and self-righteous, trying to make it clear that their desire to don women's clothes had nothing to do with, God forbid, homosexuality.

No one touched on the fashion etiquette that makes it all right for women to dress up in traditional men's clothes (trouser suits, leather boots, button-down shirts) while keeping men's gear (frilly shirts apart) on a predictably 'masculine' path. The so-called unisex trend is really a sham. Look-alike couples end up wearing trousers, never skirts.

The 'little boy look' keeps popping up for women to copy and no one thinks of that as transvestism. But any man trying to apply the 'little girl look' to himself would encounter social ridicule. Society allows females to express all kinds of sex whims through their clothes. Women don't have to rely on their husbands' benevolent natures to allow them to wear Carnaby Street ties and caps in the sanctuary of their bedrooms. They can sport them in broad daylight and be considered smart dressers too.

These socially accepted channels are closed to men. Those who have an urge to vary their rigidly sex-defined clothes are usually forced to do so in private.

This double standard must be scrapped. It's ridiculous to think that our society only allows Scotsmen and monks to wear skirts and dresses, so long as they can safely be described as national custom or religious garb.

When we reach the point where one sex isn't regarded as below or above another, but possessing equally worthwhile virtues, then the stringent rules about men's clothes should finally fade away.

Mrs. F.A.

MASTURBATION FEARS

I am a schoolboy of 17, and am extremely worried about my sex life. About three years ago I met a boy of my own age at school, and got to be very friendly with him. We used to stroke each other through our trouser pockets until finally one day we went to the school lavatories and undressed each other in a cubicle. We masturbated each other simultaneously. We enjoyed this immensely and continued to do this many times, rubbing our penises together, and squeezing each other's penises.

297

But we went no further, stopping as soon as semen began to come out.

A year ago I left that school and since then have had no other such relationships. I assure you I am not homosexual. I now masturbate about once a week and enjoy it at the time, but feel guilty about it. I cannot speak about it to my father, and dare not go to a doctor for fear that my parents will be informed.

I am worried about the size of my penis which is only 5¾ inches on erection. I have heard that it ought to be at least two inches longer. Could I, with only the amount of playing with penises that I did with the boy, have contracted any disease, and is it harmful for me to masturbate?

M.Y.

Few boys reach your age without some sort of 'homosexual' experience such as you describe and virtually every healthy adolescent boy masturbates. Kinsey found that it was the ones who did not who were 'abnormal' in the sense that, unless their reasons for abstaining were religious, they generally were of poor health and low sex drive. Your masturbation is only harmful because you worry about it and make it into a problem.

Neither masturbation, nor mutual masturbation with another boy, can have had the slightest effect on the size of your penis. The Forum Penile Survey showed that the average length of the erect penis is about 6¼ inches – half an inch longer than yours, and you are probably not yet fully developed. Only about 4% of men have the 8-inch penis you have heard is 'normal'! – F.

MARRIED CALL GIRL

My husband's salary as a civil servant is totally inadequate to sustain our marriage on a decent and humane level, but he is not fully aware of this fact because I handle all the finances in our family. The above is a brief and simple explanation of the fact that on one and sometimes more afternoons per week, while my husband is at work and my children are in school, I sleep with men for money. My husband is not aware of this fact and neither should he be. Since I pay all the bills, he has no idea what I spend.

I was introduced to the life of a part-time call girl by my girlfriend, who is also married. The men whom I meet are usually businessmen or tourists, who are obviously wealthy. Despite my work as a 'prostitute', I truly love my husband and would not do what I am doing if I didn't love him. With the extra income I earn, we are able to live comfortably and I don't have to save money from my food bill (as so many housewives do) in order to buy shoes or clothes for our children.

Before I got involved in this sort of work, I, like most other people, thought that women who slept with men for money were the lowest of the low. The truth is, many of the part-time call girls are decent, honest human beings, and most of them are married. They provide a needed service and I feel it is an honest 'profession' which is more than I can say for some men who are in the so-called honorable professions. I've never had a client who was dissatisfied and who felt he didn't get his money's worth. How many professional or businessmen can truly make that statement?

My biggest problem is my conscience. Am I truly hurting my husband (despite the fact that he is unaware of my activities) and myself by continuing to do what I'm doing? My conscience has been bothering me for some time now and I just had to have someone to discuss it with.

Mrs. A.C.

A 'NEW ME'

I was extremely curious about the letter from the housewife who supplements her husband's meager salary through part-time work as a call girl.

Despite the fact that her husband knows nothing of this, she should not suffer from the guilt which was apparent in her letter. I speak more out of experience than sympathy as I have been involved in a similar activity for the past year. However, my situation cannot be compared to hers. My husband has a responsible position and his salary is more than adequate for us both.

I would never have thought of doing such a thing until a close friend confided in me that during the afternoons she took in several clients. I must admit that I was rather shocked, but at the same time I was intrigued. My life was then rather boring. My husband spends much time away on business and the general round of coffee afternoons with other women in my circle was becoming more and more intolerable.

Consequently, in a state of great excitement I went along one afternoon to the flat which my friend keeps in town. After a few drinks I didn't care too much about my conscience and waited with anticipation for the doorbell to ring. My first 'customer' was a handsome, foreign business man. He was refined and beautifully mannered and I found myself drifting into a fantasy in which I was a glamorous courtesan acclaimed by all men, shunned by all women. Since then I have seen this man whenever he has been in London. He does not know my real name or that I am married. He is always grateful to me and leaves me an expensive present each time he departs.

There have been many others like him. Any man who I feel does not treat me with respect, I refuse to entertain a second time. Thus I have built up a clientele of men whom I enjoy as well as serve.

Of course, my husband knows nothing of my activities but he has noticed a change in me. He admits that a year ago he thought that I was becoming rather dull but since then, a marked change has come over me; consequently our marriage has become much more exciting. My 'clients' have taught me a great deal about lovemaking and I am able to implement this knowledge in my marital sex life. They also provide me with a contrast to my husband and I have come to appreciate his devotion more than ever.

Initially, I did suffer from conscience, but feel that what my husband does not know cannot harm him and the benefit he derives from the 'new me' seems fair justification for my deception.

S.R.

In the research I conducted before writing my books, The Call Girl, *a social and psychoanalytic study, and* The Elegant Prostitute, *I found that women who make such a choice are highly motivated by strong feelings of worthlessness and intense hostility.*

Both of the letter writers may be rationalizing acting out these fantasies, if the letters themselves are not fantasies. Many 'respectable' women often have prostitution fantasies based on their feelings that sex has to be dirty to be enjoyable. – H.G.

CURE FOR INFIDELITY

Just over a year ago I found out that my wife had been unfaithful to me with a man she worked with. There was a terrible row but eventually all was forgiven. Two weeks later I discovered that she was again having an extramarital relationship. Naturally, I was very upset, but because of the deep love I had for her, instead of going off and wrecking our marriage I tried to save it by attempting to discover the reasons for her infidelity.

I spent hours questioning her, and eventually found out that although she was perfectly happy with our lovemaking and satisfied with my performance, twice a week (our average) was just not enough for her. It was obvious that her sexual appetite was greater than mine.

Finding the reason for her infidelity was much easier than finding the solution. I found myself wondering what she was doing when she wasn't with me. I started imagining all sorts of things which, because I am not normally a jealous person, began to put a strain on our marriage.

We decided to have a long weekend in London and during our second evening we met an American who was obviously attracted to my lovely wife. Later, after a lot of drinks, we all went back to his hotel for a nightcap. While he was out of the room I asked my wife if she would like me to leave them alone. She said she would, so I made my excuses when the American returned and left.

Two hours later my wife returned to our hotel fully expecting another row. Much to her amazement I was quite happy with what had happened. We discussed the affair and her feelings and she told me that she wished I had stayed to watch her being made love to by the American. I admitted that I would have enjoyed watching them.

It was then that the solution to our problem became apparent. To satisfy her greater sexual appetite, we decided to try group sex and in particular, troilism with another man, and also wife-swapping.

Well, we have tried both over the past few months, and what a difference it has made to our lives! I now have no fear of my wife going astray, and she is radiant and seems more beautiful than ever. Our sex life has improved enormously by discussing our 'meetings' afterwards. We have found a new basis of life just out of discussing things from male genitals to the permutations three people can make.

With couples, we prefer to retire to different rooms, then later we find it more rewarding and stimulating to discuss in detail what has taken place.

In our case, though we took a tremendous risk with our marriage in getting involved in group sex, we both realize now that for us it was right. Our love for each other is now stronger than ever.

J.K.

DRAWING THE LINE

Exchanging partners seems to be a fairly widely reported topic in readers' letters. In my experience there is a wide, though not unbridgable, gap between discussing the subject as a means of sexual stimulation, and putting it into practice.

On a number of occasions my wife and I have talked about intercourse with other partners as a prelude to our own lovemaking. We both found that it was an exciting exchange of ideas which we investigated in great detail, but neither of us ever seriously considered translating our mutual fantasies in fact. It was therefore entirely by chance and a fortuitous chain of circumstances which involved us in group sex. Despite the fact we were carried away with the experiment on a physical plane, we are by no means convinced that we would want to repeat it.

We entertained a friend and his wife at dinner one evening and all had rather too much to drink, which gave free rein to a conversation that soon became all-embracing, on the subject of sex and our personal experiences both before and since our marriages. But this alone did no more than create the atmosphere in which we could talk and behave in a less inhibited manner than usual. In fact, the subject of sex had been supplanted by an investigation of how to keep fit – a topic close to our interests as we are all over 40. My wife, a keen exponent of physical culture, demonstrated a certain body movement to loosen the lower vertebrae which necessitated the lifting of her skirt to her waist. The exposure of her body, albeit clad in rather matronly silk panties, caused our friend immediately to have an erection which he made little attempt to conceal; indeed he admitted to this demonstration of his arousal with a jocular reference to the size and shape of my wife's bottom. The uninhibited atmosphere occasioned by the wine and conversation relaxed our normal composure, and my wife's revelation of her body, and the comment which it had already occasioned, soon prompted all four of us to demonstrate our prowess in various forms of exercise.

The two women removed their dresses and performed in their underwear, while my friend and I stripped to our shorts. The mutual excitement soon burst all bounds of propriety and my friend, seizing an opportunity when my wife was on her back on the floor with her legs over her head, kneeled before her and pulled her panties down to her knees. She invited him to take them right off which he did, simultaneously, as he bent forward between her thighs and kissed her intimately. I was extremely aroused by the sight of my wife in this situation and it was obvious that both she and my friend's wife were ready for further experiment. I soon had the other woman's pants down, placing her on my lap on the armchair. It was but an instant before I had penetrated her. We sat quite still and watched while my friend put my wife on the sofa, removed her bra, and began to make passionate love, eventually pushing his body between the thighs and entering her. The sight of my wife wriggling and twisting in the extreme of passion on another man's penis, the round curves of her bottom beneath his searching hands and, above all, the sight of his shaft moving in and out removed the last trammel of restraint on my part and my friend's wife. We had a mutually delightful few moments of frenzied lovemaking before achieving orgasm.

The aftermath was less satisfactory. As the passion subsided and the wine relaxed its hold on us, we became wary of each other. The joking was forced and the moment when my friend retrieved my wife's panties and put them on for her, which should have rounded off the evening neatly and pleasantly, was embarrassing to all. We felt that we had revealed too much of ourselves to the others, that as a group of longstanding acquaintance we had jeopardized our relationship to the point where we could never again be relaxed in each other's company. When our friends left, my wife and I felt no inclination to make love to each other. We were guarded and ill at ease and felt that by succumbing to our desires, we had totally betrayed each other. For some weeks after we were unable to communicate on anything but a day-to-day level, and our own lovemaking ceased altogether.

This is not an attempt to draw a moral for others. Men and women of our generation are deeply imbued with sexual prejudice and the guilt occasioned by our upbringing is too close to the surface to ignore. I suspect that deep within us is the lurking desire to repeat the experiment as we both, albeit with many misgivings, found it exciting and novel. We – neither of us – dare admit this to the other, however, and the rebuilding of our own love and respect for each other will take some time.

We have not seen our friends since but our two wives have been in contact by phone and it appears that all is not lost in that direction either. Incidentally, they have established that neither of them is pregnant so in that respect at least we have been lucky. It is said that no two people can damage each other in their lovemaking provided whatever they do is mutually stimulating to both. It is well to draw the line, however, when the stimulation oversteps the bounds of conduct they have subscribed to for the whole of their lives.

F.T.

LEG FIXATION

Since adolescence I have been sexually stimulated by the female leg. Now, in my mid-40s, I am still as baffled by this as I was in my youth. Perhaps the behaviorists could explain this in terms of stimulus/response and the effect of early sexual excitation in the presence of an object belonging to one's mother, or another female. But why should one be predisposed to female underwear and not combs, pillowcases or other arbitrary objects? And what is this strange aesthetic element which enters into the process? Not just any leg will excite, but only one with the right amount of curves. Not any stocking – a woolen pair would hardly warrant a glance – but a sheer well-suspendered pair will.

I first became aware of the thrill of leg gazing during early adolescence. At that time, at the end of the War, I was evacuated from London and living in the country. Puberty was a period of upheaval for me. I was particularly disturbed by the effect my foster mother had on me. She was a cheerful, easygoing woman (unlike my mother). One of her habits was to put on her shoes and stockings in the kitchen.

At first she was unaware of the effect she was having on me, but after a time she must have noticed my flushed face and intense expression and so we went through this little game of her slowly putting on her stockings, pretending not to notice me gripping my stiff penis through my pocket and me pretending not to notice her. Sometimes when her husband was out in the evening she would doze in a chair with her skirts deliberately high up on her thighs. I would sit opposite gazing over the top of my book and silently masturbating. I wonder if she knew what effect she was having on me, and if she could have done me more good by seducing me.

Up until my period of military service I was still very shy of girls. During this time I was battling with strong guilt feelings about masturbation, but still wanking all over the place; in cinemas, theatres, dance halls; anywhere where I saw an attractive girl and a sexy pair of legs. My period in the army found me relaxing and sorting myself out sexually. In my early 20s I had relationships with several girls and my fetishism became much less significant. Later, when I married, my fixation for the female leg all but disappeared. This was the time I was busy with the new home, new social contacts and later, children. My sexuality was manifesting itself in a direct person-to-person relationship.

It was when my wife took to wearing tights that I began to realize how much I missed the accidental leg show involved in her night and morning undressing. It also meant that the casual half-dressed lovings were over. (One can't make love to a partner wearing tights unless they have holes in the wrong places!) This, coupled with my wife's increasing lack of interest in sex over the years, made me take to buying girlie magazines again and tossing off as in bachelor days. Later I managed to substitute my wife for the magazines. She had 'gone off' intercourse but she didn't mind occasionally sitting watching television dressed in high heels, sheer nylons, bra and panties.

'If you get so excited, why don't you work yourself off?' she coolly said. So we got involved in this strange ritual of us both gazing at different things; she looking remote and lovely, and me hot and horny, working away at my cock.

In recent years we have drifted into an unexciting routine of a weekly fuck, with occasional periods of activity after a party perhaps. Occasionally we have a leg show and our marriage drifts on, a victim of habit and circumstances. If our relationship was only closer and warmer I feel sure that my interest in 'just legs' would have disappeared.

E.C.

CAREZZA

I am interested in the age-old practice of carezza, which to anyone adept is the most satisfying union between male and female. Carezza is, of course, the prolonging of sexual intercourse, and couples can perform it in any of the standard positions.

It is really a duel between mind and body, and though when first practiced the body takes control, repeated attempts will bring a high standard of efficiency and a great reward.

The erect penis thrust fully into the vagina, the partners then kiss and caress with hands and lips but through willpower keep the lower portions of their bodies still. The male makes no thrusting movements, but concentrates on keeping a full erection. This gives rise to a voluptuous feeling that cannot be described, and if the technique is mastered can be prolonged for almost an hour.

Eventually, still without any pelvic or hip movements, the male will have a tremendous orgasm which will immediately trigger off his partner. I offer this as an interesting suggestion to those who have tried everything else.

E.N.

CRIMEAN TARTARS' METHOD

I feel I must make a small protest against your E.N. letter.

Actually, the form of lovemaking E.N. describes is not carezza (otherwise known as coitus reservatus) but a method of coupling known as the Crimean Tartars' method, because it has been practiced for centuries by the Tartars of the Crimea.

For the greater part of their performance, carezza and the Crimean Tartar coincide, but there is one extremely important difference between them. The Crimean Tartar culminates in orgasm for both partners, while carezza is completed without either partner having an orgasm.

Dr. Alice Stockham of Chicago, who first advocated carezza as a method of birth control at the end of the last century, described it in the book she wrote about it, thus: 'Manifestations of tenderness are indulged in without physical or mental fatigue ... Once the necessary control has been acquired the two beings are fused and reach sublime spiritual joy ... If love is mutual, and if intercourse is sufficiently prolonged, it affords complete satisfaction without emission or orgasm. After an hour the bodies relax, spiritual delight is increased and new horizons are revealed with the renewal of strength.'

Whether or not this sublime end is achieved – and it is very doubtful even when the couple claim to be perfect exponents of carezza – it is nevertheless a practice extremely dangerous to mental and physical health, particularly for the man, and for these reasons.

For the man to sustain his erection for an hour or more, it automatically means that there is prolonged congestion of the various parts of the sexual anatomy involved and a terrific buildup of tension.

In the man the seminal vesicles will be flooded to bursting point with seminal fluid and the prostate will be energetically producing prostatic fluid. If he does not have an orgasm during which these vessels are emptied of their fluids, they will remain under abnormal, unnatural pressure after the lovemaking has been broken off. If this is repeated with any frequency, sooner or later the organs are going to be damaged, with the resulting impairment of health.

For both partners the buildup of tension which only orgasm can effectively relieve will in time give rise to acute pyschological frustrations.

Dr. Stockham's medical contemporaries attacked her vigorously on these grounds, and their observations are just as valid today. Carezza should be avoided at all costs.

Because the Crimean Tartar ends with orgasm for both parties, it avoids the dangers of carezza. Nevertheless, though it produces highly voluptuous sensations throughout the coupling, and the eventual orgasm-sensations are out of this world, it is very taxing physically, and should only be indulged in infrequently – saved, perhaps, for 'special occasion' lovemaking.

R.C.

PILL POWER

I wonder how many married men are in the position I now find myself in? I'm 43 and my wife is 40. We've been married 21 years and have three children. My wife had a strict upbringing and when we first got married, she was very frightened of sex. She didn't enjoy it and wanted as little of it as possible.

We never discussed her reasons for disliking sex. In fact, we never talked about the subject. As a release, I would either masturbate or else find myself a prostitute, which always left me with a feeling of disgust.

As far as I was concerned, my wife was frigid and I felt I had to make the best of a bad situation. She was a good mother and outside of sex, a devoted wife. Yet, because I was deprived of a normal physical relationship with her, I was obsessed with sex. I was always thinking about it and very often, when we were in bed together, I had to control myself in order not to 'rape' her.

In time, our marriage cooled down and it became a marriage in name only. I suppose we remained together because of the children.

Then, in 1965, my wife discovered the Pill. Before that, we had been using, infrequently as it was, the condom which I had found most unsatisfactory, so far as pleasure was concerned. With the introduction of the Pill, a most unbelievable transformation took place in my wife. After 16 years of lying dormant, so to speak, she suddenly acquired a sexual appetite that amazed me. I could hardly believe it was the same woman in my bed. After all those wasted years, the truth finally spilled out. She was in terror of getting pregnant and had only wanted two children. When she accidentally became pregnant with the third, despite the fact that we had been using condoms, she lost faith in contraceptives and felt that the only sure way of not having any more children was to have sex as infrequently as possible.

However, after reading about the Pill for a number of years and knowing women who had been on it, she felt safe for the first time in our marriage. As a result, she was able to let her true nature take over and she discovered to her and my delight that she got great pleasure from sexual intercourse.

At first, I could not have been happier. This was what I always wanted in a wife. During her first year on the Pill, we enjoyed a happy relationship for the first time in our marriage. However, a most ironic situation began to develop. Apparently trying to make up for all those lost years, my wife's sexual needs began to increase more than my capabilities. I had heard that a woman is at her 'ripest' in her middle and late 30s, but I never dreamt that I would one day find myself in a situation where my wife wanted sex more than I did. Yet, this is exactly what has happened. As her appetite increased, she became more demanding and even aggressive. She would begin the preliminaries at times when I was either not in the mood or else exhausted at the end of a long day's work. I discovered to my discomfort that the more demanding and aggressive she became, the more difficult it was for me to get an erection. She just could not understand that man is an aggressive animal and as soon as a woman takes over his role as the aggressor, he is no longer able to function properly.

This is compounded by the fact that I'm not as virile as I was in my teens and 20s. What a stupid mistake of nature to increase the female libido at a time when her mate's virility has long passed its peak.

R.W.

THE MALE AND THE PILL

As a marriage guidance counselor I'm surprised how little attention has been given to the psychological side effects of the Pill. The relatively minute physical hazards and/or discomfort produced by oral contraceptives have been blown up and examined from every possible angle until hardly a day passes without some press comment on the subject. But the easy assumption that the Pill has helped countless marriages achieve sexual harmony still prevails while the possibility that the reverse might occur at times never gets a proper airing, at least not publicly. However in some of my recent experiences with troubled couples I've noticed a few negative repercussions.

One type of problem arises when a husband is not highly sexed. Before his wife went on the Pill it would often seem as if it was she who restricted their sex life because of a wish to avoid pregnancy or a repugnance for using messier forms of contraception. At the time the husband saw himself in the 'standard' role of a man trying to make love to a woman who sometimes rejects his advances. In his mind he regarded himself as the more highly sexed of the two (as he believes it should be) while subconsciously he might have been very grateful for his wife's apparent lack of ardor.

But once she is on the Pill the moment of truth comes. She,

free of pregnancy fears, rediscovers the joys of lovemaking while he finds that he cannot keep pace with her desires. She becomes impatient and demanding. He starts worrying about his manhood and potency, feeling as if he's there just to 'service' her needs. The Pill has unearthed the sham of their previous lovemaking, exposing the game both were playing. Now they face each other with open eyes, not liking what they see.

Another difficulty arises when the husband starts getting jealous because his wife has the same sexual 'freedom' (i.e. sex without pregnancy) as he has. Many men still believe in the double standard and knowing that their wives have acquired the same sort of sexual possibilities as they have makes them angry. Sometimes they use any excuse they can to get their wives off the Pill so that they can 'keep them in line'.

Women who start marriages while taking the Pill might create other anxieties in their males. Some men interpret it as a physical and emotional passport to their wives' independence and they resent it. There was a time when a man wanting to keep his wife at home could impregnate her, thus forcing her into the mother/housewife situation whether she liked it or not. It was considered a way of making a woman 'settle down', While he longs for children, hearth and home she gulps down her daily pill, sets out into the world and there's nothing he can do about it.

When these difficulties arise it is important for the couple to understand that the Pill hasn't really caused any of these problems; it has just set the conditions for exposing existing differences both in physical and emotional temperament. Such people should try to recognize their spouse's attitudes, making an effort to meet each other's new demands with gentleness and sympathy, not immediately withdrawing with a 'let's keep things as they are' attitude.

Husbands should try to understand that their wives' sexual liberation is not a threat to their own sexuality. Wives should take it easy for a while, appreciating their husband's sensitivity to the changing situation. By acknowledging with frankness any unease that develops in their relations a couple should be able to combine sex and the Pill, producing a better love life – a recipe that seems to be working well for many Pill-takers.

Mrs. R.A.

UNRESPONSIVE

My fiancé and I began sleeping together over a year ago. I still enjoy his lovemaking and we really have great times. What bothers me is that I don't get worked up now. Before I went on the Pill I used to get 'wet' very quickly. Now I'm almost always dry till he enters me. Is there any reason why the Pill should result in my being dry and if so how can I solve it naturally?

Physical contact with someone I like usually sets me on fire, but with my fiancé this somehow doesn't happen. Usually I'm hypersensitive and the slightest touch has me in giggles. How can I make myself feel more responsive to his caresses? It's not that I'm too tense or trying too hard. I've tried to control my hypersensitivity but it just doesn't work. Also, is it usual for lovemaking to become routine and yet be enjoyable?

It is very difficult for me to reach an orgasm now. We've only achieved it three times and after more and more effort and only by oral-genital stimulation. It upsets me when I almost come, but don't, and it ruins that night for me. My fiancé and I have read, discussed and tried everything we could think of, but it hasn't helped. Both of us want me to come, otherwise I keep on feeling tense and he feels selfish.

Miss A.P.

I think you ought to discuss your difficulty with your doctor, because recently there has been evidence to show that the Pill can affect the sexual desire of some women although the cause is more probably psychological. A change to another type of Pill may be necessary.

It is difficult to suggest how you can make yourself feel more responsive to your boyfriend's caresses. I'm wondering whether you haven't yourself given a clue as to why you react as you do, when you say 'Physical contact with someone I like can set me on fire, but my fiancé doesn't'!

Ticklishness, incidentally, is a sort of defense mechanism. One theory is that it occurs under conditions which one unconsciously thinks of as an attack, but cannot treat as such, for various reasons. One might speculate that actually you don't like, or resent, your fiancé's caresses, but can hardly admit this even to yourself. So instead of simply pushing him away, as at some level you may want to do, you react with ticklishness. If this happens with other men it could indicate a fear of sex or close contact. If it only happens with your fiancé perhaps your body is trying to tell you something and you might need to take its message seriously. – F.

ANY OTHERS LIKE ME?

As a 48-year-old woman married for 30 years, I feel that my experience might be of some help to other couples.

I come from a large working-class family in London's East End, where although the surroundings were dirty and uncouth, and foul language common, a very Victorian attitude was maintained on the subject of sex. My parents were very narrow-minded, although I was one of 15 children. I was taught that it was a woman's place to do her duty and obey. When I married at 18, I soon accepted the attitude of my parents; once a week sex, just remaining on my back until my husband satisfied himself. As we did not wish to have a family he practiced coitus interruptus.

After 12 years of this Saturday night monotonous sex life, my husband slipped up, and I became pregnant. Following the birth of my baby, once again it was back to the old routine, only I was more scared of another baby, and insisted he was more careful. We tried practicing birth control with pessaries, and condoms, but my husband disliked either method, and went back to coitus interruptus.

After frustrations, dissatisfactions, and numerous rows over my reluctance to have sex, my husband drifted off and started going out with other women for a while. Whether he gained any experience from these wanderings or not, I shall never know, but some time later he suggested to me he would like to have sex again, this time withdrawing much earlier and finishing himself off by performing what I now know to be cunnilingus. He claimed that by satisfying himself in this manner instead of waiting until the last second before he came off, there was no chance of my becoming pregnant again.

Although I was shocked at this suggestion, I wanted to try and mend our marriage and agreed. With butterflies in my stomach I waited for him to do this to me. Within seconds of his mouth making contact with me, however, all my earlier fears disappeared, my feelings were indescribable and within two minutes for the first time, after 15 years of marriage, I had an orgasm. My husband also climaxed, and my thighs became his pillow for the night. We slept soundly.

This experience changed our lives completely. I allowed him to do this every time we had sex. Gradually however, I began to withdraw from my husband earlier each time and invite him to suck me. Each time this happened, my pleasure increased, and I began having multiple orgasms waiting for my husband to climax. Eventually, coitus was no longer the foreplay and whenever my husband felt like sex he automatically carried it out orally.

Since then, having no fear of becoming pregnant, I have slowly become sexually awake. I no longer lie passive and submitting to my husband; but have gradually become the aggressor, dominating him and making him submit to my desires. I started to force him to suck me off. He never objected and our roles were reversed. It has become my turn to be the boss in bed, and he lies on his back whilst I crouch over his face making him kiss me.

Now that I have complete domination over my husband, I make him perform in this manner at least four times a week, and kiss my vagina every night and morning before leaving for work. I have even made him perform in our motor caravan in a public car park, deliberately leaving off my pants before we went shopping.

I recently asked my husband if he would like to resume sex in the normal way, as I am now in the menopause. We did, but neither of us were completely satisfied. There was no satisfaction, only disappointment and we resumed cunnilingus, our great thrill.

Recently I asked my husband why it was he preferred to do this instead of normal sex. I was pleasantly surprised to discover that it was the smell and taste of my glandular secretions that turned him on; once he had started to suck my 'lovejuice', he said, he couldn't stop until he came off.

I did suggest fellating him once, and masturbating him whilst I was on top of him, but he didn't wish me to do so. I hope the continued habit of my husband sucking and swallowing my juices, now that we do this so frequently, will have no harmful effect on his health. Although we both are completely satisfied by doing this, no longer row, sleep better, never reject each other, we would like to be reassured that we are not abnormal.

Are there other married couples like us?

Mrs. L.Y.

Twelve years of coitus interruptus is bound to drive anyone to extremes – you both reacted by eventually rejecting penis-vagina contact altogether. Bad associations are hard to wipe out and the fact that you both climaxed satisfactorily for the first time during cunnilingus made this activity the magic formula for you both.

However there is another factor here. There has been a total about-face on both your parts in your psychosexual relationship with each other. After all these years you are rebelling against what your parents taught you. Although your mind accepted the traditional view of a 'woman's place' your emotions, on a subconscious level, never could stomach the idea that your job was to lie passively under a man, obeying and accepting his demands.

Achieving orgasm for the first time in your life made you feel as if you'd been conned into foregoing one of life's greatest pleasures. Years of subconscious hostility and resentment welled up in you and you channelled these feelings into sexual dominance and aggression. Now that you're 'the boss', you make your husband 'perform' – you call the tune. Very luckily for you your husband has not reacted against this situation; in fact he seems to find it stimulating. It's quite likely that he too has been playing a role all these years, and is now happy to react in a way which is more natural to him, rather than what he thought a man should act like.

What you are both doing is not abnormal in the sense that it is not an unnatural reaction to what has gone before. But in the context of what most other people do it is not average. However, if you're both happy with this new relationship, enjoy it and don't worry about the national statistics. – F.

ACCOUNTING FOR TASTE

When a woman comes, is there any distinctive taste in her release? My wife has a special taste about her. She bathes constantly, uses perfumes and creams and is exceptionally clean when it comes to her vaginal region, so I am convinced this taste is natural. Her vagina has a dry, slightly salty taste to it. I would describe it as a warm, feminine and not unpleasant smell. On the contrary it is very pleasant indeed.

Do all women have this particular salty odor and flavor in the vagina or is my wife different? Does she need something extra to cleanse herself with?

Mind you, I am not complaining. Without this taste, cunnilingus to me would not be half as stimulating. I would simply like to know whether her taste is natural in women.

P.W.

As a rule every natural secretion has an odor and a taste. This includes the vaginal secretions, whose taste is often described as 'salty'.

The smell and taste of these secretions are thought in most societies to be powerfully aphrodisiac – as indeed is the case among most mammals. Several experts, such as Dr. Alex Comfort, feel that the current preoccupation (especially in the U.S.) with douching, deodorizing, etc., far beyond the requirements of ordinary hygiene, is unhealthy and a sign of a repressed and sensually inhibited society. It is also thought that the vaginal odor is an important factor in male stimulation, even if it is not perceived consciously, and that the woman who continually douches, deodorizes, and artificially perfumes her vulva may be affecting her partner's potency.

So P.W.'s wife is perfectly normal, and the pleasure her vaginal taste and smell give him is natural and healthy. – F.

HANDY TECHNIQUE

I feel that a very valid area for discussion is precoital techniques, that is, the loveplay which is essential in order to have a satisfactory orgasm. This is most important when one considers that one of the characteristics of the average Englishman as a lover is his lack of imagination, and reluctance to try anything new.

Just one example of technique – the vaginal insertion of the thumb instead of one or more of the fingers. This digit's quasiconical shape results in considerable pressure on the labia minora and the clitoris as well as the vaginal walls. A technique to which some women respond with extreme intensity involves the deep vaginal insertion of the thumb while the remaining four fingers clutch at one of the buttocks or thighs.

Personally, I find the loveplay almost as enjoyable as the climax. What must be remembered is that the sexual enjoyment one derives from an act of coitus will be determined not by the act itself but the imaginative and prolonged loveplay which precedes it.

C.D.

Many males believe that vaginal finger insertion should accomplish only one thing: contact with the vaginal walls. This belief probably is the result of the misconception that the vaginal walls are the most sensitive area of the female genitalia. However, both the labia minora and the clitoris generally are far more sensitive than the vaginal walls. Usually finger insertion which places pressure on those organs will produce much more intense sexual response. – F.

THUMB SUCKER

My wife has always derived a great deal of pleasure from the act of sucking in fellatio. This made me wish very much that I could experience the sensation, but as I could not bear another man's penis in my mouth it did not seem possible. Then my wife had a wonderful idea. She put her thumb inside her vagina, and then let me suck her thumb. We were both amazed at how exciting it was, and she actually achieved a climax. Do other men experience this desire to suck or am I unusual?

R.S.

INSATIABLE DESIRE

I am in my middle 50s and have been happily married for 30 years. For many years my sex life was very satisfactory, both of us enjoying most varieties of sex including oral practices. As my sexual appetite was always much stronger than my wife's, the gap widening with the years, I have had a lot of affairs, which never made the slightest difference to our marriage.

I have never had any homosexual tendencies until some years ago, and they were brought about by a woman! After fellatio, she insisted on giving the semen back to me with a kiss. Nothing had ever excited me so much. I wanted more and from other people. She helped me by inviting a young student she knew and after fellating him, gave me his semen. She then advised me to get it direct from his penis and it is from that day on that I have an insatiable appetite for fellatio.

I am not a homosexual. I don't know whether my age and the resulting diminishing sexual potency have anything to do with it, but it certainly makes life complicated and difficult. I wonder if I am unique in this respect or if any of your readers have the same problem?

J.S.

Almost everyone has a degree of homosexuality in them, and it seems you are no exception.

You are finding fellatio stimulating because you have been weaned onto it by heterosexual activity, thereby making the jump to homosexuality a little easier and less emotionally traumatic.

You are acting out man's oldest fantasy – that of association with the desirable. The African warrior who wears the skin of the lion he has killed and the Polynesian wearing the teeth of his defeated shark are acting out this same fantasy. The same idea held true in times gone by when eating the flesh of your enemy meant being able to absorb his strength. It was even thought that by eating the sex organs of man or beast one could, by association, absorb the sexual potency of the devoured.

You are anxious about this homosexual aspect of yourself, having been proud of your abundant sexual drive (you probably got a lot of ego-boosting from your affairs) and now feel bewildered by the turn of events. Don't be – you are far from unique. – F.

LONG-DISTANCE FRIENDSHIP

I want to tell you about the most erotic things that have happened to me and also the most unusual.

I once formed a friendship over the telephone with someone whom I have never met and with whom I had only had a business relationship. One evening, feeling somewhat down in the dumps and being alone (I am a divorcée), I remembered his invitation that if ever I wasn't doing anything to ring him, so I

317

did. We talked for two and a half hours over the telephone, and after about half an hour we started to talk about the usual subject of conversation, sex. He thought I had a really fantastic sexy voice and he started to feel excited and began to masturbate while he was talking to me. The conversation became somewhat difficult, and he switched the phone to the extension, took all his clothes off and lay on the bed while talking. I was very inhibited because I felt I didn't know him very well, and although I was excited to think that he was masturbating I couldn't bring myself to do the same. He had a fantastic orgasm and told me afterwards that it was the first time he'd masturbated for years.

Over a process of many telephone conversations, he gradually 'seduced' me and I used to lie nude, stretched out on the rug in front of the fire, while I talked to him. He would meanwhile lie on his bed in a similar state. We formed such a good telephone friendship, so totally uninhibited, that we agreed never to meet as we felt that it would spoil our friendship.

We have done many other things over the phone. I read him sexy stories and he makes up stories to tell me while I am masturbating. Also he asked me to make up a story about my seducing him, if I ever meet him in real life, and we had a gorgeous time reading it. (I felt such a fool reading it over the telephone at the time because I hadn't much faith in my literary talents but the effect was really good and we both came off together listening to each other over the phone.)

Not only do we get very aroused by each other's voices over the telephone, which I think must be a little unusual, but also we manage to climax together although we live a good 20 miles apart!

Our friendship is still intact and we are very attached to each other after three months, but we can't help feeling that our relationship is somewhat unusual and wonder if other readers have had similar experiences. Also we both have close friends of the opposite sex, and always tell each other about our recent escapades without any feelings of jealousy or possessiveness. We have such a good thing going between us that we have absolutely no desire to meet. Incidentally, we are also very interested in each other in various other ways and send each other presents, cards, etc. He is older than I by 18 years, but over the telephone there is no difference at all.

Mrs. J.B.

Quite a distance for a climax. Who pays the telephone bills? – R.G.

THE FRIENDLY ENEMA

Throughout my boyhood I was given frequent enemas by my mother, and except for the fact that I was made to go to bed immediately afterwards I secretly enjoyed being syringed in this way.

The enemas always gave me certain pleasurable sensations, and these were intensified by the fact that my mother's free hand would gently caress my genitals while the syringing was taking place.

As I grew older I began to get erections on these occasions, and because of these erections I started to associate an enema syringe with sex. Whenever my mother was out of the house I would steal into her room, take the syringe from its box, fondle it with one hand, and masturbate with the other.

I was 13 when the enemas finally tapered off, and as I grew up they faded from my mind, although from time to time I did recall them when masturbating.

Some months ago however, at the age of 50, I became very, very, constipated and my wife said she would give me an enema. I agreed and while she prepared the warm soap suds I undressed myself. Even at that stage I found it all very exciting and sexually arousing. An erection took place, and as I felt the syringe entering the passage and the smooth warm fluid pouring into my rectum, memories of my boyhood were revived, together with the sensations. Before my wife had finished syringing me I had come.

She was somewhat understanding for she herself had been given enemas as a girl and because of them, always expected titillation of her anus during loveplay.

This enema had thrilled and excited me so much that ever since I have been syringing myself in this way two or three times a week, and in doing so have given myself intense sexual pleasure, not, I might add, to the detriment of relations with my wife.

I have also experimented with a cylindrical piece of rubber, some five inches long and five-eighths of an inch in diameter, with a rounded end. After thoroughly greasing with vaseline I introduced it into my rectum, and the resultant sensations were so intense that I experienced a violent orgasm.

I have, however, been scared to use it again, in case it is dangerous. Is this so?

Could you please give me some information about enemas – do people in this day and age use them, and do they affect others as they affect me, sexually? Also, are they harmful? I can't believe that they are for I certainly haven't been upset by them.

A.R.

The passage of a short, soft, lubricated rubber tube into the rectum will not cause harm unless hemorrhoids or some similar disease is present. Such a procedure would tend to aggravate any trouble.

Enemas are used today, but in medical practice they are 'small volume' enemas containing an active principle to stimulate the bowel, and hardly perceptible when given. Usually circumstances in hospital and the reason for emptying the bowels preclude any possibility of sexual interest in such a procedure.

The use of large volumes of fluid as in years past would lead to sexual feelings in many men if circumstances were favorable. There is a close relationship between sexual feelings from the rectum and penis – this relationship is less marked in women. No harm would come provided the enemas are used in moderation – if excessive, or soap or other materials are used in too strong a concentration, a colitis (an inflammation of the lower bowel) would arise, and hemorrhoids and fissure formation would be likely. – F.

CLASS REUNION

I have been happily married for 15 years, and my husband has been an excellent partner in every respect. The physical side of our marriage too has been perfectly satisfactory and I have no complaint on that score.

For the past year, however, I have been having an intimate affair with an old schoolfriend, an attractive but unmarried 'career woman'. It began when she came to stay with me to keep me company while my husband was on a business trip.

We had always been used to giving each other a friendly kiss on meeting, but the first night when she kissed me goodnight, the friendly peck became a passionate kiss. It left me lost in confusion, and though I had always frowned on same-sex relationships I must confess I was a willing partner to the events which followed, which culminated in mutual masturbation.

This first experience left me eager to continue our activities and we shared many beautiful moments over the next few days, making love at every available opportunity. It seemed natural to try sexual variations, including cunnilingus, which I had always found too personal to let my husband do. Eventually we moulded a dildo from a liquid rubber compound, complete with straps, and using this in turn were able to simulate the sex act to perfection. I can honestly say that when I was on the receiving end it was difficult to differentiate between the dildo and a man's penis, and in fact it was more satisfactory, since after I had come my friend could keep it inside me and we could lie joined together for as long as we liked. Something that has always disappointed me about sex with my husband was that, while I was still enjoying the feeling of my husband's penis inside me after orgasm, it would become flaccid and he would lose interest and withdraw.

It would be impossible for me to break this wonderful friendship now because we love each other dearly. But I am tormented with the feeling that it is unfair to my husband, even though this has not affected my love for him in the slightest or put me off intercourse with him (in fact I enjoy it more). He is a kind, understanding man, but how would he feel about this association? Should I continue to deceive him, or should I tell him the truth?

Mrs. M.F.

In general, relationships work better if there is trust and openness between the two partners. However, Mrs. M.F. has to decide for herself how much risk is involved in discussing this with her husband and how much risk she is willing to assume.

Is she aware that many men would be quite stimulated sexually by such a situation and rather than find it intolerable, might even ask to join the party? – H.G

IF ONLY ...

My husband has left me for another woman, and only now do I realize that I was really to blame. If only I had had the sense to see the obvious, we would still be together.

We have two teenage children, who naturally took up quite a bit of my time, and I feel I have sacrificed my married life for them; as while I have always made myself 'available', I realize now that my husband's lack of interest and virtual impotence during the last few years could well have been brought on by my complete failure to appreciate his needs for stimulation, although he was shouting them at me in the shape of gifts of pretty and sexy underwear of all kinds, including G-strings, fancy stockings, tights etc. I would, on rare occasions, put something on when lovemaking was to take place, but for the most part, the items were put away in a drawer, and that was the last he saw of them. Usually I wore tatty old and faded underwear, when not only had I all these items laid away upstairs, despite hints from him, but to purchase new ones from time to time would only have cost a few dollars in the local stores. Too late I have realized he would not have bought them if he hadn't wanted me to wear them and be seen in them.

I suppose I must have felt they were not quite 'the thing' for women turned 40 to wear, and now I am paying the price of my blindness. On one occasion he persuaded me to go out with him wearing one of his specials, and on another occasion without any panties at all, and his caresses as he drove, and while walking through the woods, should have told me here was stimulation with a capital S. If only I had followed this up by doing this sort of thing of my own accord, and surprised him, and dressed for him even when not a prelude to lovemaking, I would not be a lonely (but enlightened) wife at this moment. I have made a clean sweep of all my old clothes, particularly underwear, and if ever he should return to me, whenever he lifts my dress to caress me, there will be all the variety he can wish for, at my instigation. Also, he will find my language absolutely filthy during intercourse, and the variety of acts he will be permitted to try will amaze him, including those I have always considered not nice.

I know the other woman well, as several years ago she spent a holiday with us. My husband expressed interest in what she was likely to be wearing, and so one day when she was out shopping I suggested he have a look in her case. When I think back and

322

compare her holiday underwear to mine, no wonder that night he made love as never before! She is within a year of my age, but I am sure my husband is now cured of his impotence. Perhaps she even makes love in the car, parked down a country lane, or has cut the tips out of her bra, wears open crotch tights, or even satisfies herself with a rubber dildo, all things I remember my husband expressed interest in.

In the case of the latter, he even produced a catalogue of sex aids, at which I only expressed disgust and criticized the high cost. But I realize now I have paid a far higher price by lack of interest. If writing this letter will help other wives to go a little bit mad at times, and so keep their husbands, it will have been worth it.

Mrs. A.G.

The problem, Mrs. A.G., is not one of individual blame. You cannot blame yourself for early familial and societal influences. Probably you were both unable to communicate effectively with each other; otherwise, the problem could have been handled with less pain. In my experience I have found that the ability of two people to speak with each other is of tremendous help in working out differences and getting more pleasure out of their relationship.

The most important question becomes, 'What are you going to do now?' – R.G.

THE OTHER WOMAN

Can you please publish a few words in defense of the 'other woman'. There must be thousands of us who, like myself, are not wicked sirens making designs on other women's husbands. It is just our misfortune to fall in love with a married man. I know most wives' reaction would be to say a girl shouldn't look at someone else's husband, that both are to blame if an affair is started, and it's always the woman who's deliberately trying to break up the marriage. This just isn't true. I have seen, and heard of, a few affairs that started because the man lied about being married.

In my own case, I knew the man with whom I fell in love was married but he only spent the weekends with his family. He told me there was nothing between him and his wife and that they were discussing divorce. I believed him and waited. A few months later he announced that he thought he should try to make things up with his wife for the sake of the children, but insisted he still loved me.

I was broken-hearted but there was nothing I could do. I wanted his wife to know about me, hoping she would divorce him, but I soon learned that she knew about me all the time and didn't intend to do anything. Perhaps she has been through this many times before. For a while they spent a lot more time together, while I stayed at his flat and spent my evenings washing his shirts and cleaning house for him.

After a few months, something went wrong and they got round to seeing lawyers. It was just like the beginning for us: this time I was sure he was serious. It hurt me when he went to visit the children – I felt I would always be shut out of that important part of his life. But I loved him so much I was content to take what he gave me of himself.

My happiness and hopes for the future did not last long. The divorce plans were dropped again, this time because his wife had threatened suicide and he felt responsible for her because of the children. I had no part whatsoever in their unhappy marriage, it existed before he ever met me, and yet everyone who knows of our arrangement thinks I am a terrible woman not to leave him and help him mend his marriage. No one ever stops to think that he *wants* me with him and that I have spent years of my life as if walking a tightrope.

I never know if he is suddenly going to move back with his wife, and I have no assurance that if our relationship loses its glamor or becomes too much of a stress he will leave me for another girlfriend. I am also rather miserable about the fact that I am now over 30 and would seriously like to have a baby; but, of course, in my situation I am forced to take the birth pill.

I suppose the only advice I will ever get from anyone is to get out of this situation, because it is pretty obvious that he never intends to get a divorce. But when we are lying close together in bed I feel I couldn't live without him and until he tells me there is nothing between us, I am hanging on to that little thread of hope that there is a future for us. If the break must come, then he must be the one to do it. Am I so wicked because I can't bring myself to leave the man I love?

Miss B.N.

The position of the 'other woman' is frequently a painful one, and I can understand your despair at seeing the years pass by with no chance to enjoy the complete and fulfilling relationship you want.

I have found that when many women in situations like yours break up with one married man, they frequently become involved with another one. Freudians would see this, and I am inclined to agree, as someone trying to recreate the situation in her childhood home when her mother, the hated rival, had her father. Now the young woman is trying to win her surrogate father, her lover, away from the surrogate mother, the lover's wife. One young woman who had been involved with four or five married men told me that she never found a man interesting unless there was another woman involved with him. Part of my reason for believing that the rivalry of the older woman is important to you is your statement that you wanted the wife to know. It's true you rationalized this by thinking she would then divorce him, but this is not how it usually works out. In fact, many women who might have divorced a man because they found him unsatisfactory, will hold on all the more when they find that he is involved with someone else.

It might be helpful to you to seriously consider the reasons for your present choice and your unhappiness. – H.G.

TRAUMATIC EXPERIENCE

I have always believed in complete sexual freedom. When we first married, it was my husband who was a little inhibited and shy, but I soon taught him all the joys of sex and impressed upon him I didn't feel I owned him because we were married; he was perfectly free to have another girl if he fancied her and I would never question him. And, of course, the same would hold true for me, if I wished to take a lover. Funnily enough, we were married for six years before I was attracted to anyone else, and after I had had sex with this man a couple of times, I suggested he and his wife should spend an evening with me and my husband and we should all get to know each other better. That was the way I introduced my husband to partner-exchanging and he thoroughly enjoyed it once he was able to let himself go. From that moment on, we have had a full and complete sex life, doing everything we fancied together; and we have brought our children up to know sex is a joy, enriching mind and body, and nothing of which to be ashamed.

We have three children, two girls aged 9 and 15 and a boy who is 13. It is about one of my children I am writing to you for advice. How is it possible that any child, growing up in an atmosphere of love and freedom of expression, can have a traumatic experience as regards sex? All our children are completely aware not only of all the facts of sex, but the emotional implications as well. We have never made it a secret from them that we, their parents, enjoy each other sexually. And yet, something inexplicable has happened. Recently my husband came home at 1 p.m. as he usually does on Mondays. We had lunch together and lay down to relax on the couch. Before long, we both felt in the mood for sex, and were having intercourse, oblivious to everything else, when our 15-year-old daughter walked into the room. She had been sent home early from school. She screamed and ran from the room. For two days, she locked herself in her bedroom, only coming down for meals when the other children were present, and refusing to talk to either me or my husband. She has been out with her friends in the last few days, but still ignores us. I have tried so hard to reach her, but she tells me never to touch her again and that I'm disgusting to her.

Why should a girl her age be so frightened of sex, especially when we have been so free about it? Nobody could accuse either of us of being puritans. I dread to think of her reaction if we had ever been caught in one of our exchanges. Parents are so often condemned for inhibiting their children; we have done the opposite, so what is one to do? Is there anything I can do to help my daughter?

Mrs. C.W.

Love and sex are not necessarily the same.

Although a child is brought up in an atmosphere of love and freedom of expression, what may be freely discussed might be only the biological differences *between the sexes. Until children reach sexual maturity in a psychological sense, and seek out the company of one of the opposite sex, the emotional aspect of sex tends to bypass them almost completely.*

At puberty, there are mood changes which are probably due, in part, to hormonal imbalance and can be quite serious.

During this particularly unhappy period, the sudden shock of seeing one's parents in the act of intercourse can be a disturbing experience. The child can hardly believe that this is how her parents behave! Sexual intercourse, about which she probably knows 'everything', is for the 'others', not her own Mother and Father. Hence as a general rule the actual deed performed in front of children, particularly during adolescence which is such a time of extreme sensitivity, can be shattering.

If attempts to 'explain' the situation to the child are not at first successful, keep the lines open between you. – F.

THE QUESTION OF NUDITY

Although we are not practicing nudists, we've brought up our three children (two girls and one boy) not to be ashamed of their bodies, and in fact, very often walk about the house nude. Our eldest daughter, now 16, as a result of being influenced by her friends, now demands complete privacy when she dresses or undresses, something she never did before. When I mentioned this fact to a friend of mine, she agreed with my daughter's actions. She insisted that parents can cause a great deal of harm by allowing their children to see them in the nude. Is there any validity to this statement?

Mrs. J.D.

It is very difficult these days to avoid the sight of nudity – what with films, magazines, posters, books, pictures, offering ample opportunity. It is, of course, different to see nudity 'in the flesh' and in one's own home. But your daughter's behavior may be a simple phase in her psychological and sexual development. Whatever the reason, you ought to respect her attitude – though you might ask her why she has changed in this respect. – F.

ART FOR LOVE'S SAKE

Prior to actual intercourse, I insert several different colored chocolate beans into my wife's vagina which I then proceed to extract orally. This gives us both extreme pleasure.

After this, we have normal intercourse, and on withdrawing my penis, the many different colors which adhere to it (giving it a sort of psychedelic effect) give prolonged pleasure to the two of us.

I am now seriously considering covering my penis in harmless watercolor paints. When making love, all the senses should be employed – including the visual. Artists of the world unite!

J.J.

SEX SHOULD BE FUN

Everyone seems to take sex much too seriously. Perhaps that's one of the reasons why so many of our marriages turn flat like an opened bottle of ginger ale. The only way to keep the fizz within marriage is to inject it with fun.

I speak from experience. My first marriage couldn't have been more miserable. When I think back how completely unprepared we both were for marriage, I shudder. Sex was something which was only done in bed and in a dark room. It was never done on the spur of the moment. Whenever I got in the mood and was raring to go, everything would come to a stop while my wife went through the long drawn out process of inserting the diaphragm and then the spermicidal gel. By the time she was ready, I was either asleep or out of the mood. The time she needed for her preparation seemed endless. Why couldn't she be ready and anticipate my needs? Well now, decent women don't do such things, do they!

If my marriage proved anything, it was that an unhappy sexual relationship colors the other aspects of the day-to-day living. Dissatisfied sexually, I began to see my wife in a new light. Minor defects which under ordinary conditions I would have ignored suddenly increased in intensity and importance. After five years, our marriage ended in divorce. There is no question in my mind that had we had a good sex life, we would still be married and possibly happily so. But how do you go about having a good sex life if your wife treats sex as an obligation, as a serious enterprise which requires the same intense preparation, discipline and stamina as cleaning the house?

Like most men who have tasted the bitterness of a dull, predictable marriage, I was determined not to try it again. Less than two years after my divorce. I met a woman with a fantastic sense of humor. She had been married to a man who sounded like the male equivalent of my ex-wife, little sense of humor, meticulous, dull, uninspired. It didn't take us long to see how both of our marriages had gone on the rocks, because they had become so serious, so planned and so very boring.

My girlfriend and I soon proved just how much fun sex can be. Gone were the long waits between desire and fulfillment. She used the Pill and was always ready. What a blessing! Chasing her around my flat, both of us in the nude and laughing uncontrollably, finally making love wherever I caught her, was sex as it really should be. It was great fun and made the whole thing exhilarating and joyful! What a difference between this and my five years of planned copulation, always in bed and always in the dark!

Needless to say, I soon changed my mind about not remarrying. That was four years ago and I haven't regretted my decision at any time. While our sexual bouts are not as frequent as they were when we first got married – whose are? – we both see to it the fun is never taken out of sex. We've tried and mostly enjoyed every possible variation of human sexuality. If you're not obsessed with guilt and keep your sense of humor, it's amazing the laughs and pleasure you can get out of any of the variations, whether necking or making love in a naturist camp – those nudists are such squares – or swimming in the nude at night at a non-nudist beach, or even playing the game of group sex with several other happy-go-lucky compatible couples.

We both feel marriage can be a most enjoyable, enriching and wonderful relationship if the two people use their imaginations, all their senses, get rid of their stupid guilt and understand that sex should be fun.

T.M.

A strong taboo against the sex-is-fun equation still exists in our culture, perpetuated by many of the most enlightened pundits of sex.

Recently I was on a beach at Fire Island speaking to a young writer, and commented on the physical attractiveness of two bouncy bikini-clad young women passing by. My writer friend stared at me shocked and said, 'I'm surprised at you, a psychologist, talking that way. My shrink says it's an expression of hostility to be interested in other women when you're married.'

His doctor was enforcing the Puritan dictate against sex-for-fun by defining it as hostility. Among the aversive stimuli used by therapists in controlling their own and their patients' tendency to sexual encounters are: 'It shows lack of commitment.'

'You are orally fixated, looking for another breast all the time.' 'It is a defense against feelings of sexual inadequacy.' 'It is a reaction formation against deep-seated fears of homosexuality.' When you reach the proper age it becomes: 'You are a dirty old man'.

If you wish to maintain your interest in sex-for-pleasure, it is necessary to take effective measures against such statements and turn them into compliments. For example, since I have been apprised of my dirty-old-manhood on more than one occasion, I have convinced myself that it is a testimonial to my continued potency and virility. After all, the ability to respond to external stimuli is a characteristic of living organisms, and the more ready the organism is to respond, the greater the intelligence. – H.G.

SEXUAL SNEEZING

Occasionally, when sexually excited, my wife sneezes continuously – sometimes nine times in quick succession! It usually happens when I am away on a business trip and she is reading erotic literature or thinking about masturbating.

This continued sneezing does not worry her at all – in fact I find it quite amusing – but we should both very much like to know what causes it.

My dear wife has experienced the sneezing phenomena for the past ten years, ever since she first discovered the absolute joy of masturbation at the age of 30.

R.W.

The association of sneezing and sexual stimulation has been noted before and is mentioned in literature. One explanation given is that, in susceptible individuals, a sudden sensory stimulus will provoke sneezing. This is commonly seen when a person enters bright sunlight; many people will sneeze then.

It is an individual idiosyncrasy of no significance and might be reduced or avoided if the nose is blown before exposing oneself to the stimulus. Another person might encourage the phenomenon by regarding it as amusing or attracting attention and they will find that 'nothing I do can prevent this' is quite proved by the fact. – F.

A SENSUAL WIFE

I wonder how many people who have had an unhappy first marriage are too frightened to gamble on a second? Perhaps my case might ease the minds of those who might otherwise be missing out on a good thing.

To all outside appearances, my first marriage was a 'happy' one, but the truth was quite different. In my wife's case, sex played a secondary role. It worsened during the war years while we were separated. Despite the fact that she was an excellent housewife and mother, she became less and less interested in the physical aspects of our marriage. Our breakup was inevitable.

When I met my present wife, I knew I had found what I was looking for. She is a very sensual, sexual woman, which is exactly what I needed. Despite the fact that we are both in our 50s, our lovemaking is exhilarating and passionate. It has given me a whole new lease of life.

My present wife, I am happy to say, is very beautifully built. Her 41-inch bosom combined with a slim waistline inevitably draws admiring glances from the men. She is a very feminine woman and at no time coyly attempts to hide her obvious charms.

I glory in her nudity. To me, her body is an enchanting work of art. Just drinking in her curves and mounds is sufficient to arouse me to great sexual heights. I need no other aphrodisiac.

Her pre-coital preparations should be a useful guide to those women who are incapable, because of their lack of imagination, of sexually arousing their mates. As she slowly undresses, she sensuously caresses her breasts, while at the same time weaving her plump bottom from side to side. As a finishing touch, she parts her legs and softly strokes her vagina, which is constantly moist and ready for the ensuing loveplay. This visual aperitif never fails to quicken my pulse and to arouse within me all of the sensations with which the male is blessed. No matter how tired I might have been, my partner's ambrosia, as if by magic, transports me into a fantasy world of sheer erotica.

Progressive psychiatrists today agree that all is permissible between a man and his wife on their marital couch with the obvious exceptions of one injuring the other or one of the partners being forced to do something against his/her will. With this in mind, we continually experiment, and are delighted at discovering new sensations, new nuances, new positions. Our loveplay, for instance, is varied and uninhibited; sometimes wild and savage – other times, sensitive and poetic. My wife employs all her senses to the fullest. She knows exactly when to touch and taste – and her timing is almost a sixth sense. She anticipates my moods and makes love accordingly.

Whereas during my first marriage I would have been most reluctant, or even ashamed to have discussed sex openly, today, because of my newfound happiness, I am of the opinion that sex should be discussed and appreciated just as any other of the great works of art which are capable of stimulating the most civilizing senses of man.

I am aware that my comments might be shocking to those readers who are still guilt-ridden when it comes to sex. But they, more than anyone else, should be made to realize that the full enjoyment of marital relations is the healthiest and best means of guaranteeing a happy and satisfactory marriage. As one who had to suffer through a sexless, guilt-ridden marriage, I speak from experience.

M.M.

SHARING

I was interested in your correspondent who wrote regarding exhibitionism and voyeurism bringing pleasure and excitement to one's married life. I certainly agree with his remarks and can give scores of instances which have made my life a thousand times more exciting and have given my wife and me greater sexual satisfaction than any other married couple we've ever known.

The first time I can remember was during a holiday at the seaside. One evening we were watching a firework display on the beach, and my wife being rather tiny I managed to find a seat she could stand on to see the display. I stood at one side behind her. I always took every opportunity to excite her sexually, so I put one hand under her summer frock between her thighs and was soon playing with her there. (As she always wore wide-legged French panties which she made herself, this was quite easy.) After a time I decided to light a cigarette and, as this was a two-handed job, took my hand away to do so. I was surprised when I put my hand back between her thighs to find another hand already there doing what I had previously been doing. I tried to pull the hand away and saw it belonged to a man standing the other side of my wife, who must have been watching me earlier. He was much taller than I and I knew I would be outclassed if I tried to use force, and as I could see my wife was enjoying it by the way her bottom was moving, I did nothing. I thought I would have been jealous but instead found I was getting more excited than I'd ever been before. Of course, I never told my wife and we had a wonderful night sexually; it seemed to excite me enormously every time I thought of the stranger's hand fondling my wife's intimate parts.

After that, I persuaded my wife to be more of an exhibitionist and she soon began to enjoy showing her undies and legs in front of men friends who used to come and play cards with me.

One day she told me that one particular man who came into our shop while I was out on business had said he wanted to make love to her. I asked her if she would like to and she said that, since she'd never had intercourse with anyone but me, she was curious and would like to see what it was like with another man. I told her to go ahead.

One evening shortly afterwards she did so, while I kept out of the way. Of course, she told me all about it that night and we had a wonderful session as she described her feelings. After that first episode, I encouraged her in every way to have more lovers and eventually took part myself, with the three of us sleeping together.

I found my married friends were the most appreciative and everyone, without exception, told me I was a lucky man to have such a marvelous wife, since their wives seemed to treat sex as a duty and not as fun.

We had scores of exciting experiences over the years and remained very much in love. Only very occasionally did I stray, since I found my wife was more exciting than other women in every way.

J.R.

WIFE-SWAPPING WANTED

My wife and I lead a fairly active and varied sex life and are very much in love. Virtually everything we do, we do together, both in business and in the home. Despite this seemingly idyllic setup I have a strong desire for a little sexual adventure every now and then.

333

I do not wish to visit whores or to conduct an affair behind my wife's back. Ideally, I would like to form a friendship with another couple and get together about every month or so. Obviously this presents us with the problem of finding a couple that we both find reasonably attractive. This, however, is a small problem compared to the problem of explaining my wishes to my wife without offending her.

Each time she has read of wife-swapping she has always said something like 'They can't have much respect for each other.' This is primarily because she is of the opinion that people can't enjoy a sexual relationship without being in love. I just cannot think of any way to tell her that it is possible to enjoy sex without love, without convincing her that I am a sex maniac or depraved.

F.J.

This is one of those difficult situations which needs to be thought through carefully, especially with regard to the probable consequences. In fact, the problem of sexual fidelity is one of the most important that affects the survival of marriage or lifetime partnerships. Your desire for a 'sexual adventure' is totally understandable, as is your desire not to deceive your wife. Most people do long for sexual variety as well as an enduring, honest, monogamous relationship. To combine the two is a rare and difficult achievement, but would certainly be 'the best of all possible worlds'.

However, your wife's feelings in this matter cannot be discounted lightly. Only you can judge how strong they are. If, as you suspect, she would find a preplanned, wife-swapping session distasteful, then there is little that you can do to change her feelings which are probably deeply rooted in her personality. Even if you were able to talk her into it against her will, it is likely that the whole thing would backfire. She would probably feel guilty and 'degraded' and would blame you, which would ultimately harm your marriage. – F.

NEVER 'HUSBAND-SWAPPING'

Strange how this activity of swapping partners is never called husband-swapping. Perhaps this is because it is always the husband who suggests the idea to his wife and never vice versa.

I think that a wife accepts the idea reluctantly and with pretended enthusiasm because she does not want to be accused of being a spoil-sport and because she loves her husband and will do anything to make him happy. In her heart she must wonder why her husband wants to swap partners and make love to another woman. Perhaps she feels that if she does not agree to the idea she is in danger of losing him altogether. It is, in fact, an act of moral blackmail on his part. The wife really has no choice but to agree. If the husband is set on the idea he will indulge in extramarital sex with or without his wife knowing or participating.

I think any wife should be most offended if her husband suggests swapping partners. He is saying that he is not satisfied with their sexual relationship. A man whose sexual needs are completely met by his wife has no need to go to another woman in order to titillate his appetite. Not only does it appear that the sexual relationship is unsatisfactory in their marriage partnership but also their personal relationships with each other.

It is a well-known fact that most people who indulge in extramarital sex are emotionally immature and incapable of establishing and maintaining any kind of real personal relationship. Invariably these people are very shallow and incredibly selfish despite their charm, wit, good humor, intelligence, broadmindedness and apparent respectability.

They are selfish insofar as they are first and foremost concerned only with their own happiness, even to the extent of deliberately taking the risk (and it is a risk) of hurting the feelings of their marital partners. They are shallow inasmuch as their sexual appetites can only be satisfied by withdrawing their emotions. They themselves state that wife-swapping can only be a success if the participants are not, and do not become, emotionally involved with each other. Yet can sex ever be really and truly satisfactory when the emotional element is missing?

Without emotional overtures the act of sexual intercourse is relegated to a simple physical and biological level of experience. There is no love involved, no feeling, no possession of mind, body and soul, no giving of oneself completely, no sharing of intimate words or whispers of true love and affection. Nothing. Just a physical act to satisfy sexual lust: selfish in that the participants are not giving anything of themselves except their bodies; shallow in that the experience is unrewarding, except in a physical manner, and in itself has no meaning;

335

gratifying in that the man is capable of ejaculating into another woman.

For those with an inferiority complex the experience will boost their ego and assure them that in some way they are still attractive to the opposite sex. With their morale boosted and the experience over, they are now able to return to the arms of their marriage partners and make love successfully – usually immediately afterward before the effects wear off. How pathetic! How juvenile!

They give as their reasons for wife-swapping, sexual monotony and marital boredom. People who resort to wife-swapping or regular group sex have problems. Wife-swapping or group sex is not the answer. It might provide temporary relief, but wife-swapping will never remove the root cause and so solve the problem completely. For a permanent cure they need to psychoanalyze themselves. Both husband and wife should get together to solve the problem between them. It is pathetic for a husband to depend on another man's wife to stimulate him sufficiently to make love to his own wife. Variety may well be the spice of life but self-indulgence is the road to ruin. Is it really a change of partner or a change of attitude that is needed?

Wife-swapping is simply another means of having extra-marital sex. It is antisocial, irresponsible and very dangerous. Only the mentally, emotionally and spiritually immature could ever indulge in such a practice. At a time when everything else in our society is being devalued, please let us not devalue sex. The value of sexual intercourse is measured by how much we put into it, not how much we get out of it. It is a thing of joy and real beauty only when it is an act of love. Who would settle for less?

M.C.

PRACTICE MAKES PERFECT

I have found that the following simple exercises do strengthen the pelvic-vaginal muscles and would like to pass them on to others.

1. Lie flat on the floor or in bed with legs straight. Point the toes and strain to make the ankle bones meet. Now flatten the small of the back to remove the arch and repeat the exercise.

2. With back flattened, draw toes up instead of pointing them

336

and try to make the·ankle bones meet. If this movement is carried out correctly, one can feel the muscles tighten across the lower abdomen. These positions should be held momentarily and repeated as frequently as possible. After childbirth they are particularly beneficial. Incidentally, they are also figure improving.

The vaginal muscles constrict when the buttocks are squeezed together and the pelvic floor is pulled taut as though the body is trying to hold back water and trying to prevent an attack of diarrhea at the same time. The movement can be a quick twitch, a series of twitches, a long sustained grip or a sucking action which starts at the entrance of the vagina and ripples upward. This latter movement requires practice.

My husband and I engage in considerable foreplay and a depilating session in which he gently removes all my pubic hair with a safety razor. The sensation of the hot water and cold soap is exciting in itself and the naked pubis, perhaps just covered by a see-through nightie, is a stimulus to both myself and my partner.

Mrs. T.P.

The exercises described above are basically those taught to mothers in the post-natal phase; they help the pelvic floor musculature to improve and strengthen following the severe stretching received in the process of childbirth. Conscientious attention to these exercises will greatly diminish the frequency of prolapse of the uterus and bladder in later life.

The exact details of the exercises will vary from one physiotherapy department to another, but the principles remain the same. Similarly, in cases of 'stress incontinence', i.e., where urine passes on exertion, coughing, laughing or sneezing, when lifting heavy goods, etc., these exercises are particularly helpful.

All these exercises take time and concentration and only perseverence will produce results. – F.

THE COMPETENT QUIM

As regards vaginal muscle control, some societies train girls when young in the basics of copulation so that later they, themselves, will benefit from using their expertise on men. The critical word is 'expertise'; the stage in which the basics have become second nature and the body reacts automatically and leaves the mind relaxed to enjoy the oblivion of orgasm.

One of the reasons why so many women are frigid is that they cannot relax while concentrating on the basics. These are not, as most textbooks suggest, a matter of knowing a variety of acrobatic contortions that allow the penis to get into the quim; rather they are knowing what the quim can do with it once it is in. Few women know that with practice they can make their quim open wide or close tight; make it draw into itself a flaccid penis which when erect it can hold against all efforts to withdraw it; make it suck at the penis until it ejaculates and when done, or even before, expel it; make it expel the ejaculate also. But such expertise needs practice, impossible to obtain as a virgin. Only when such actions become second nature can a woman set the quim going on its own work and then lie back and float relaxed into orgasm. As in swimming, any striving invites failure.

Here we have arrived at the crux of the virginity concept. Men are afraid of the 'competent' quim. They have given it a name – *vagina dentata*, the vagina with teeth. So they prefer the inexperienced virgin who will not know how incompetent her man may be. She, poor lass, has to take what she gets and be grateful. Add to that the threat of perpetual pregnancy, and it is easy to understand her lack of any interest. But the Pill has put an end to the latter. (Beware vasectomy, a male device to avoid risk to himself but keep the risk of pregnancy hanging over her head.)

To summarize: girls, get rid of your hymens yourselves as fast as you can, shave and take pride in your quim's appearance; develop your clitoris to the full, and train your quim to do what it was designed to do without your having to think about it. Having done all this you can lie back and relax and enjoy the orgasm which is your natural right. Then you will be meeting man on equal terms sexually and therefore as persons in your own right. You will respect yourselves the more, and the wiser men will respect you for it. The others are not worth a second glance.

O.A.

VAGINISMUS

I've read about the condition 'vaginismus' but am not clear about what it actually means. Can you clarify this point?

E.F.

Vaginismus is the term used to define an extreme sensitivity of the female external genitalia, such that any physical contact, i.e., medical examination or an attempt at intercourse, or even in the more severe cases the 'threat' of contact by finger or penis leads to a reflex spasm of the sphincter vaginae and levator ani muscles, the whole perineum and even the adductors of the thighs. In extreme cases the patient will draw up her legs, roll on to her face, and prepare to defend herself by pushing away the 'attacker'. As is appreciated by all today, these extreme cases are of psychological origin. – F.

FINE PIECE OF ENGINEERING

There have been a number of letters on the rear entry position. In this connection, it might be interesting to recall that when humans were wild creatures they probably lived in packs, rather like some species of monkey. The females of the pack would give off a scent when they were ready for copulation and this would alert the male, who, acting on his instinct, would come up behind the female. He would grasp her forearms, and pinion them in front of her chest. Her buttocks would then be nestling against his lower abdomen and upper thighs. A woman's buttocks are always colder than the rest of the body, and this would have an aphrodisiac effect on the male. His penis would start to rise and would naturally come up between her thighs.

The human penis has a slight curve along its length, and this curve has the effect of keeping the knob at its end tight up against the female's body.

As the male thrusts his penis forward, the shape of the knob is ideal to part the labia majora, and to travel on, coming into contact with the clitoris, being brought to a halt where the lips join together beyond the clitoris. As the clitoris is stimulated by the penis knob, the female bends forward to obtain more of the pleasant feeling which the stimulant produces. The female now bends still further forward, with the result that the penis, instead of travelling on to the clitoris, enters the vagina. When it has got to its limit of the stroke in the vagina, the female has bent so far forward that the back of the penis at its base is rubbing against the clitoris.

The orgasm-producing nerves now come into play. As the male thrusts in and out, so the female rocks her pelvis on an axis through her hips so that her vagina is travelling along an arc of a circle, the same as the male's penis.

All this is a fine piece of engineering by nature. When entry is made from the front, the full benefit of this well-designed machinery is lost, especially on the sequence of events for the female. If a virgin hymen has to be broken this rear entry position is ideal, but it is essential that it be done standing up. Perhaps this explanation of the rear entry position may help some of your female readers to understand and not feel disgust at a position designed by nature to afford exquisite pleasure.

F.D.

ONLY MONKEY BUSINESS

I don't know why human beings have to rationalize their actions. The more unnatural the act, the lengthier the rationalization. If a man likes to make love to a woman from behind, let him just say he likes it that way and leave it at that. But no more long and silly explanations on why we should all do it. I'm not saying I don't enjoy this position at times. My husband and I have been married eight years so we know each other well enough to experiment and also to feel intimate and relaxed in all our lovemaking. It's rather cozy to have him cuddle up to me in bed, take me by surprise and enter from the back. But I can quite understand that a young girl, or equally a mature woman, making love with a man at the beginning of a relationship would object and feel it to be an unnatural position. Because that's exactly what it is.

The rear entry position is perfect for monkeys. But man has evolved into an upright creature, walking and performing all his everyday tasks on his two feet, using his shortened arms for tasks entirely different. During the course of evolution all the sexual attraction symbols have become displaced from the back (as in monkeys and other mammals) to the front. No other mammal but the female human has protuberant breasts so we may suppose that the main purpose of the breast is not to suckle the young but to serve as a sexual stimulant to the male. Similarly, no other mammal has the rounded, sensitive lips that humans have, nor do they verbalize (in the natural position, facing the person they are talking to), nor do other mammals use their eyes to convey subtle emotions to each other.

All these symbols come into play during human lovemaking. I have not yet made mention of the most important feature of all – the vagina. This has changed shape considerably since ancient man was running around much like his monkey cousins. Instead of the tract running parallel to the outer stomach area, it is now at an angle to the pubic area, going straight up inside the woman, in her upright position. This explains the natural position of making love lying down so that the seminal fluid does not escape but lies in a pool at the entrance to the uterus. Add to this fact that male and female erogenous zones are at the front of our bodies, breasts, lips for kissing, hands in a free position to caress each other, and it's simple to see that the 'natural' position to make love is to lie down facing each other. If all the devotees of the rear entry position disagree with me let them read any good book on biology. I would particularly recommend Desmond Morris' *The Naked Ape*, which explains fully our sexual evolution.

No one minds someone saying they like doing something, or don't like doing it, as long as they don't try to talk us all into their own particular kick, or give us an intellectual, pseudo-scientific explanation along with their view. Right now I can't resist adding a little explanation of my own. It would seem to me that any man who likes to enter a woman from behind, exclusively or preferably, does so because he's afraid of women. He can't meet her face to face, tenderly and on an equal footing; he must grab her from behind where she can't see him, make him feel inferior, or perhaps gobble him up. Could I be right?

Mrs. B.G.

INCIPIENT PRUDE?

We have piles of magazines all over the house, among them goodness knows how many copies of Forum, Penthouse and similar magazines. Our daughter, who is nearly 15 months old, loves turning the pages to find pictures of dogs, horses, and so on. I never really gave this much thought until I found her kissing a drawing of an overdeveloped mermaid.

I am not looking for any perverted sexual connotation in this but it did set me thinking. During the next few months she will become aware of the pictures, and while I know there is nothing pornographic about the photographs and that the cartoons are supposed to be funny, she will take everything at its face value.

Therefore, ought I to remove copies of Penthouse, etc., to a less accessible place, or should we leave them where they are in the hope that familiarity will breed boredom?

Incidentally, when looking at this type of magazine with her, I tend to find myself carefully skipping over photographs of well-endowed women and the more explicit cartoons. Could I be an incipient prude? Am I using my daughter as a front for my own unacknowledged distaste for sex?

Mrs. C.H.

'Shoulds' and 'oughts' aside, I think your embarrassment when looking at these magazines with your daughter will most certainly communicate to her. I would suggest that you let her look at them by herself, answering straight questions if she asks them. The more natural you can be physically with her, the less likely she is to become hung up on the 'ideal' of womanhood as a sexual object so often presented by 'cheesecake' photographs. – F.

PROCREATION VS. RECREATION

My girl friend and I see eye to eye on most things with the exception of sex. Because of her strict Catholic upbringing she feels that the primary purpose of sex is procreation, and that any sex act which does not permit procreation to take place, that is any contracepted act of coitus and all noncoital sex acts – violates the primary purpose of sex.

All my arguments to the contrary, that the world is changing, the problem of overpopulation, the popularity of the pill, etc., seem to have made no impact on her. While I admit that the most important aspect of sex is procreation, there is absolutely no reason why married couples should not enjoy the act or any type of noncoital lovemaking, if they want to make love just for the pleasure it brings and nothing else!

After each one of our lovemaking sessions, my girl friend

becomes overwhelmed with guilt, and feels ashamed of herself. She assures me that if I did not wear a contraceptive, she would not have any guilt. She is of course aware of the danger of getting pregnant if no contraceptive is used. Since I'm not prepared to get married within the near future, fatherhood is the last thing I need, or want.

C.J.

The belief that the primary purpose of sex is procreation is often thought of as Victorian, but in actuality it dates back to the early Christians. A similar tenet may be found in the Hebraic codes of the post-exiled period. The view once was accepted unquestioningly throughout the Judeo-Christian world; however, modern theologians appear to have reevaluated their position.

For example, Rabbi Samuel Glassner, in an article in Encyclopaedia of Sexual Behaviour, *suggests that the reason behind the early Hebraic proscriptions of nonprocreative sex might have been more political than theological. He points out that leaders of the Hebrew tribes were faced with the continuing problem of defending themselves against several different enemies and therefore had a very definite need for increasing their numerical strength. Support for this contention comes from the fact that there is no record of proscriptions of nonprocreative sex during the pre-exile period, when defense was not a problem.*

Other faiths seem to have adopted a similar questioning attitude. For example, the Church of England has joined the majority of the other Protestant religions in approving of contraception and even abortion under certain circumstances. Of all major religions, only the Roman Catholic Church still forbids both practices, but in recent years, the Catholic view has been growing considerably less inflexible.

In any event, to say that the primary purpose of sex is procreation is to presume that there actually is a primary purpose to sex, and that it is within the speaker's power to make positive identification of that primary purpose. These are presumptions which science cannot accept without proof, and no proof seems to be forthcoming. If anything, the evidence at hand seems to favor an opposite point of view. For example, there can be little doubt that procreation is the primary, indeed the only purpose of sex among certain species of fish. Bodily contact does not take place. Instead, the female lays eggs, the male fertilizes them and both adults die shortly afterward.

However, the fact that human sexual behavior can be made to serve two functions, one procreative, and the other pleasure-producing, suggests that both are legitimate purposes. Why assign primacy to one? And, if primacy must be assigned, why not assign it to pleasure, which is present even when the potential for procreation is not? – F.

PREGNANCY PROBLEMS

My wife is at present three months pregnant. As with her previous two pregnancies, at this stage she no longer desires sexual relations. She says she is fast reaching the stage when she cannot bear me to touch her.

This is an exact repetition of what happened before. In fact, during her last pregnancy, toward the end she was so distressed by my presence that she moved into the spare room.

We have talked the matter over, as this situation upsets my wife as much as myself. Normally she is very loving and enjoys frequent coitus. Yet she freely admits that even the thought of lovemaking at present is abhorrent to her.

What we want to know, is, is my wife abnormal in this respect?

J.L.

No, it is not abnormal. Pregnant women react individually to sexual relations during the various stages of pregnancy – some of them actually find that their sexual desires increase during it. – H.G.

PATIENCE REQUIRED

I suffered feelings of coldness towards my husband for a long time myself during and after my pregnancies, but worked them through on my own by acting a part in our sex lives until a more natural feeling for sex came back to me. I'm not saying all women should or could do this. Neither does the original thrill of lovemaking ever come back, if it's forced. It's much better for the married partners to talk freely to each other during or immediately after the problem arises.

This kind of frigidity is caused simply by the fact that the vast majority of women really do not want sex during pregnancy. No matter how we may try to accept the modern intellectual approaches to sex, we cannot change the biological fact that once the female is impregnated she ceases to have a biological urge. If she is unaware of this fact, her change in feelings towards her husband may frighten her. She may fear she's not in love with him any more, which fear many women cover up by pretending to be more sexy in case their husbands sense their feelings or turn to another woman for their sexual outlet. A lot of women are aware of their feelings and say they don't want sex as much as before in case it damages the unborn child.

In most cases, a marriage can well endure the strains of the first pregnancy. The experience of creating a child is new and thrilling and perhaps the couple haven't been married long enough to have grown out of that great 'in love' period of wanting each other sexually for purely psychological reasons. Where there's a great deal of tenderness on both sides, the physical aspects remain largely unconscious. I found that because my husband was very gentle with me while I was expecting our first child, I had little problems during my pregnancy. It was after the birth I began to feel less sexy. My husband felt that after a week or so in hospital, I should have come home ready for all the more strenuous bedroom romps we had denied ourselves and which he had been waiting for. But a woman is just not able, physically, to have sex immediately after giving birth. It takes a good six weeks for the body to settle down, not to mention those first few exhausting weeks with a new baby.

Any problem arising during and after the first pregnancy will become magnified during the second and subsequent pregnancies. If a husband doesn't know how to handle his wife during these times, he is bound to cause frigidity in her. We know he needs a sexual outlet. However, more important, his wife needs an extra amount of love, attention and reassurance from him, and if he gives her, instead, the impression she's undesirable because she isn't satisfying his needs, she's just naturally going to withdraw, perhaps for good, once her image of him as a lover has been smashed.

Mrs. R.M.

REDUCED SENSATION

Since the birth of our fifth child my husband has complained that because of my enlarged vagina he no longer receives the sensations he did during our early years of marriage. Is there a method by which my vagina could be tightened?

Mrs. L.W.

The problem of a 'loose' vagina is usually the result of slack genital muscles. These muscles can be strengthened through exercise.

Occasionally, vaginal looseness is the result of the tearing of the perineum during childbirth. If this is the case, the problem can be corrected through relatively simple surgery. Consult your family doctor. – F.

MASTURBATION AS AN ART

I have been a regular and fairly frequent masturbator for 30 years or so. I feel that masturbation, as an art, is something which has long been neglected as a vital part of sexual experience, so long as it takes its natural, and to my mind rightful place. Nothing, but nothing, in this world can surpass the joy of a good fuck, but in its place, a wank, pull-off, or whatever you like to call it can come a good second. As a serviceman, whose duties often take him to parts of the world where female company is often unobtainable, masturbation has played quite a significant part in my sex life, and I have, over the years, become quite adept.

I use the thigh method by lying flat on my back, bringing my knees up to my chest, then pushing my erect penis up between my thighs. By squeezing my legs tightly together and lifting my legs in a rocking motion, I can bring myself off.

Another method, requiring a little more agility, employs the feet. To achieve this, one squats down on the floor with feet close together and knees apart, then, supporting oneself with one hand, turn the feet inwards so that the soles point together, and the outside edges are on the floor. The erect penis can then be introduced between the feet by bending the body forward. Friction is obtained by lifting and lowering the crotch, and can be adjusted by squeezing the feet together. A variation of this is to use a double toilet roll, with one end of the outer wrapper

346

removed and the center tube well greased, the end of the roll being clasped between the feet.

Artificial aids can be adapted from almost anything with a hole, or capable of having a hole made in it; two of my recent successes being with a large grapefruit, and a square of soft sponge rubber. I have, however, always been careful never to employ anything which could be harmful, or liable to get stuck. For a long-term sensation, I strap the erect penis against my belly with a broad belt. This can be worn under the clothing quite easily and every movement of the body produces excitement.

The possibilities are endless, it only needs imagination and improvisation to produce almost endless variations. I suppose people do exist who can obtain all the satisfaction they need from sexual intercourse, but as far as I am concerned there are times and circumstances when masturbation, be it solo, mutual, or homosexual, forms an essential and gratifying part of a full sex life. If both men and women were not made to feel so guilty about masturbation while growing up, their sexual lives today, I am convinced, would be much happier.

Y.J.

Guilt about masturbation is frequently preverbal. In other words, the guilt feelings arise from early physical restraints put on masturbation. When an infant or child first discovers the capacity for pleasure which his little organ provides him, he frequently runs into parental uneasiness about this activity. To this day, mothers still remove their children's hands from genital play, slap them, shame them, and utilize a variety of methods to try to control this behavior before the child understands speech. That is why it is so difficult to deal with this problem merely by explaining it rationally to the adult. The shame has been imprinted by the early physical prohibitions. – H.G.

ORANGE MAN

I am 64 years of age and have been married for more than 35 years. Recently, for the first time since my marriage I have spent two weeks alone. My wife took a short holiday with a woman friend.

While she was away I indulged in the most wonderful sexual experimentation, although not with another woman. I turned the clock back 50 years and masturbated every day, as I did when I was 14.

I cut a hole through an orange and inserted my penis into the pith and juice . . . believe me, no vagina can produce such a sensation. I then applied lots of hot water and soap.

Please do not print my name and address as I am a respectable citizen of this town and a sidesman at our local church.

Sidesman

PIP PIP HOORAY

I am extremely interested in the letter from a respectable sidesman aged 64, who obtained such pleasure from an orange.

It would be interesting to hear how he managed to achieve such an enjoyable climax without damaging himself on the pips.

K.B.

LEGIONNAIRES' LESSON

I was amused to read the elderly gentleman's experience with an orange. Why an orange? It is cold and irritating. Perhaps he would be amused to hear the experience I enjoyed while I was stationed in Southern Algeria during World War II near the home of the Foreign Legion, but not so near that we could enjoy their bordellos.

After several weeks in the hot sun and away from females (except for goats) we learned of a masturbatory device invented by the legionnaires – a cactus leaf! After removing the spines and needles, you slice it open on one side the width of a large knife blade. Now the insertion takes place. You can also cut a slit across the leaf, and penetrate this way. The juice of the cactus is moist, very softening, and similar to sperm or vaginal liquid. The sensation is extraordinary. The leaf is warm (sun-warm) and it cleanses as you masturbate which in these lands of no water was a marvelous device indeed!

By the way, cactus pulp was used during World War II to make artificial shaving cream which was quite satisfactory.

R.C.

SEXY MELONS

K.B. indeed has a valid point as to 'the respectable sidesman' damaging himself on the pips in his orange.

The British soldier in the Middle East Forces (who only saw a white woman on his annual 14-day leave) was much more sophisticated in his choice of fruit, using ripe melons which were plentiful and cheap.

One end of melon is sliced off, a hole is punched with a finger, and then the penis was thrust firmly in. The melon was slippery and juicy, and the vacuum created by withdrawal made delightful, squelching noises. For optimum pleasure it was best to have the melon held rigidly in place, and addicts used to design their own special mounting blocks.

In the army there is little privacy, and usually one performed to interested comments from a tent-mate. Indeed, if the melon was resonably long, one would slice off both ends, for two people to satisfy themselves at the same time. You started by operating in rhythm, but at the climax you were both thrusting home simultaneously, thereby meeting (or even overlapping) in the soft center.

But I do agree that you finished up encrusted in melon seeds, and it was quite a job getting rid of them.

H.M.

Sidesman, K.B., R.C., are you all vegetarians? – H.G.

SPANKING DESIRE

I am an ordinary housewife who receives regular sex-spanking from my husband. What happens afterward makes it well worth it. He is never too severe, I have always accepted this as normal as I believe it is the man who must play the active role and the woman has to be passive.

However, lately I have had the feeling that I would like to spank my husband but I do not know how to go about persuading him to allow it. I am afraid he might think I am abnormal and I am wondering whether I am in fact being abnormal in having this desire. There seems to be quite a lot written about husbands spanking their wives but not so much about husbands being spanked. Is it because it is considered abnormal?

Are there some men who do not mind being spanked by their

wives? How can I find out whether my husband would agree?
Am I abnormal in my desires?

Mrs. B.M.

*If Mrs. B.M. would enjoy sex-spanking her husband, why
doesn't she ask him? He might not only enjoy this sexually, but
also be relieved that he doesn't have to be the sole initiator.*

*The fear of being 'abnormal' for feeling like spanking a man
– a mate, a husband – is largely tied to the image of what is
considered masculine and/or feminine behavior, a very restricting idea when one then has to behave as one 'should' rather
than as one feels. After all, many men may be just as tired of
being active and strong at all times as some women are of
continued passivity. It's a drag all around. – R.G.*

SUDDEN URGE

I am 53, fit and have lived a normal, active sex life. About 12
months ago I felt a compelling urge to be caned by a member
of the opposite sex – something I have never before experienced, even in childhood.

This urge, which was accompanied by dream fantasies,
became so strong that I told my wife about it to see if she might
oblige but she refused. I am convinced that, had she accepted
the challenge and given me a severe caning, I should have hated
it, and the whole business would have been finished.

As, however, she did not, I must now look elsewhere and I
remain convinced that if only I could find some young lady
who would enjoy performing this act and would do it with the
object of effecting a cure, my problem would soon be over. Is
there any explanation for this sudden urge to be caned, coming,
as it were, out of the blue?

D.S.

*Occasionally, as sexual interest wanes, men look for new forms
of stimulation that were not previously required. Before this
time your masochistic wishes were probably latent. Now that
you have become aware of them, you experience 'the return of
the repressed' as a 'sudden urge'. – H.G.*

350

HAIR FIXATION

I am 29, single, working as a representative for a firm selling hairdressing products. My work naturally brings me into contact with very many attractive females of all ages and so my sex life is very full and varied. I have always had a penchant for women with long flowing locks, much preferring this style to the closely cropped styles. The feel of long hair on my body really sets my adrenalin going!

If the woman I'm with has no objections – and so far, very few have – I like to wrap their hair around my penis and scrotum, massaging the silken tresses against my skin. Standing behind a seated woman is, I find, the best position for this, as I'm able to snuggle in close to her hair, at the same time leaving my hands free to play over her body. During oral sex play, if the woman's hair length permits, I become roused to a climax almost instantly if she uses it as a massaging agent on my scrotum and stomach and thighs.

As I said, very few women object to this; in fact many say they themselves are roused by doing this and feeling my penis on their scalp, or in contact with their neck and ears. (I might also add that I have tried masturbation with a false hairpiece. Although some satisfaction is obtained, the sensation is nothing approaching the real thing.)

I would be interested in knowing if this particular fetish of mine is common, or if any of your other readers make use of their women's hair during sex play.

C.L.

Obsession with and use of long female hair as an erotic stimulant is one of the commonest fixations encountered in males.

The Kinsey researchers, after studying the responses of 16,392 men and women, stated: 'Persons who respond only or primarily to objects which are remote from the sexual partner, or remote from the overt sexual activities with a partner, are not rare in the population. This is particularly true of individuals who are erotically aroused by high heels, by boots, by corsets, by tight clothing, by long gloves, by whips, or by other objects which suggest a sadomasochistic relationship, and which may have been associated with the individual's previous sexual activity.'

As evidence that such fetishistic arousal was not peculiar to their respondents, the Kinsey Report pointed to the fact that a number of magazines which featured fetishistic objects and attire were, in 1953, enjoying a wide circulation. Today, in the United States, and in England, there are a considerable number of such publications, and they are enjoying an even wider circulation.

C.L.'s fetishism, by today's standards, would not be classified within the realm of sexual pathology. That is to say such fetishism does not necessarily impede the fuctioning of the individual. Thus, if a person cannot achieve an erection except by kissing his partner's hair, let him kiss her hair. If she does not object, neither should the psychiatrist. – F.

AN UNUSUAL TASTE?

I am a homosexual, middle-aged, and I have a terrific fetish about moustaches!

The very first man I ever had in my life had one. I never look at a man without one; especially a moustached policeman!

I have one myself, and I admire them all. I recently read in some book: 'A kiss without a moustache is like a potato without salt.' How true!

N.R.

A DOG'S LIFE

My husband and I have not come across, in your columns, the peculiarity that we share. Some might call it a perversion, but we feel that so long as we both get fun out of it, there can be no possible harm in continuing.

I love my husband to pretend to be a dog! He takes off his clothes and goes down on all fours, and I attach a collar and lead to his neck, and he follows me around the house on his knees, or, if not on the lead, behaves as any normal dog would – sometimes curling up in front of the fire, or rubbing himself against my legs while I sit quietly knitting or watching the television.

The view I get of him, especially from the back, with his penis in permanent erection, really sends me, and before long we are both making love wherever we happen to be.

I remember one hilarious and exciting evening when we persuaded a friend of my husband's to join in the fun, and he and my husband made believe they were dogs and spent a lot of time sniffing each other!

Occasionally I spank my husband's bottom with the end of the lead, and he whines and barks and strains away from me, the collar around his neck getting tighter as he goes red in the face. This, together with him rolling on his back, legs apart, is the thing that gets me most excited of all, and I can barely wait for him to enter me before I come, sometimes up to four times.

I should add that far from looking ridiculous in this position, my husband, who is a beautifully well built and muscular man, with fabulous flat stomach and very long penis and with balls that really hang down, looks to me even more desirable when I see him as a dog, than as a man.

Are we as weird as we sound, or are we as normal as most, with an interest shared by others?

Mrs. A.W.

To say that I am surprised by the content of your letter would be an understatement; incredulous would be a better word! However, to take it at face value, the following comments seem pertinent.

Your 'canine capers' are certainly rare. I have had a wide experience in most types of sexual variants, but I have never come across such behavior as you describe. ... I have also made an exhaustive search of the appropriate medical literature and have not been able to discover a single case. There are a number of reports of the type of practice you describe figuring prominently in sexual fantasies, but not in actual behavior.

'You ask whether or not your practices might be called 'perversion'. Briefly, to my way of thinking, the word 'perversion' is emotionally loaded and should not be used since it tells us nothing valuable about the particular type of behavior under discussion. I prefer the term 'sexual variant' which implies only that any particular sexual stimulation is practiced by the minority – nothing more and nothing less. Thus, the prejudice associated with the word 'perversion' is removed, allowing a much more rational approach to the subject.

Your particular preference may be referred to as a 'sexual variant' which is extremely rare. I think most people would view your behavior with hilarity rather than disgust. Certainly I feel this and the tone of your letter suggests fun rather than prurience.

You ask whether or not your practices could be harmful. If I may end on a rather facetious note, your husband sounds such a 'hot property' that my only suggestion is to keep him away from other 'bitches in season'. Otherwise you might lose your dog – sorry, I mean man! – F.

'PENIS SMACKING'

During the past year I have become very keen on bondage, which I find adds quite a lot of fun to our sexual activity. My husband is rather passive and it is left to me to make most of the sexual advances. I don't mind this at all, in fact I prefer it. I have always loved to tease him and enjoyed making him wait as long as possible for any relief, so of course when I introduced bondage into our loveplay, it seemed ideal.

One of the methods which gives me a delightful feeling of being in control is to take my husband up into the bedroom during the afternoon. There he is secured with wriststraps, lying on the bed. I then explain to him that I am going to give him lessons on self-control. I make it quite clear that he must not allow his penis to become erect, or woe betide him. I take down his trousers and shorts and then have a nice sexy talk to him.

It doesn't take long for his penis to come to life, in spite of his efforts, and as it does so I fondle it and remind him of what I promised. Then I take out a springy wooden rule which I keep in my dressing table drawer.

I give a few playful taps with it on his penis, then a sharp slap; this is followed by five or six more slaps spaced out at about half-minute intervals. Were I to continue, I could bring him to a climax with slapping alone, but of course I never do.

I leave him alone for half an hour, then return and fondle his penis, asking teasingly if it's learned its lesson. It hasn't of course and soon rises to attention. This earns it another series of smacks perhaps just a little harder that the previous ones.

These sessions are repeated – and he has had as many as ten of them during the afternoon and evening. As you can well imagine his penis becomes quite tender and I must confess it looks it too.

In between smacks I playfully kiss it better which of course

354

teases it all the more. The vigorous erection which my husband achieves like this excites me considerably and by the time I decide to set him free we are both feeling so sexy that we get fantastic results.

My husband complains that I am too severe with my slaps and that he is sore and tender for the next few days. Yet I have only to remove the rule from the drawer, tap it in my hand and ask, 'Shall I?' and he gets an instant erection. I can only surmise that he enjoys a little pain with his pleasure.

I have never read any letters from readers about penis smacking and I wonder if I am alone in my passion for doing this?

Mrs. P.E.

Your practices of 'penis smacking' will do no harm physically or emotionally providing common sense is used, the stimulation is light enough to provoke a pleasurable sensation and not cause welts or bruising, and you are both willing, even eager participants, deriving pleasure from the situation.

The soreness and reddening are natural results and should pass in a few hours, causing no permanent damage in a fit young person. – F.

ANY HARM IN THIS?

A very passionate female friend of mine is so fond of me she has expressed a desire to drink my urine. I have heard of 'urolagnia' before, but what I want to know is can drinking urine occasionally do you any harm?

I could imagine that if I had any kidney or liver diseases it could be transmitted via the urine, but would it do any harm if the person is healthy?

C.G.

The desire to eat up, swallow or ingest the object of one's love is quite common and has been extensively explored by the psychoanalysts. 'You are so lovely I could eat you all up' is said by loving mothers so frequently that we all must have heard of this expression of love to a young child. But it is of course merely an expression indicating the intensity of the love.

Oral-genital contact, an extension some feel of this mode of love expression, is so common today that it is to be regarded as

355

a normal act in lovemaking. Many women wish to ingest the ejaculate and some actually say they believe this is beneficial to them, claiming it improves their bust line. There is no shred of evidence that this is so, but on the other hand this habit will do no harm, and people can be left to please themselves in what they believe.

When the ingestion of the urine or the feces is considered, then we might regard this practice as so unusual that it leaves the realms of normality, and not one to be encouraged. As C.G. says, any disease of the kidneys or bladder might infect the drinker. If the person who passes the urine is perfectly healthy, then the occasional intake of urine will do no physical harm.
– F.

AN OLD, OLD STORY

I would appreciate your advice in the following matter. A girl I know claims to be a virgin and says that she has no sex experience at all, not even of masturbation. She is 25 years old.

However, I have discovered that her inner lips (or labia minora) project at least ½ inch outside her body, pushing the outer lips apart, and are clearly visible in all positions.

I am told that female genitals like these are very experienced indeed, and this is a sure sign. I would be grateful for any comments you would care to make.

B.C.

It is an old, old story that masturbation will leave physical signs to be detected by examination of the genitalia and other parts.

In fact, normal sexual activities will leave no trace in most cases. It is possible to say on examination in some cases that any sexual practice is unlikely, or the reverse, but any categorical statement is as likely to be wrong as right. This applies so much to medical practice in general that it leads to the comment 'doctors can never give a straightforward answer to a straightforward question!'

The size of the labia minora varies enormously, and no conclusion can be drawn from the fact they are apparently large.

The modern use of tampons or internal sanitary appliances

and the indulgence of so many girls in strenuous physical activity make the detection of a true virgo intacta a difficult task requiring much experience and expertise. – F.

INSENSITIVE GLANS

I was mutilated as a child by circumcision, for a reason that I have been unable to ascertain, and have suffered years of mental torture as a result.

In middle age my glans has lost all sensitivity and stimulation of this so-called erotic area goes unnoticed.

Is there any appliance that we 'round heads' can wear during the day to protect and help this membrane regain its sensitivity?

I am married and the proud father of three uncircumcised sons.

M.M.

Your letter expresses the kind of rage that a minority of men feel about their circumcision. The 'mutilation' exists in your mind, not on your penis. In middle age many men become generally less sexually active and harder to stimulate. It is unlikely that your condition stems from circumcision. The same plight occurs to uncircumcised men.

Nonetheless, you could try wearing a glans or 'tip' condom during the day as it has been claimed by some men that this type of sheath, which covers the extreme tip of the penis only, has been of some benefit in increasing lubrication and sensitivity. However – beware – this sheath should not be used as a contraceptive as it slips off easily. – F.

FEMALE VIEW OF CIRCUMCISION

My husband has finally persuaded me to write to you following the lengthy correspondence for and against circumcision. Why not, he has said, give the 'customer reactions'. Having strong views on the subject myself I am very surprised that all the letters on it seem to have come from men. Yet, as I fully know circumcision is a factor which affects sexual efficiency.

I am as fond as most sexually awakened women of

357

pre-intercourse foreplay, of cunnilingus and the rest, but, after all, these are only the preparation for the real thing which is having a firm active penis inside the place it is intended to be. For me it cannot be too active and it certainly must be capable of lasting for it is poor (and unusual) lovemaking when my husband and I do not go through three or four positions before orgasm. As far as I am concerned the measure of a good penis is not length or even circumference but its ability to stay erect. This is where the circumcised man gains; if he does it at the expense of quick sensitivity he gains immeasurably in the end.

I was first married at the age of 18 knowing little of sex and my first sight of an erect penis was on my wedding night. I can remember to this day the fascination of seeing it push through the foreskin but as the days passed fascination turned to frustration because it was so sensitive that foreplay was out of the question and it became a race to complete penetration before ejaculation. There is no doubt that this was the root cause of our breakup for in spite of our efforts and the use of thick condoms we could never satisfy each other.

Three years later I met and fell in love with my present husband though with the unhappy sex experience behind me I was very diffident about risking a second marriage.

Fortunately he was understanding as well as persuasive. One weekend was all that it needed to cure my sexual inhibitions. I remember also seeing his penis for the first time and being a little disappointed at the stumpiness that circumcision caused but I can assure you that the disappointment soon disappeared with the performance. We have two daughters but if, as I hope, a son will be forthcoming he will very quickly have his foreskin removed!

Mrs. L.W.

Masters and Johnson report that in their research they could detect no difference in sensitivity between the uncircumcised and circumcised penis. – H.G.

SIMULATES ORGASM

I have a problem of a sexual nature which I am most reluctant to discuss with our family doctor. The problem is – whenever I engage in coitus with my husband, I simulate an orgasm. The truth is, I have never experienced an orgasm in my life. During our first year of marriage, my husband became terribly upset when he saw that he was not capable of bringing me to climax. Because it was beginning to adversely affect our marriage, one night I pretended that I had reached orgasm. My husband was beside himself with joy. His reaction was so positive that I decided to do the same thing when next we made love. His attitude toward me changed. He was more considerate and loving and was very much easier to live with. With his confidence as a lover restored, his sexual appetite increased which meant that I, too, had to carry out my deception more frequently.

Try as I might, I have never been able to truly reach a climax. Perhaps it is due to the fact that I had a very strict, religious upbringing during which time sex was usually associated with sin. I cannot recall ever completely enjoying lovemaking since I got married, and I find myself in a position where each time after the completion of the act, I feel dirty and guilty because I am lying to my husband. Yet, I know that if I did not lie, our marriage would have ended by now. I do love my husband and I feel we are doing a fine job raising our children. I cannot give you more personal details because I feel it would be tragic if my husband found out that I wrote this letter.

Do you feel that I am justified in deceiving my husband as I am and have been doing – or, is my behavior as immoral as I think it is?

Mrs M.L.

'It's not surprising that in a country as achievement oriented as America, the new female status symbol is the orgasm,' wrote Colette Dowling and Patricia Fahey two years ago. 'And not just any old orgasm counts, mind you. It has to be the climax of climaxes. The Quality, or simultaneous-multiple orgasm, referred to as the Big "O" by those who haven't yet achieved it and therefore feel compelled to devalue it . . .'

The cult of the orgasm can be just as exaggerated and lopsided as any other cult. Perhaps it started with D. H. Lawrence who, in Lady Chatterley's Lover displayed a monumental ignorance of feminine libido and physiology. But now the reaction has set in. Sane and balanced sexologists deny it the supreme importance which writers like Maxine Davis (The Sexual Responsibility of Woman) ascribe to it.

It is obvious that any male wants to give his partner, wife or

mistress, pleasure. It adds to his own, it swells his ego and cer-
tainly it is desirable. But not the supreme goal nor absolutely
essential.

Sex is an art, not a science and is often a matter of trial and
error. Some couples can catch fire at a slight, casual touch – on
the nape, the inner surface of the wrist, the most unexpected
erotogenic zone. Others need 'heavy petting', manual or oral
stimulation of the genitals. One is not superior or inferior to the
other because of these individual differences. – F.

You have yourself in a no-win situation, Mrs. M.L. Since you
are so concerned that your marriage may break up as a result of
your lack of achievement, how can you consider yourself im-
moral or deceitful?

The problem becomes part of a much larger one of female
orgasm as a symbol of masculine achievement. As long as you
are busy faking an orgasm, you are less likely to have one.
Perhaps if you can learn to relax and enjoy what you have, you
won't need to fake it. – R.G.

ORGASM 'PROOF'

A recent best-seller on sex instruction says there is one infal-
lible way of finding out whether a woman has really reached
orgasm, namely that erection of the nipples will be observed:
'no nipple erection, no orgasm', according to this book.

If it had not been for reading this, it would never have occurred to me to doubt that my girlfriend reaches orgasm when
we are making love. She shows all the obvious signs – tension
and excitement, culminating in vaginal contractions, followed
by relaxation. But she *doesn't* experience any noticeable erection of the nipples.

This has us both worried since we wonder if she is really
coming off properly. In addition, it has me wondering if her
apparent symptoms of orgasm are all a sham, designed to cover
the fact that she just isn't feeling anything at all. She strongly
denies shamming anything. But the book is so positive on this
point that I still feel some doubts.

I would appreciate your views on this problem. Is it the case
that orgasm in a woman is invariably accompanied by nipple
erection – or are some women exceptions to this rule? And is

the nipple erection supposed to happen before, during or after orgasm? How pronounced is it supposed to be, and how long is it supposed to last? *Is* there any way of knowing whether a woman has really reached orgasm, and, if so, what is it?

I.S.

There is no foolproof way to discover whether or not a woman has really reached orgasm. More important than orgasm detection is why I.S. is so concerned about whether or not his girl-friend has an orgasm. If she doesn't complain it is only looking for trouble to demand that she have the kind of orgasm he read about in the latest sex book.

One of the unfortunate consequences of reading many of the popular 'how to' sex books is that some people then become dissatisfied with an enjoyable sexual relationship because it does not measure up to the author's description. Nothing could be more absurd. Why not enjoy what you have and stop looking a gift horse in the mouth or any place else? – H.G.

MULTIPLE ORGASMS

I am often struck by the frequency of reports of women unable to experience orgasm or the amazement expressed concerning women being capable of multiple orgasm. Kinsey gives figures showing that many women never achieve orgasm even after several years of intercourse, and he offers a figure of 14% for females experiencing multiple orgasms – the majority of these having two per session. My experience is so at variance with Kinsey's findings that it might justify a deeper investigation if other capable males can offer similar experiences.

I have only considered relationships where ample time was available for all the lovemaking desired and have therefore excluded all those where through limited time it was necessary to aim at one mutual climax. Although I have travelled widely, only four, all in the multiple group, were foreigners. Of my 21 affairs two *never* had a climax. Three never had more than one. Sixteen had multiple climaxes.

Of the first two, one could achieve climax if her clitoris was stimulated for a sufficient period of time, but this was the only way and could be exhausting, difficult and tedious. The fact that only three women were unable to have orgasm more than once, whatever length of time the man functioned, must be compared with the 16 who readily achieved multiple orgasm under the same circumstances.

The female has to be brought to climax by the male's activities, and in my view *if the male is capable the female is almost always able to climax many times each session.* I should explain, I have trained myself to be able to withhold ejaculation as long as desired (but if I am not at ease with my lover, this can fail me), and I am particularly well developed. All the 16 women had one thing in common – having reached their climax, if strong thrusting was continued, they had a second almost immediately, a third and even a fourth on occasion, all within a minute. Once they were there, it was easy and entirely up to the man to be vigorous, and to have full control of himself. Only three were in their 20s, and the rest were 40 and more.

Although I can defer my ejaculation, I always achieve it – indeed my partner has only to ask me to come with her next time and I am powerless to do otherwise.

The proportion of women I know who can have multiple orgasm and the number of such orgasms are matters so different from figures publicized or difficulties expressed in letters, that I wonder whether a few cold women are not receiving disproportionate attention. My experiences clearly indicate that the female is not cold and almost all are able to climax many times if loved correctly

I recall one author stating the view that the single climax was stronger and more satisfying – he couldn't have had much experience!

B.F.

Our society is obsessed with the need for achievement. Unfortunately this obsession has invaded the sexual realm as well, and instead of sex being a source of pleasure, for many it has become another indicator of success or failure.

A few years ago the emphasis in many of the sex books and journals was focused on simultaneous orgasm, and the men and women who did not come together often felt themselves inadequate. Now there has been increasing attention paid to the phenomenon of multiple orgasm based on the motion that if one is good, two, three, four or ten are that much better. Sexual pleasure is not based on the 'numbers' game, but on sexual appetite. – H.G.

SICK OR WELL?

One theme annoys me very much, mostly expressed in letters from women – the idea of the great importance of the orgasm for women. It's almost become like the suffragettes' cry for the vote; it's not the means, it's the end that counts. Of course, it's wonderful to have an orgasm during love-making but if, for some unaccountable reason, a woman can't always make it she should realize it's being close and having such wonderful contact with a man she wants that really matters, not the physical action of orgasm.

I am separated from my husband because of personality clashes; when we were together and on good terms he always brought me to orgasm when we made love. I now have a lover whom I absolutely adore and desire the moment I see him, but in all the months we have been going to bed together I have never had an orgasm during intercourse. When he leaves me in the morning I masturbate thinking of him and his semen inside me and I have a wonderful orgasm and am thoroughly satisfied mentally and physically.

I suppose a lot of experts would think this is a sick relationship, but we're very happy and I'm not looking around wondering if other men would satisfy me better in bed.

Mrs. J.L.

STILL HAS INHIBITIONS

I personally have always had a secret yearning for my wife to tease me gently to orgasm while I am asleep. I would not ask that she deliberately lay awake and lose sleep just to give me this pleasure, but often one awakens during the night and is unable to go to sleep straightaway.

What a delightful surprise to experience this pleasure while progressing from the unconscious. And what a joy to know your wife cares enough to do this for you!

For my part, I often awaken and have a desire to fondle my wife, but am not sure whether she would welcome this, and even after 25 years of married life, I am too shy to ask!

P.K.

Perhaps it does take some courage to overcome the inhibitions of training to discuss a subject like sex with one's wife after 25 years of silence. However, the experience of so many of my patients has been that silence can prove much more destructive to a relationship than open communication, even if difficult. A simple way to do it is to broach the subject, and then ask if the other person wishes to continue. It is advisable to be guided by the response and not to force conversation on a person, just as one would not force any other kind of activity. Communication is a two-way street. The person who wants to talk should also be wiling to listen and vice versa! – H.G.

OUTSIDE THE BEDROOM

One of the most basic problems in any marriage is how to maintain a mutually stimulating sex life between husband and wife once 'the first, fine, careless rapture' has worn off, as it must inevitably do.

My wife and I have been married for three years, and during this time we have practiced every conceivable positional variation when making love, preceded by and/or interspersed with all manner of non genital-to-genital arousal procedures to ensure that our sex life was kept on the 'front burner' as much as possible. About a year ago, however, we frankly admitted to one another over the breakfast table that the almost electrical spontaneity which characterizes truly great sexual experiences was slowly but surely ebbing out of our relationship. As we'd exhausted all of the procedural variations that we knew about, we seemed to be stumped for a remedy. Then my wife suddenly said, 'We always make love upstairs in our bedroom – why don't we try it in other parts of the house?' I must confess I laughed. 'Such as,' I answered jokingly, 'right here and now on the floor of our breakfast nook?' 'Why not?' said my wife. To my amazed surprise, the prospect of imminent coitus in such an original locale stimulated me greatly. I suppose anyone seeing us a few moments later, rolling around under the breakfast table in a frenzy of uninhibited lovemaking, would have thought that we were nuts, but it was the fullest and most meaningful sexual experience that we'd had for some time.

Afterward, we knew that we had stumbled onto a good thing and that it had been nothing more than the routine familiarity of our own bedroom that was dampening our zest for each other. We decided to take short trips together, staying in motels for the night, but interestingly enough, it was not just our *own* bedroom that seemed to put us off – it was bedrooms in general. I think that we had both associated sex with the bedchamber for so long, that no matter what we tried between the sheets, it was old hat, and therefore lacking in that marvelous animal abandon when lovemaking is really sensational.

We have now taken to making love, whenever possible, in all the different rooms of our house, bathrooms included. In this way every area of our abode is a potential venue for sex. And as we have an 11-room house, and there are God knows how many sexual variations that two people can indulge in, our sexual varietarianism must run into five figures. Making love on the floor of the laundry room or under a billiard table may sound ridiculous, but our room-to-room romancing works beautifully for us, and surely that's the important thing?

H.C.

AVERAGE TIME

So many articles and letters refer to the importance of the female partner having orgasm and many advise how to bring this about. But none mention length of time or the female 'going off the boil' even when the thrusting is continuous.

Length of time is my immediate concern and I would be glad of advice on it. At 58 I can keep going for 25 minutes. Young people tell me it's all over in about four minutes, but one lad says he can keep going for an hour and a half! What *is* usual?

G.C.

It is absolutely impossible to give an average time for the man to bring his partner off. The partner will likely vary in the time she needs for coming from occasion to occasion, depending on a number of factors, such as the degree of tension to which her sex drive has brought her before lovemaking was initiated, her psychological mood, the skill of her lover on this particular occasion, and so on. This period may be anything from a minute after the penis has been put into the vagina to 10, 15 or 20 minutes. According to the Kinsey Report, 52% of all males take longer than two minutes to reach orgasm during intercourse. So that while one man may reach orgasm in four minutes, another may take fifteen. Because of this wide variation, the term 'normal' or 'average' time in sex is practically meaningless. All that is being described is a statistical figure which is only arrived at by averaging a great many widely disparate figures. – F.

G.C.'s problem is not one of timing, but rather one of determining why he feels that he has to produce an orgasm under all circumstances. Too often this demand makes it impossible to have a really joyous coupling and produces instead an arduous task. – H.G.

A MALE CYCLE?

I know that women have a monthly sexual cycle, but I think I have detected something of this sort in myself. Is this a sign of illness, or do men also have a sexual cycle?

R.M.

Many researchers have asserted that there is no male sexual cycle, but recent studies are beginning to point the other way and it has been shown that many sexually normal men do have a measurable monthly emotional cycle, swinging between mild depression and mild elation. The Swedish zoophysiologist Dr. J. E. Kihlstrom has investigated the question in animals and claims to have found male monthly cycles in cattle, rats, mice, rabbits, and sheep.

Among the factors which he found to vary cyclically were the volume of the ejaculate, fertility, body temperature, the number of spontaneous ejaculations, sexual drive, and the number of sperm cells. These and similar phenomena appear to correspond with hormonal fluctuations.

A possible use of his findings in man would be to chart the times at which a man is most fertile. 'Peaks of seminal volume and number of sperm cells per ejaculate are followed some days later,' Dr. Kihlstrom says, 'by a peak in fertility'. There are technical difficulties in determining this peak, but further research might show that the presence or absence of certain crystals in the semen might be used as an indicator. – F.

RETRACTED NIPPLES

I am 41 years old and have five children.

I have always had retracted nipples. I have tried nearly everything, including breast plates and massage, but nothing seems to happen. I have a 44-inch bust. Can I be helped in any way?

Mrs. R.G.

Retracted nipples can be of any degree from a slight loss of the normal prominence, to complete inversion, where the skin edges have to be drawn aside to allow the nipple to be seen at all. In these cases the breasts appear to be surmounted by an umbilicus (navel). These severe cases are apparent at birth, but the less marked retractions will not be obvious until the breasts develop at puberty.

Milder cases respond to the use of nipple shields and gentle traction (massage), particularly when the breasts are developing during pregnancy. If the milk ducts are congenitally short, then, as these cannot be lengthened to any significant degree, only surgical division will be of value. These form the more severe cases.

This operation although surgically simple is not to be undertaken lightly as late complications can occur – e.g. blockage of the ducts may give rise to retention cysts in the breast after a few years. As the operation will usually be performed for cosmetic reasons these rather frequent and unpleasant late complications will deter most surgeons. Few would advise, I'm sure, any active measures in a woman of 41 with five children. – F.

A LESBIAN TECHNIQUE

About 12 months ago I became emotionally involved with a colleague who worked in the same office, and this resulted in a lesbian affair. At the outset we had one thing in common, and that was that we had both been practically raped when we were still schoolgirls, and the experience had made us shun the opposite sex. We share a flat together and are devoted to each other. My reason for writing is that in our lovemaking we have discovered a wonderful technique which we have not heard about before.

The method we adopt is that one lies on top of the other making sure that the respective clitorises are in direct contact. The one on top makes slight pressure and then moves backwards

367

and forwards so that each clitoris is being manipulated. Slow uniform movements at first induce sexual excitement with the result that each vulva is well endowed with secretion. Then as each reacts to this situation, rapid movements become inevitable thus terminating the act with the most wonderful simultaneous orgasm. The only explanation we can think of for this achievement is that we each have an exceptionally protruding clitoris, so that perfect contact is not difficult to maintain.

Needless to say, some considerable time is spent beforehand in preparation for the act, such as passionate kissing, body stroking, penetration of the vagina by fingers or artificial penis and the genital kiss, so that we are each in a state of complete sexual excitement before the 'marriage' of the clitoris.

Have we achieved the unusual? Or is this method practiced by a number of females who have sex together? Sex books never appear to describe methods used by lesbians and information regarding this is nonexistent. It would be most interesting to hear examples of the techniques other women use – this I am sure is a subject which will interest many lesbian readers, who, like us until recently, have never departed from the usual conventional method of manual masturbation. I can truly say without hesitation that the delights of female lovemaking are out of this world.

Miss M.B.

GAY PARTIES

Since I was 19 and had a sad love affair I have been a true lesbian and I am now 30.

It started when I met a glorious girl at a nudist camp who seduced me after several encounters.

At first I was rather shocked by my indiscretions, but soon came to feel that they were all right.

Later we met others who shared our way of life and very often we have the most heavenly parties, sometimes with eight or nine of us naked and having fun and games without a blush. It all seems natural to us.

Women are our main critics but we feel sure that they themselves are confirmed masturbators and live on fantasies they dare not put into reality. They are unaware of what they are missing.

Most of us shave our pubes. We believe in hygiene and oral-genital kisses are far nicer on a bare pubic region. We, of course, shave one another at the small parties and we are adept hairdressers by now!

We get up to every sort of prank at these parties. We spank one another very gently with little canes and we play around with battery vibrators at times. We feel no shame whatever in sitting in a room completely naked admiring one another's charms. Conversation never lags, humor is always present and we are above all sincere with one another.

We believe that there are thousands of secret lesbians. I have been told by a masseuse friend of mine that nearly all her clients come to her for one reason only, to expose themselves and to be comforted sexually by feminine hands. I am sure she is right. Let us be frank about these things. We require no sympathy.

Miss M.L.

DISTURBING TENDENCIES

I am somewhat worried about a recent incident which occurred to me. My girlfriend asked me whether a female friend of hers could be present when we next made love. I was quite taken back by the request and, after much discussion I agreed.

I was absolutely overcome with embarrassment when the evening arrived. There is great intimacy when one is making love to one girl, but I could not even start when there were two girls in the room. My girlfriend's friend, however, was obviously quite experienced in these matters, and started off, with the help of my girlfriend, by taking off all my clothes. Some intimate caresses from both of them eliminated my embarrassment, except I could not allow them both to see my erection, and kept it covered.

When the two girls stripped off, I was very keen to make love to my girlfriend, but she made me sit down while she and her friend made love to each other. Following this, they again caressed me at which time I had an ejaculation.

Without going into further details about what happened, I will only say I performed what for me seemed miracles of sexual endeavor. I am still not sure I should have enjoyed it as much as I did, if just the two of us were alone. I am also a little disturbed by the fact my girlfriend exhibited such enormous and obvious pleasure during her 'performance' with her friend, far greater it seemed to me than the not-inconsiderable pleasure experienced during our previous lovemaking, after which she always expressed extreme satisfaction.

Is it possible she is basically of strong lesbian tendencies, and if this is so, would it be unwise for me to contemplate marrying her as I had hoped?

J.L.

We are continually asserting there is nothing wrong about most things a man and woman do sex-wise in the privacy of their own home, provided neither is compelled to do what the other desires, and both are satisfied and happy at the end of it. I can see no reason why this should not apply where more than two people take part.

J.L.'s partners obviously enjoyed the experience, and I think the test J.L. might apply to himself is 'would I like to do it again?' If his answer is 'yes', then there is no reason why he should not have enjoyed it as much as he did.

Marrying a bisexual can raise problems unless (1), the heterosexual partner is unaware of it or the bisexual is satisfied with heterosexual contacts and (2), if he does know and genuinely does not mind if she takes a female partner now and again. J.L. must sort this one out himself. – F.

BISEXUAL

I wonder if any of your readers can explain the following: I am 32 and have been happily married for ten years, with a perfectly satisfactory sex life, two children, and no major problems.

In my work I travel quite a lot, and a year or so ago I was on a visit to Germany, staying, as usual, in a very good hotel. I sleep nude, and had ordered breakfast for 7 a.m. having set my alarm. However, the alarm did not work, and the first thing I heard was the waiter setting down my tray at the bedside. The feather-filled cover, which is used in certain countries in place of sheets and blankets, had fallen onto the floor during the night, and I was lying on my back with (as usual in the morning) a large erection.

The waiter, who was young and good looking, did not pretend not to notice, but smiled and commented that I must have

370

been having an interesting dream. I was somewhat embarrassed, so I got up and went into the bathroom, closing the door behind me, and got under the shower to wake properly, assuming that he would have gone by the time I was finished. However, the door opened and the waiter stood there asking if he could be of further service to me. As a result of the ensuing conversation (my German is fluent) he approached and proceeded to soap my back for me, gently massaging all the way down, and finally inserting his soapy finger into my anus. At the same time his other hand crept round to fondle my genitals, which I found distinctly pleasurable.

Presently he stripped and joined me in the shower, so that I could reciprocate, and before long we had both returned to the bed for a lengthy and enjoyable session of what can only be described as homosexual love.

But the point is that I am far from homosexual. I am still in love with my wife, still enjoy sex with her, and carry on normal sexual activity as much as ever. I return about every three months to the hotel in Frankfurt, and on each occasion the waiter, Hans, comes to my room and we make love.

I have never been attracted to any other man, but when I see Hans, under whatever circumstance, I have an immediate erection. When he enters my room we can hardly wait to tear open our flies, and enjoy the sight and touch of each other's penises. Then we do the most outrageous things.

Yet, above all, I am essentially heterosexual, and my wife knows nothing of this strange second life of mine. I cannot give up going to Frankfurt, and indeed would not, as I like it so much. Are there others who are capable of enjoying sex with both men and women?

P.M.

You appear to be very taken with this man because of the totally uninhibited relationship you've developed with him. Many of the 'outrageous' things you do with him you've probably never done before with your wife, from the tone of your letter. Perhaps you would find your marital life much enhanced if you tried out some of these variations with your wife. Your 'perfectly satisfactory sex life' might then take on new dimensions which you never thought were possible. – F.

OVERENDOWED

I am overendowed rather than merely well-endowed. My penis when erect is 9¾ inches long with a girth of six inches (nine inches and four inches when slack).

As a lad and when in the armed services my penis was the envy of the other males, and I became very proud and arrogant about it – in fact, it turned me into an exhibitionist, since I used to walk around the barracks room in the nude, and stand well back when at a toilet stall.

As a young teenager my services were in considerable demand by mature women, and I liked this role. On reaching full development, however, I discovered that it was virtually impossible for me to find a woman prepared to have intercourse with me. They were invariably fascinated by the size of my penis but were not prepared to receive it; it was the length that most feared rather than the girth. Moreover, the glans swells to a size that disallows fellatio. I am now reduced to having a homosexual affair.

I should like to point out that in Kenya the boys used to wear 'cock stretchers' from an early age. These consist of a stone with a hole through it which is suspended from the penis, the size of the stone being increased as the boy grows older. This method does not improve the girth, and I don't suppose either that it would be of any use to a fully developed male.

P.K.

From time immemorial men have desired to increase the size of their genitalia and sexual powers. Little has been left untried.

To increase the size of the penis all sorts of creams, lotions and ointments have been used and every type of 'exercise' and massage that the human mind could devise, apparatus to encourage erection such as suction cups (very popular in India), constriction bands and rings, and elastic devices to elongate, etc. Primitive tribes also have their methods – the use of living ants, or the juices of crushed ants and other venomous creatures, nettles and thistles and other irritants, and the use of weights, bands of grass, and bamboo 'sheaths'.

None of these methods stand the scrutiny of modern science and all must be relegated to the mumbo-jumbo of the past and included with the old wives' tales, the black magic of sex and the unsubstantiated claims of certain cures, now long since forgotten.

The dangers of the method of using stones through which the penis is threaded are obvious. Any rigid band can cause such congestion that it becomes impossible to remove without special aid. Few hospital emergency room orderlies have not met at least once in their career with the case of a man with a ring over the penis, which can only be removed by cutting with heavy shears. All surgical textbooks quote the famous case of a gentleman arriving at a hospital in a taxi shrouded in a long cloak and holding a bottle, into the neck of which his penis was impacted.

Although the use of weights might increase the length, this is at the expense of girth. Like a rubber tube, if the penis is pulled longer it will become thinner. No additional tissue is added by such methods.

So the answer remains – at present there is no easy, certain, and safe method of increasing the size of the external genitalia by mechanical means. In certain cases hormone therapy can do this, but it is not a remedy generally applicable.

Conversely, if the penis is too large, there is no easy method to reduce its size. In general, the penis can be easily accommodated in a normal receptive vagina. The fear that the organ is too large to be accepted is of a psychological origin, not physical. Any penis is too large if owing to fear of insertion the perineal muscles of the female are contracted. Under anesthetic in gynecological surgery, the size of the vagina, when the muscles are relaxed, is quite remarkable.

To be 'reduced to having a homosexual affair' suggests that a latent homosexual tendency was always present and this might account for the lack of success in recent heterosexual affairs. – F.

SMALL PENIS

Just spare a thought for me – and perhaps thousands of others like me – for I may have to revert to homosexuality for quite the opposite reason. (I was once a bisexual, but that is another story.)

My penis when erect is between $4\frac{1}{2}$ and $4\frac{3}{4}$ inches long with a circumference of hardly 3 inches. My first heterosexual experience at the age of 22 left me in a psychologically disturbed state. The woman I went to bed with was so scornful (she even said that her little boy had a larger penis than mine), that subsequently for a long time I used to shy away from girls. I remember another occasion when a little girl of 17, about ten years my junior, humiliated me and in the middle of our intercourse, got up, put on her clothes and went away, because she thought she could do better than that with her finger!

I was married twice. My first wife left me within a year and before she left she had the cheek to advise me that I was best suited to become a 'nancy boy'!

My present wife is much older than me, not much to look at, has below average intelligence and hardly any education. Although I knew all this at the time of our marriage, yet I married her because I thought she would stand by me – at least for the sake of her security. For three years now we have been together; clinging to me she is indeed! But what a hell life is now. I can count the number of occasions we have had sex together. I have to beg for it, literally beg for it. Even then she relents only once or twice a month. And the urge for sex is so strong that I have to masturbate at least once a day – in the privacy of a toilet.

My only drawback, Mr. P.K., is my size!

R.C.

MASTERY OF TECHNIQUE

Of late there has been considerable discussion as to which physical feature of the penis has the greatest bearing on the quality of lovemaking. Some correspondents insist that circumcision is essential, others claim that a bulky penis is necessary.

From my experience – I have been married twice and have had a number of affairs between marriages – there is only one vital factor, and that does not concern size or circumcision. Successful lovemaking depends on mastery of technique and control, by the man, over his ejaculation.

My first husband, to whom I was married for 14 years, had an average-sized penis which had been circumcised. We made love about four times per week.

My present husband, to whom I have been married for nearly two years, has not been circumcised and his penis is approximately nine inches long with a girth of five and a half inches. We make love at least six times each week.

374

Comparing the two, my present husband's technique is far superior and although I am 35 years old I am enjoying intercourse as never before. However, once the penis is in the vagina I cannot recognize any real difference between the size of each. Where I prefer my present husband and his monster, as I call his penis, is in the foreplay and this is particularly so when we include fellatio in our lovemaking. I take a great delight in doing this. Although it is never my intention to bring off my husband while he is in my mouth, sometimes this does happen and I can assure any other woman that this is not an unpleasant experience.

To complete our lovemaking, whenever possible, we use a deep penetration position so as to obtain the maximum benefit from the length of his penis. We use the rear entry crouching position a great deal but the one I favor more than any other is where I adopt the rolled up or 'trussed-fowl' position. Although this is a little bit uncomfortable for me I derive great excitement from the fact that I am completely open to him and utterly defenseless. In this position I never fail to have at least one climax which is very intense. Afterwards I feel very relaxed and have a good sleep, unless of course my husband wishes to make love again, when we would use a side-by-side position.

I cannot imagine a better lover for me than my husband, but I am sure that with a smaller-sized penis he would still be the master he is. It is technique, which all men can learn, that is important, not size or circumcision. No man should, therefore, give up hope.

Mrs. M.W.

MALE PINUPS

Whether she wants to be or not, a woman, in the course of her everyday life in a city, is faced on every side by pictures and words on female nudity in connection with sex: those happy girls flaunting their breasts on railway station billboards, a lovely maiden admitting halfway up the tube escalator that next to herself she likes her underwear, magazines (produced by men) which 'daringly' expose to view every charm of many half-gone girls as we walk to the office.

Alongside this, how many pictures of nude men do we see? How often can we feast our eyes on an undressed male in a semi-orgasmic state as we drift up the escalator? Any nude male photographic magazines are thickly cloaked in the aura of 'men for men only'. Try to get in on that scene. There's not much fun in being a peeping Tomasina.

No, every effort of the media reinforces the mental association between women and sexual freedom, happy nudity, and erotic enjoyment. 'They're the ones that will give you a good time,' it all says. If there are prudes left in our society, they are the men, who remain coyly veiled behind trendy gear and ego-boosting aftershave.

We also see the nude girls on the bookstalls as ourselves, enjoying our uninhibited sexuality, and putting it at men's disposal. But where is the reciprocal favor? So, many of us like looking at handsome men. And not just their faces. So how about a sexy picture magazine for women? Not only would we girls not mind if the fellers let it all hang out – it would be only fair and just. And can't they see? We'd really enjoy it.

Mrs. J.G.

EROTICA FOR WOMEN

As for lack of sexy picture magazines for women, I think the simple answer is supply and demand. Just look in at any local shop selling magazines and take note of the clusters of males around the saucy magazines and notice the absence of females. There is a shop in my district that deals exclusively in saucy magazines and books. If you peep inside the door you will only see male faces and I have yet to see a female enter or leave this shop. What publisher could risk printing magazines for such a rare buyer?

It is just not true, of course, that the male form is not on display. On some statues a figleaf is provided for the mere male but in many thousands of cases the penis and testicles are exposed for all to see. In some of the paintings shown in our museums that most intimate part of the male is uncovered and you can gaze upon the bare glans. On what statue is the labia minora or the clitoris exposed? I have never seen either on a statue or in a picture.

It has been very noticeable that the sunbathing magazines have been printing natural pictures for some time along with many other magazines where the male form, circumcised and uncircumcised, can be seen in all its glory, in all sizes and shapes and in full color. Again I notice that the female in all cases retains her modest covering of pubic hair revealing nothing sexy to the common gaze, though in the same pictures the penis is revealed with no such coy veiling.

I think I have proved beyond a shadow of doubt that there is more exposure of the male sex organs in magazines etc., than there is of the female sex organs.

W.R.

NIPPLE PIERCING

I am an ear-piercing specialist of twenty-six years standing, and I have had a considerable number of unusual requests for piercing, which might be of interest.

The piercing of the nipples is as painless as ear piercing if done properly. The nipples are first sprayed with ethyl chloride to deaden any pain. Unfortunately, there are many jewelers who do not know the exact amount of ethyl chloride to use. The amount various considerably with each individual. Also, the instrument used by the majority of amateurs is very hard to sterilize satisfactorily. If done properly by a professional using sterilized equipment, the operation is completely painless.

After the nipples are first pierced, gold sleeper earrings are inserted. Healing usually takes from six to eight weeks, but this again varies according to the person. After the nipples are healed, anything can be worn in them. Most women wear gold rings or dumbbell-shaped rods about 1 inch long.

You might rightly ask – why have one's nipples pierced? There are several reasons for this. During the early Victorian times the operation was quite often carried out on young children when they were having their ears pierced. This was quite a painful operation as nothing was used to kill the pain. The Victorians believed that the movement of the rings against the clothing helped to strengthen the breast muscles, and with this goes a certain amount of satisfying tickling. Many men today like to see their wives wearing jewelry in their nipples. Women also like having it done in order to be different. Not only does it make them look more sexy, but the women who have had it done say they also feel more sexy.

Other unusual requests I have received are for pierced nostrils. This is done in a similar manner and a gold stud, pearl, or diamond is immediately inserted, or if the piercing is to be invisible, I put in some small flesh colored plastic thread.

This is quite invisible and can be worn if no stud is required.

I have also had a few requests for piercing in the outer lips of the vagina, for chastity reasons and also for those women who love to be different.

P.B.

ARTIFICIAL MATES

When my wife was ill, and we could not indulge in intercourse, I obtained a battery vibrator of the 'male' variety. This I attached by means of elastic bands to the underside of my penis, so that the business end of the machine was touching the knob of my penis. I then switched the vibrator on, and in a very short time gained the satisfaction of a tremendous climax.

I wonder why the makers of such instruments don't devise a sort of 'substitute vagina' for men who are sexually deprived because of their wives' illnesses?

F.W.

A SEX SLAVE

Living in Paris has more advantages, sexually, than one even anticipates before arriving. I recently acquired the most wonderful mate for my bed partner and I am sure your male readers would be very interested to hear about her. She is 5′ 5″, with the most beautiful shaped legs, perfect bust and little waist and a bottom that is perfection itself. We have the most wonderful intercourse together, in any position I happen to fancy; sometimes lovingly, with her legs wrapped around my waist, we make love face to face, sometimes I climb on top of her from the back, leaning over a low table. At times I feel like tying her spreadeagled to the bedposts for deep entry, or whipping her and dressing her up in exquisitely designed bondage outfits which I have bought her.

Whatever I feel like doing, she never protests. She never nags me if I stay out all night, get drunk, or bring home another woman. and she never talks to me of marriage. In fact, she never talks at all; you see, she's made of rubber! Soft and velvety to the touch and sweet and clean to smell, she comes all the way from Japan.

Apart from the fact that she gives so much pleasure and asks nothing whatever in return, what a useful little creature she could be to society. Just think of how many men get married for sex alone because their fiancées won't say 'yes' until after the ceremony. Invariably the poor man becomes disillusioned with what he gets; guilt-ridden, inhibited girls who can't relax and enjoy sex, refuse altogether to do the things he most enjoys; and he's saddled with another human being to house, feed and clothe. Most marriages are a mockery of the word and would never be entered into if the boy had a permanent sexual outlet before tying the knot for life.

Then consider the institutions where men are confined together; prisons, the army, even public schools. If these 'females' were provided for the use of the men, we should see a sharp decline in the homosexual practices which cause such concern to the authorities. Also, what better way to control the near epidemic rise in VD in the last few years? And unwanted, illegitimate children – 'she' never has to take the Pill!

Possibly the best reason why society should sanction such a sex partner is the fact of the frightening population explosion, which by the year 2000 will see our present world population doubled, with resultant unheard-of starvation in many of the poorer countries.

As for me, I'm enjoying the best of both worlds. When I'm in the mood for 'the real thing', I'll make love with a woman. But since I acquired my 'slave', I find that I'm more relaxed, get more sleep, and spend a lot less money. Paris, in case you haven't heard, is terribly expensive, especially when it comes to entertaining a woman.

Before anyone starts calling me a degenerate and accuses me of perversion, just answer one thing – who am I hurting? Certainly not myself. I'm enjoying my sex with both varieties more than I ever did.

P.B.

BABY MAN

I am a man in my 30s, unmarried. From earliest memory I have always derived intense sexual satisfaction from indulging in a fantasy world. I imagine that I am being forced, against my will, to live life completely and permanently as if I were a baby.

In my fantasies I am always treated by females exactly as if I were a baby. In real life I find that anything to do with the baby world arouses strong sexual emotion in me. The sight of a feeding bottle, a rattle, large high prams, diapers, baby clothes and rubber toys all affect me. However, the article that most arouses me is the all-rubber pacifier. Other types of pacifiers affect me only slightly.

When I indulge in my fantasy world I imagine that girls or women – usually someone who is known to me – put me back permanently to living as if I were a baby.

They destroy my adult clothes and dress me in baby clothes – diapers, rubber pants, shirts, dresses, bonnets, bibs and shawls.

The women tease me and feed me with a baby's bottle, However, the most humiliating thing of all is when at the beginning of my fantasy they roar with laughter as they produce a large rubber pacifier and force it into my mouth, making me suck it in front of them.

I imagine that a large cot has been bought for me and I am always put to bed in this. Rubber toys have also been purchased and some of these are given to me when I am put to bed in the cot.

At other times, in my fantasies, I imagine that I am taken on holiday. I am carried about the hotel in my baby clothes, always with a large all-rubber pacifier in my mouth. Everyone in the hotel thinks that I am a real baby. To taunt me, I am put in my pram in the garden with other real babies in their baby carriages.

But that is enough of my fantasy world. In real life I try to surround myself with as much of the baby world as possible. I have several large, all-rubber nipples, two feeding bottles, large rattles, rubber pants (baby style but made in an adult size), a bonnet, rubber toys and baby books.

I always use a pacifier in bed at night. I simply could not do without one any more.

I live alone and bought myself a large pram some years ago. I used to balance the pram handle on chairs so that the pram would not overbalance when I climbed in. I was, of course, too large for the pram and my feet stretched to the handles. In spite of this I spent many lovely hours lying in it covered by blankets.

After two years I reluctantly disposed of the pram. Although I always kept it out of sight I was always apprehensive, in case friends should accidentally see it.

Over a period of years, I have seen psychiatrists for treatment for this condition. Although this treatment has been carried out at considerable expense I am afraid that I am as bad as ever. I have come to the conclusion that I must simply come to live with this (fortunately harmless) abnormality.

B.G.

The still ongoing taboos against sex in conflict with strong sexual desires lead to a whole series of psychic compromises, Infantilism is one such compromise.

In the fantasies described, the letter writer sees himself as the infantile victim of strong aggressive women and thus does not need to feel guilt about his sexual behavior since it is imposed on him. – H.G.

INFANT IDENTITY

Thanks to a woman's letter describing how she treats her husband like a baby I was able to solve my own personal problem.

To be precise, for a long period of time, sexual relations between my husband and I were nil, but I could never understand the reason as I did everything to excite him.

After reading the Forum letter I became aware that when my friends came to visit with their babies and my husband was present, he always appeared agitated and restless if he saw them change the diapers of their offspring. After the visits he always wanted to make love. I also noticed that whenever I read ads from books and newspapers about baby buggies, beds, etc., the result was the same – my husband would become agitated and restless.

Aware now of what might be the problem I decided to try a plan. One night, after he had gone to bed I told him to remove his pajamas, explaining that I was going to try an experiment which I hoped would give us both pleasure. I then proceeded to put a diaper on him as well as rubber pants and one of my shorty nightdresses. He was speechless and embarrassed at first and demanded to know what I was playing at. I was worried, thinking that my conclusions were wrong, but after what seemed ages he broke down and confessed that he had wanted me to do this ever since our marriage but had never been able to tell me for fear of ridicule and losing me.

Needless to say now that I know about this I can help him. I think of all kinds of things I can do for him which I know will please him such as giving him his evening drink from a bottle, putting a bib on him at mealtimes and giving him a pacifier to suck. I have even thought seriously of either purchasing a baby buggy or having one made in which he could lie. I do all this because he is a wonderful husband, kind, considerate and generous and I feel nothing is too good for him.

I sincerely hope this letter will help any wives who are faced with a similar problem. Believe me ridicule is not the answer.

Mrs. A.D.

A COOPERATIVE HUSBAND

The subject of nymphomania is of great interest to me as I am married to one. I discovered this fact quite by accident after our second year of marriage. One afternoon, unexpectedly returning home from work, I decided to check something in our garden and, while passing the living room window, got the shock of my life when I saw my wife with one of my friends, in the act of making passionate love. Although very jealous at first, I was incapable of doing anything except watching. I soon discovered that instead of wanting to burst into the living room, the sight of my wife being made love to had the most stimulating effect upon me. I became very aroused sexually, and decided not to disturb them. Instead, I went for a walk.

When I returned home at the usual hour, my wife was in the sitting room reading a book. She greeted me as though nothing had happened. When I confronted her with the fact that I had seen her having sexual intercourse with my friend, she broke down and confessed that she could not help herself – that she constantly needed sex and realized that I was not capable of fully satisfying her. She was afraid to tell me of her constant sexual desires because of the fear that it might end our marriage.

Since I was very much in love with her, I decided that it would be foolish to terminate our relationship because of something over which she had no control. As mature people, there was no reason why we couldn't find some sort of compromise. I admitted to her that I had actually enjoyed the sight of her making love and that it excited me. But what I didn't want was her indulging in extramarital affairs behind my back. As long as she told me about her lovers and described everything that happened, I felt that it would benefit both of us. She happily agreed. That night, we were so aroused that we made love until the wee hours of the morning just like young lovers. This discovery about myself had obviously heightened my sexual appetite.

We are both delighted with the new arrangement which has been going on now for four years. My wife has had a succession of lovers, but she makes sure that no affair lasts more than a week. This fact is made quite clear to the man before starting with him. Since she is very beautiful and extremely voluptuous, she has no trouble finding the right type of men.

Because of her omnivorous sexual appetite, there are occasions when she needs more than one man. I am of course, always present whenever she arranges a multiple sex evening. My wife, incidentally, claims that many women deep down would love to occasionally take on a group of men at one time but obviously do not do so because of the society we live in. She has read of other cultures where such things were permissible.

On one occasion, when she brought home four American airmen, we decided to have a party. At first, the Americans were rather uneasy because of my presence but after I had reassured them, we all settled down to what became a most exciting, stimulating evening.

I justify my acquiescence in her affairs by the fact that I alone could not possibly satisfy her continual craving for sex. Rather than her having lovers behind my back (as so many women do with their husbands), I find that our solution is much healthier all round in spite of the fact that many of the people reading this would refer to our marriage as 'sick'. The truth is, we love one another and are able to differentiate between love and sex, and we are mature enough to realize that whatever we do is permissible just as long as no one is hurt. Perhaps our solution might help other marriages faced with a similar problem.

L.C.

LESBIAN DREAMS

I hope this letter will prove of interest to the men in understanding the female psyche.

Until my first-pregnancy four years ago I had always viewed

lesbianism with some distaste. I was of the 'liberal' opinion that if women choose to indulge in lesbian relationships then they should be free to do so without social ostracism, but I recoiled at the thought of being made love to by another woman. I suppose that because I couldn't relate it to myself in any way, I didn't understand it, and we are always a little afraid of what we do not understand.

However, a couple of months after conception I began to have lesbian dreams and fantasies. I still wanted my husband and we made love just as often, but the dreams went on. These dreams were extremely sexual. In the dreams I was participating in lovemaking with both women I did not know and female acquaintances. I felt no guilt over the dreams nor distaste; in fact I found them quite pleasant. I began to look on the subject of lesbianism in a different way. I realized that I was not a lesbian nor did I have repressed lesbian tendencies, but that it would be possible for me to make love to a woman to whom I was sufficiently attracted. I thought that the feeling might advance to the point where I was looking for a lesbian experience, but this did not happen. I had my baby and afterward never thought much more about these dreams and fantasies, which ceased.

However, I now find that I am pregnant again and with my pregnancy the dreams have returned. Obviously they are related to pregnancy, but why? I have thought a great deal about this over the last month and think that I might have come up with a reasonable solution. I am sure that during pregnancy a great many women have a fear of penetration. I know that this is true of myself. Although I still enjoy lovemaking there is always this little nagging fear that penetration may harm the baby. Perhaps sexual relations with other women appear so attractive simply because in such a situation the fear is eliminated. I am sure that there is something in my theory as I recently met another pregnant woman who told me that for the first time she too was thinking of other women as sexual partners.

J.H.

ORGASMIC CAPABILITIES

It is only infrequently that a woman will not reach orgasm if skillfully stimulated. Masters and Johnson's *Human Sexual Re-*

sponse really opened my eyes to the orgasmic capabilities of the female.

I had been consorting with a young lady of 25, a nurse, and had bought a copy of this book. We read it together and the subject of her masturbation was brought up. I remember one 'report' in the book stated that a female subject had reached orgasm in 12 minutes. She told me that she could do it quicker than that. Jokingly I asked her to prove it. Half reluctantly she agreed to, and, although we had had intercourse only a short time before, she brought herself to orgasm in just over four minutes. Needless to say, watching her aroused me very much, and shortly afterwards I had intercourse with her again, and again she reached a climax.

Afterwards we discussed masturbation, how we had both discovered it and how frequently we indulged in it. She had been brought up in a convent boarding school and had little or no knowledge of sex when she left. She went to stay with an aunt and her female cousin taught her the delights of lone sex in bed at night. By the time she was 18 and took up nursing she was in the habit of masturbating three or four times a week. At 19 she began courting.

In due course she lost her virginity, but was not orgasmic the first time although subsequently she learned to respond and so aid her own climax. The relationship broke up because she wanted to become an RN before she married, and she found that she had to masturbate every day to satisfy her sexual urges. She even went so far as to buy a vibromassager to aid her in this and as it 'did all the work for her' it was not so tiring and she could experience multiple orgasms on quite a number of occasions. She had tried inserting objects into herself but still had to stimulate her clitoris to obtain orgasm and she would dearly have loved to try out the Masters and Johnson electrically driven artificial penis!

This ultimately led us to trying out our own experiments. One day she achieved five artifically induced orgasms in an hour. She masturbated by hand, then with the vibro. Her next attempt was with a dilator, a plastic expander used in hospitals to stretch the rectum after an operation for hemorrhoids. She found it tiring to use upon herself and so I did it for her. The fourth orgasm was also induced orally by me.

We tried other experiments. She could not achieve orgasm by thigh pressure alone, not even when her bladder was full. She took longer to reach orgasm when masturbating with a full bladder. She said she found it difficult to concentrate. I wondered if she could involuntarily void urine from a full bladder at the moment of orgasm if she masturbated, so one evening in my flat she filled herself with tea and waited until she was all but wetting herself. We went into the toilet and she began to masturbate. She got herself to the point of orgasm and then, to use her own words, everything stopped. She couldn't come and she couldn't urinate. She had to wait a few minutes before she was able to empty her bladder and then bring herself to orgasm.

Another time when she was dying to go to the toilet, I insisted we make love and found that she very quickly roused and came off before I did. However, on another occasion when the call of nature was even more urgent her reaction was the same as when she tried to masturbate to orgasm.

I tried bringing her to orgasm by nipple sucking alone but failed. However, if I inserted my fingers and moved them around inside her while sucking her nipples then she quickly reached orgasm.

J.I.

SAVE MY BOY!

My son, our only child, is 15, a tall, mature-looking boy but has so far shown no interest whatever in girls. My wife seems quite pleased about this and feels it is because he is spending all his energies in sport and study and is not frivolous. I feel very strongly that this is unnatural; I have observed him closely when his friends come to visit us during the school holidays. There is only one boy he appears to idolize and copy in every way; to me this is a danger signal. When I ask him about girls he blushes and says he's not interested; at his age I was very interested. I feel let down and disillusioned by him. If he does not grow out of this and one day becomes a queer, I shall disown him. But I don't know how to avoid it happening.

Am I right to do all I can to avoid a possible tragedy, or is one right in assuming that if a boy is destined to be a homosexual nothing can be done to help it?

W.S.

There is considerable controversy over the origin and course of homosexuality. Some believe that once the homosexual course is set, it is incurable and incapable of change. Many others, including myself, see no such inevitability. During the last five years of my practice I have helped at least twelve people to become heterosexual. They have been homosexual for varying periods of their lives. One, a man of 50, became one of the most vigorous heterosexuals I have ever encountered.

In the case of W.S.'s son, there is no evidence that he is homosexual. It is not unusual for a boy of 15 to avoid the company of young girls because he finds them threatening. In fact, the very sexual excitement which he feels for the opposite sex may cause him to avoid their company. It is also not unusual for a boy of that age to idolize an older boy and use him as his ego ideal. Frequently his wish to achieve masculine identity causes such idolization. In his effort to establish himself as a male, he is patterning himself after one who he feels is quite male-like.

It is important that parents not get too upset over potential homosexuality. Sometimes an anxious attitude may encourage a young man who feels resentment and anger at his parents to choose homosexuality, a choice which he knows will make his parents most unhappy. – H.G.

IN DEFENSE OF HOMOSEXUALS

May I direct this letter in particular to W.S. and to any parents who may find themselves in similar circumstances.

W.S. is worried by the fact his son may be homosexual. He said in his letter, 'if he does not grow out of this and one day becomes a queer, I shall disown him'.

As a homosexual, I ask W.S. to sit down and think in a calm and logical manner what his actions ought to be, as his immediate thoughts and intentions are so very wrong.

Homosexuality, in this modern age, is not as taboo as it has been in the past, and although it is an obvious shock and disappointment to discover that a son (or daughter) has homosexual tendencies, it is a fact which has to be accepted. It has been indicated clearly that for some people, homosexuality is present at birth and not acquired, and is usually impossible to cure.

We don't ask to be born or turn out as we are, neither do we expect sympathy from people. What we *do* want is understanding so we may make the best of the lives we must lead. Our wish is to be *included* in society, not as a peculiar and different section, but *accepted* as part of the community.

Most of us are not flamboyant simpering pansies walking around with limp wrists seducing innocent little boys. Indeed, the majority have ordinary jobs and try very hard to appear normal to their business colleagues and neighbors. We have our own pubs and clubs, meeting places where we can mix with our own kind, so we don't need to lead normals astray.

Now that the laws governing homosexuality have been reformed with no apparent bad effects, it is time the public was a little more tolerant and understanding in its attitude. In my case, when I read of the deviations which some people *need* 'to turn them on', I begin to wonder who is normal, after all?

A.B.

IRRATIONAL ATTITUDE?

I am a homosexual, 35, and until recently, I was lucky enough to be living with a 'friend' of the same age. (When, incidentally, will someone come up with an acceptable word for a homosexual partner?) Since I began to masturbate at 11, I have enjoyed countless sexual experiences, the vast majority of them with my contemporaries. But in recent years, I have had to face the fact that without doubt, the object which has the strongest sexual attraction for me is the sight of almost any reasonably good-looking boy between about 11 and 15. And yet this does not mean I pursue these boys.

What people seldom realize is the almost total impossibility of seducing a child who does not want to be seduced, besides which there are no recognized meeting places where boys can be picked up. On the half-dozen or so occasions when I have had sex with a boy, the boy has not hesitated to make it perfectly plain he wanted to go to bed with me, and the degree of experience, lack of inhibition and general desire for uncomplicated enjoyment shown by these lads has been an eye-opener to a guilt-ridden product of the public schools like myself.

In puberty I too enjoyed freedom from guilt. It was in adolescence that sex turned sour for me, and my adult life has constituted a series of crippling emotional crises in which sexual pleasure has suffered. I therefore tend to think my attraction for boys is rooted in a subconscious desire to return to puberty.

388

Society's attitude to pederasty is almost totally irrational. The majority of sexual assault cases concerning children which come to court only do so because a boy or girl who was originally a willing partner, if not actually the instigator of an 'offense' has been persuaded by the police or parents to give evidence for the prosecution. Short of rape, there is virtually no sexual *'offense'* an adult *can* commit with a boy to which the boy does not consent. Children are very capable of looking after themselves. If a boy does not wish to be masturbated or buggered, or does not wish to do these things to you, he will walk off, change the conversation, laugh at you, run away, tell you to do up your fly and stop being silly, or sock you one.

Of course, I am prejudiced, but I honestly believe no harm and much pleasure and useful release both to myself and my partners has come from my infrequent sexual adventures with boys. The *real* danger with pederasty is that some boys who start their active sexual career with men may be tempted to cease offering their youthful charms, and instead spoil their personalities by turning sex into profit. Male prostitutes, like female, are on the whole an unlovely lot.

S.B.

If one can make a general comment on such an extremely complex and broad subject, it is to establish the general principle of voluntary choice and preference and the harm, physical and psychological, that intrusion or compulsion can cause, both in homosexual and heterosexual relations. However, we would hesitate to endorse your opinion that the majority of sexual assault cases involve boys or girls who were originally willing partners. As far as we know there are no reliable statistics or psychiatric material available about these cases nor can ordinary methods of statistical analysis or psychology be applied when so many intangible factors are involved. And you yourself point out the 'unlovely' aspects of male prostitution, a breeding ground for blackmail. – F.

CAMERA BUFFS

Just before Christmas my husband bought a camera which develops its own prints. Since then he has experimented with taking pictures of me in various poses and stages of undress. I

389

am considered to have quite a good figure and the wonderful thrills and sexual pleasure I get out of the various poses are out of this world. This also excites my husband and, needless to say, we have a marvelous time after the photographic sessions.

Mrs. G.C.

SHOWING OFF

My wife and I have always used the four-letter words and are pleased to see that they are now accepted as normal. We also feel that sex should be indulged in whenever a couple feel like it, and not reserved solely for the bedroom. It's very rarely I go to sleep at night without my hand on her cunt.

One thing we could never understand though was why some men obtain such a thrill by watching another man having intercourse with their wives. But not long ago something happened which has made us more sympathetic to them.

We were sitting on the couch one evening having a snogging session, and one thing led to another. To cut a long story short I had just finished removing my wife's panties as the doorbell rang. I rolled her panties up and hid them under a cushion. It was my pal at the door. He came in and sat on the couch with me while my wife sat on a low stool in front of the fire facing him. After a time I noticed a look of excitement on his face and a fixed look in his eyes. I followed his gaze and found he was enjoying a perfect view of my wife's quim. Instead of being annoyed, I felt excited myself.

Not long after my wife went into the kitchen to make some coffee, and the spell was ended. That night when I was performing cunnilingus (which I think is the most exciting form of foreplay) I was amazed when she came off almost at once. She admitted that she knew my pal had seen her quim and said that it had got her excited. We made love twice that night!

I wonder if all women have a streak of exhibitionism in them?

F.B.

REVIVING A MARRIAGE

I am 35 and married my husband, who is a few years older than myself, 14 years ago. During the last few years he has become less interested in the physical side of our marriage and this has distressed me.

Reading in Forum about wives who wore short skirts and left off wearing panties at home, I decided I would do the same. I have been surprised at the almost instant renewal of my husband's interest in me.

I used to wear my skirts at almost knee length but I have shortened them all. Several I have made into microminis for wear at home. I have given up wearing tights indoors and instead wear grip-top stockings. This makes it less troublesome when my husband wants to make love and I think the sight of bare flesh above the stocking tops excites him. I have spent rather more than I usually do on buying two new bras. However, they are worth it because of the improved shape they give and I pull up the straps a wee bit more than before so as to get an extra uplift.

The result of all this is that instead of my husband wanting lovemaking only about twice a month, and then only in bed using the man on top position, we now make love in our living room three our four times a week in the early evening and sometimes later in bed. My husband has become quite experimental and I never guessed that he knew so much about oral love which I am enjoying with him for the first time.

If my husband is slow in getting interested, I sit opposite him and cross and uncross my legs several times, letting my skirts ride right up. I do this quite casually but it never fails to turn him on and his paper or the TV is quickly forgotten.

Our lives have really changed for the better. The tension and frustration that I suffered from have vanished. My husband tells me I look ten years younger and says that he never realized before that there was so much to get out of the sexual side of marriage.

Mrs. J.W.

SEXUAL FANTASIES

My guilt has forced me to write because frankly, I can't discuss what I have to say either with my husband or with my doctor.

I have discovered that the only thing that will excite me during the loveplay and actual coitus with my husband is if I close my eyes and visualize the most erotic fantasies, such as

391

being made love to by a group of men, or participating in a wild Roman-type orgy. Without these fantasies, I am incapable of being stimulated to the point of orgasm.

I, of course, have never told him what is on my mind while he's making love to me. After the climax, my guilt is unbearable. I feel dirty and ashamed, as if I had cheated on my husband.

R.R.

HORSEPLAY

My wife confesses that her secret fantasy is to ride on the back of a stallion while he is mating with a mare. This came about as a result of a visit we made to a farm soon after we were married. A young couple we know run a stud farm, and we were asked if we would like to watch the stallions mate. My wife eagerly answered yes, as she had never seen horses doing it before. I had only once before.

The four of us walked over to the paddock. The mare was tethered, and the stallion was in an enclosure separated only by a gate. Immediately the gate was opened, the stallion charged in and pawed the ground and nuzzled the hindquarters of the mare with his nose, and soon she was quivering and swishing her tail. Suddenly his penis shot out to its full length, and this made my wife gasp.

Immediately he mounted her his monstrous organ entered the mare's body. I must admit that it was rather exciting watching the powerful thrusts of the stallion's hindquarters, working away as if his life depended on it. Lather and sweat were running down his legs, his nostrils were flared, frantic noises came from his throat, and in his eyes was a look of agony rather than ecstasy. Suddenly, a series of spasms shot through the stallion's body as he had his climax. His thrusting movements became so quick that his hindquarters were just a blur, and with one final whinny, he seemed to collapse on the mare's back. Then he withdrew from her body, and his organ was still as big as when he entered her, but it was quite limp and hung down from his body.

I could see that my wife was excited, and we made our excuses and drove back to our flat and had a marvelous session in bed. Couples should tell each other their secret desires and fantasies.

D.R.

TO TELL THE TRUTH

There is a current American trend for total honesty in our personal relationships which can sometimes have a detrimental effect that is totally unexpected. In this context, 'telling all' about your sexual past is regarded as a positive method of explaining yourself to your lover or spouse.

My own experience taught me how erroneous this attitude is. I now wish that I'd let 'sleeping dogs lie' but unfortunately it is too late. My husband was a virgin when I met him, while I had several affairs under my belt plus a lot of one-night stands. I more or less taught him everything he knows and while our sex life was not exactly anything to rave about, it was quite satisfactory and fulfilling.

Of course he knew I wasn't a virgin, but we never talked about my past lovers in the same way that we never really delved into why he was still a virgin when I met him. Then a few months ago, while reading a sex instruction manual, I felt like bragging a little and mentioned to him that I'd tried out many of the positions before and found them very stimulating. He seemed very interested and began asking me where, when and how in what I thought was a truly interested, mature way, not jealous or anything, just a bit awed and curious. So I started talking. It was as if the lid had been blown off and my whole sexual history came out in one long stream of consciousness.

Deep down inside I'd always longed to tell him about it but somehow we'd always avoided the subject, especially as I knew he had no similar stories to reciprocate with. Somewhere along the line I noticed that his thoughtful interest seemed to take on a sharp edge and it was then that I got a whiff that something was wrong. He said, with what sounded like bitter humor, 'I guess I have a lot to catch up on, don't I? Maybe I just won't make the grade.' 'Don't be silly,' I said, 'you're the only one I've ever wanted to stay with. I love having sex with you.' But somehow he didn't seem convinced.

From that time on things haven't been the same. When we make love he often makes sarcastic remarks like 'Is this the way Mike did it?' or 'What kind of memories does this bring on?'

I've tried everything I could to make him feel wanted and loved, but it seems as if I've opened a Pandora's box of jealousy that I never knew was there. Now if I go out alone he wants to know details of where I'm going and how long I'll be – questions he's never put to me before. Sometimes he even asks jokingly if I'm not slipping out to meet some boyfriend, as my present diet must not be as varied as before.

Another worrying thing is that we don't make love as often as before. I've tried to pretend there's no difference, but the gaps are getting longer and for the first time since our marriage I'm really beginning to feel frustrated. Before my revelations, we spoke about sex now and then without making anything of it but now that's all he ever seems to talk about, pumping me for more information as if my past sex life was some pimple which he is trying to squeeze all the pus out of but never manages to get it all out. His sex is getting to be all verbal and the inquisition goes on.

I hope we can ride this out and go back to the way we were. I've never cheated on him and don't intend to. I can only hope he'll finally understand that. Unfortunately, nothing I do or say now can erase the images of my past lovers that are now imprinted firmly on his brain. He has a great imagination and it seems to have been working overtime with the information I fed it.

I would certainly advise other people (men and women) to think twice before going into details about your past loves to your husband or wife. No matter how understanding or unjealous they may seem or even think they are, they are very likely to feel some jealousy or bitterness at your revelations. Mate-swapping apart, sex for most people is still an intimate relationship to be shared by two people. When you start talking about others you've been with you somehow break this intimacy by introducing other lovers, even verbally, into your lovemaking. For emotional reasons it's often best to keep these things vague. When you love someone you want them to be yours – past, present and future.

Mrs. J.D.

ZOOPHILIA

The subject of zoophilia does not seem to raise much interest which is understandable because, quite frankly, I do feel that it is practiced only by a very small number of people. My own three experiences, however, may be of interest to your readers.

My first experience happened at the age of 12. This was the first and only time I have ever taken part, but I must confess I remember it gave me quite a thrill.

I was sent off for my first holiday on my own to spend four weeks with my aunt and uncle and my 14-year-old cousin, William. It was a large house in the country. My uncle was, of course, at work all day, and my aunt, a great social worker, spent several days a week out on her calls, leaving Bill and me to look after ourselves and to find our own pleasures. We spent much time out in the fields or in the house at play, but often, at least once a day, sometimes twice, and every night in bed (we slept together) we would indulge in homosexual practices.

One day, when we were on our own in the house, Bill showed me how he played with his dog, a large mongrel bitch. Covering most of his genitals with butter, he allowed the dog to lick it off, which it did with eagerness, giving Bill much pleasure. Wishing to try this for myself I found that the experience was exciting and ended in ejaculation.

My second experience came at the age of 18. I was a lorry driver, working for a small local firm, delivering corn, etc., to farms. Making a delivery one afternoon I could find no one at home, and therefore started to look into some of the out-buildings to find someone to sign my delivery sheet. Hearing sounds coming from the barn, I approached it and as I passed the window I saw the farmer's wife bending over some hay, doing her best to guide the penis of a large dog into her vagina. After entry was effected the dog worked away with gusto, to the obvious and extreme pleasure of the lady.

My last experience came in France during the war. We were resting, that is, out of action behind the lines. I joined a party of six one evening and some heavy drinking of wine took place. Early in the evening we were joined by one or two local Frenchmen, and by about midnight we found ourselves in the large barn of a farm. There were some animals tied at one end. I am not sure how many, or what they all were, the memory being dimmed by the wine, but there were about six or eight of them.

I was not sure how or what led up to it, but during the evening, I recall that it was suggested that we should have an exhibition, and for about an hour, two of the Frenchmen performed with the animals, having sexual intercourse with a sheep and a pig, and one performing fellatio with a lamb. It was obvious that they enjoyed themselves immensely.

In the last 20 or so years I have led a full sex life, with several homosexual episodes, but ever since that time in France I have never come across zoophilia, and indeed have never even discussed the subject with my friends.

M.G.

Zoophilia is one of the least discussed 'deviations'. It has, however, been practiced for centuries and provides the content of such myths as Leda and the Swan, Io and the Bull, and Jupiter who, disguised as a white bull, pursued Europa. Both Dionysus and Pan were often personified as sacred goats. The disgust with which Western man regards zoophilia – or bestiality, as it is also called – may originate in biblical condemnation of the practice, although some taboo was probably in existence before the scriptures were written. In Leviticus it is stated that any man or woman who 'lies with' a beast shall be punished by death, and in England during the Middle Ages the animal was executed along with the human.

People raised or working on farms are more likely to indulge in this practice due to the constant proximity of animals and familiarity with their copulation techniques, and most prosecutions for bestiality occur in rural areas. Kinsey calculated that about 17% of boys raised on farms experience orgasm after the onset of puberty as the result of contact with animals. Sexual activity with domestic creatures, such as cats and dogs, is also more common than is generally supposed and pets often figure in some way in the sexual development of city-bred children. From personal experience, I can remember how as a child I ran about the house naked and often played with our cat because I found the sensation of its fur on my bare skin pleasant and exciting.

There is virtually no species of animal which has not at some time or other been involved in sexual acts with humans. Modern mythology, in the form of horror films and 'dirty' jokes, provides endless stories of maidens abducted by gorillas and sex-starved men seeking relief with anything from a crocodile to a camel. Such stories often involve servicemen who find themselves without female companionship and seek the sort of diversion that M.G. witnessed in France during the war. Elements of exhibitionism and voyeurism are also often present in such situations, and displays of female coitus with animals, boasted by certain brothels, contain these elements, too.

It does seem that animals are mainly used as sexual objects when the possibility of contact with another human is either absent or threatening. In other words, they are substitutes rather than primary sexual objects. However, when this is not so, bestiality can be said to be part of a pathology which Krafft-Ebing called 'zooerasty'. – F.

INCESTUOUS RELATIONSHIPS

I had an older and a younger sister and at an early age we all started to examine one another. Later this led to masturbation and eventually to intercourse. In due course we were discovered by our mother who I think dealt with the matter wisely.

There was no recrimination, no punishment. We were not even told to stop. First, she had a heart-to-heart talk with us about sex and love; it was a very candid discussion on all its aspects. She also told us about contraception. We were allowed to carry on our previous activities but now quite openly and were even able to talk about them to our parents.

Following this, they steadily started to encourage our friendships with other children of our own ages and regularly invited them to our home to stay.

Our parents were always there in the background ready to help and to talk over anything we wished to discuss. Yet they never seemed to interfere with our activities.

Before very long these friendships had developed into boy and girl friendships of a normal kind and we were far too busy with our own immediate dates to bother with one another. We all eventually made lasting and happy marriages, and not one of us is any the worse for our early experiences and no harm was done to anyone.

What our parents did teach us was that a family was built on love and understanding. And when our family gets together we number over 20 and cover four generations.

I think, if the truth were known, brother and sister relations of this sort are a lot more common than we are prepared to admit.

C.A.

You are fortunate in your choice of parents. They handled the problem with rare understanding and wisdom. One thing your letter demonstrates is how often deviant sexual practices are used as an act of hostility against the parents. The fact that your mother accepted your behavior but encouraged other outlets seemed to rob it of its hostile element, if there was one.

It is usually not the behavior itself, like incest, which causes problems later in life, but the reaction of significant individuals, like parents, in one's childhood. Your mother's understanding and sagacity at the time made it possible for you and your sisters to deal more easily with the matter.

One of the special problems about incest is that aside from the moral attitude involved it has been my experience that individuals who engaged in incest often had difficulties in establishing mature relations. For example, older sisters who had relations with a younger brother, frequently find it difficult to be involved with any but passive men; women who have been involved with incestuous relationships with their fathers are frequently frigid in later life. Apparently at some level, they experience the incestuous relationship with a father or a much older brother as an invasion of their rights of choice, and this leads them to give up sexual relations in general.

Of course, one of the problems with incest, as Freud long ago found out, is that reported incest is frequently based on fantasy rather than fact. The child, having strong sexual desires for a member of the family, proceeds to translate that desire into fantasy, and then the fantasy becomes reality. Investigating stories of incest by various patients with the use of hypnosis, I have often discovered that the incest was imagined rather than real, although the real frequency of brother-sister relationships is greater than one might expect. – H.G.

HOMOSEXUALITY – PLEASE UNDERSTAND

A homosexual is a person who has emotional and sexual relations with another of the same sex. What forces cause a person to be inclined this way? Many believe that it is a gradual process, with its roots in early childhood, progressing through adolescence, which, instead of resolving itself in young adulthood, eventually asserts itself, often with soul-searing strength. Some say that sexual trauma – psychological or physical – causes the individual to undergo a 'dramatic and heartbreaking' change in sexual development, so channeling him toward homosexuality. Others again believe it is congenital, that one's genes and chromosomes play a highly important part.

I think the subject has a high individual strain. All homosexuals, male or female, have their own theory as to the cause of their own inversion – whether correct or incorrect one can never be certain.

Many young people – I think it safe to say most young people – go through a 'bisexual' stage where the sexual balance is a little uncertain; and they may feel equal attraction to both sexes. I also think that would explain the emotionalism and difficulties most adolescents feel. Everyone has homosexual inclinations. Some admit it; but do not practice it. Some admit it only to themselves. Some would rather die than admit it – even to themselves. Who said: 'He who protests too loudly?' So where is the dividing line? How can one know how, when or why homosexuality is released from man's subconscious? And why in some cases it is accepted, embraced and taken as a way of life?

Attraction – both hetero- and homosexual – is an intangible subject. One person meets another and bang! there is attraction. Sometimes it is physical, sometimes emotional, sometimes intellectual – and sometimes a combination of all three. Others may not perceive what the couple see in each other. One cannot generalize in these things, and especially so with a homosexual relationship.

The general idea of a lesbian is a big, 'butchy' woman, very domineering, watching jealously over her smaller, more delicate, and definitely 'femme' partner. Or there's the male 'queen', mincing his way from one relationship to another – at high speed. Of course there are examples – hence the public image – of these types; they could be called the classic examples. But there are a very much greater number of couples – two women, or two men – very happy, very ordinary, neither 'butchy' or 'poncy'; but usually very much in love with each other. Their relationship, although passionate on occasions, is often based on friendship and strong affection for each other. Usually there is one more dominant sexually than the other; he or she feels his or her sexual role is to be dominant, and gains satisfaction from dominating and satisfying his or her partner.

In a prolonged homosexual relationship, I think there is a need for a far more basic love between the partners than is often found in a heterosexual relationship. I do not mean that heterosexual love is not deep. I know it can be, but – they can

399

marry and generally, all being well, have a family. They are equally bound to each other, and a long bitter legal wrangle must ensue – often damaging the children – should they want to dissolve the marriage. On the other hand, the homosexual relationship cannot be legally binding. The couple are able, and free, to part whenever they please. There are no children. Society, to a large degree, deplores their relationship. They indeed have only their love for each other, and a genuine desire to be together.

Please understand. I am not putting an argument for or against hetero- or homosexual relationships. I am not trying to 'boost' homosexuality! I am just attempting 'to enlighten the black cloud of ignorance which surrounds the subject, and can cause so much heartache to the homosexual. And there are a lot of us, you know.

V.P.

SEXUAL TIME-BOMB

Female orgasm has for a long time been understood to originate in the vagina. Recently, however, it has been suggested that only a minority of women actually achieve orgasm by intercourse alone, and furthermore that the vagina is not capable of sufficient responsiveness, so that in fact all orgasms originate in the clitoris. Whether or not this is true, it is clear that most women's sex pleasure is only indirectly associated with the 'reproductive act'.

The average man is ready for orgasm well before the average woman and has been expected to use his skill to accelerate the woman's orgasm or delay his own or both. Now it appears that his efforts have been expended in the wrong area and that in fact the penis is not essential to female pleasure at all. However the clitoris is usually small and difficult to find and it generally needs a very gentle form of stimulation. Considerable skill and perseverance are required on the part of a man to induce orgasm under these conditions.

Taken together, these factors expose the idea that men and women are suited sexually as a myth in subservience to which women have endured frustration and simulated orgasms while men have sweated through hours of fruitless toil.

Looking at the situation objectively, one is bound to admit that the homosexuals have a more efficient arrangement. Men can adjust to each other's reaction time more easily than to women's and understand intuitively each other's erogenous zones – and women too, since the clitoris responds more immediately to the gentleness of another woman's hand. But isn't homosexuality illogical? Certainly a penis would seem to be suited to a vagina and vice versa and it can be argued that the anus is designed for expulsion not reception. But the vagina, too, is 'designed' for expulsion of a baby; moreover, there are pleasure nerves at the anal sphincter which may be more susceptible than the vagina.

The fact has often been cited as evidence of their 'unnaturalness' that homosexual unions are sterile, but as has been shown heterosexual bliss depends greatly on cunnilingus, which is itself sterile. An American doctor recently said that homosexuality in parts of America was reaching 'epidemic' proportions. This accords with a definition of homosexuality as a disease. Why a disease? Because it is officially regarded as a threat to marriage and the birth rate. But most scientists concerned with the effects of the population explosion are already seeking ways of reducing the birth rate and there is already a debate on the place of marriage in the modern society: a number of weaknesses are being criticized and changes in younger people's living habits are putting pressure on marriage from other directions, so we can expect developments in this quarter in any case. We shall therefore have to entertain the possibility that homosexuality not only will increase but may have to be institutionalized.

This is the sexual time-bomb waiting to explode as a new phase of the sexual revolution eradicates the mistakes of the first, and I believe we should prepare ourselves for the advent of the Gay Society.

C.T.

According to Wardell Pomeroy, Kinsey's collaborator, there has been no increase in the actual incidence of homosexuality. What has happened, he told me, is that it is now more open. Since then the Gay Liberation Movement has encouraged more homosexuals to come out and openly announce their sexual preferences.

The Gay Liberation Movement has helped many homosexuals deal with their feelings of passivity, inadequacy, and social victimization. But there has been another even more interesting result which I noted among some of the people I treated who were active in Gay Liberation. At first some became involved in the movement in a search for people with similar preferences. As they became more and more active and assertive, some of them for the first time began to be interested in relationships with women. They did not necessarily want to become heterosexual. They did feel, however, that they wanted to be able to make the heterosexual choice when they so wished and not be compulsively homosexual. Three young men whom I had the opportunity to see within the last two years have gone through this interesting transition.

There are those who fear that the open announcement of homosexual activity by various people involved in the Gay Liberation Movement, including some prominent writers, will lead to a growth of homosexuality. This is probably untrue. What it will lead to is a greater openness about homosexuality. Like any other form of human behavior, as homosexuality becomes open and subject to public discussion there is a greater likelihood of an individual being able to choose other forms of behavior if he so desires. – H.G.

MARRIED HOMOSEXUAL

I am 32, married, with a child of four. When I was a little boy of four there was a young man living next door who used to give me sweets, buy me toys, etc. I started going to his room as he would show me books about animals, jungles and motor cars. My parents thought that it was all innocent and harmless.

Then one day as I became very familiar and friendly he made me sit on his lap and touched me all over. He took my penis in his hand and rubbed it gently. At first I did not know why he should do that to me and then I felt a little pleasure. I asked him if he had one. He told me it was called a penis and that every boy has a little penis and a man has a big one. I was very curious and wanted to make sure he was telling the truth, so I asked him to show me his. This led to mutual masturbation, which took place many times. Later, during my boyhood and adolescence. I had several other homosexual encounters.

With my wife I enjoy intercourse to the extent I would enjoy it with a man. But I can only make love with her once a night.

When I am with a woman she has to bring her vagina very close to my penis, rubbing it gently, for me to get an erection. I can't get an erection just thinking about her or seeing her naked, while the thought of a penis makes me feel deeply moved. So I think about an erect penis when I make love to a woman and I satisfy her well. I like to watch myself making love to a woman in a mirror simply because that gives me a chance to see myself naked.

I am afraid that some day my wife is going to find out all about my weakness for males. She might leave me and take the child away and I don't want to lose them. Sometimes I wish there was a way of finding other men like myself and satisfying this unnatural urge. But to reveal my secret longing would involve great risk. It might cause what I don't want.

Sometimes I think I should tell my wife and ask her if she would let me have men in the house. If she wanted to we could share them. But would it be right to suggest this, as she isn't that type of woman?

I am very worried and feel very helpless, especially when an attractive man is around and my wife is present. Not that I would make advances if she was not there. But I am tormented and sad when I can't do what I want to.

I don't even have the courage to tell my doctor about my problems. So far my wife hasn't discovered my faults. If I can't make love more than once she assumes I am just too tired after a day's work.

Please advise me. Is there any cure for men like me, or should I try to find men having the same sexual tastes as myself?

P.S.

You present the classical problem of the married homosexual who although proficient in coupling with his wife is preoccupied with unfulfilled homosexual yearnings and fear of succumbing to his desires. Again you demonstrate the usual illegal childhood seduction at the hands of an adult male which started you on a series of homosexual adventures throughout your adolescence. By adulthood your homosexual preferences were firmly established. Despite your basic orientation, you have however made a satisfactory marital relationship, especially it would appear in the sexual sphere. The fact that you 'can only manage intercourse once a night' would suggest that you have a very high sex drive (the average male of your age performs coitus about two to three times per week) and not, as you think, a low one. At any rate you give me no reason to suspect that your wife is other than eminently satisfied with the level of your proficiency.

Regarding your fantasies and preferred stimulative techniques, i.e., watching yourself make love in a mirror, etc., these are entirely private experiences, to be used and enjoyed by the fantasizer alone. You are not being deceitful, only diplomatic, in keeping them to yourself.

Although you secretly desire to be a practicing homosexual, in my opinion there seems little risk in this happening at present. Your obvious anxiety and determination not to disrupt your marriage, even in the face of your powerful yearnings, will I think protect you. Regarding your musings about inviting men into the house presumably for homosexual purposes, you answer the question yourself in the next sentence by rejecting the idea. My advice is for you to continue to get 'sexual relief' from coitus with your wife. By all means indulge both your fantasies and 'mirror' techniques. By enhancing your own pleasure and performance you do likewise to your wife and that cannot be bad, can it? – F.

I have known and treated many men with similar problems. If they are strongly motivated, it was possible to help them find increasing pleasure in their heterosexual lovemaking and leave their homosexual urges in the realm of fantasy. Frequently they have used the homosexual fantasies to enhance their lovemaking with a woman. If they can give themselves permission to indulge in such fantasies, the fantasies usually fade away. – H.G.

HE WHO GETS SLAPPED

If some people find extra pleasure in black lingerie, and others in plastic or latex clothing, there is nothing evil in it. However, there is danger and evil in 'wife swapping' because this cuts across the bonds of marriage. In any case, a sensible and clever woman should learn enough varied sexual approaches to satisfy her partner in every possible way.

Many continental countries are ahead of us in allowing an

open discussion of sex variation, and in publishing uncensored books free from Victorian hypocrisy, but this does not make the continentals 'perverts' or interested in 'sick sex'.

Being a modern girl, conscious that at last we are reaching more than equality, and knowing it would take only a little effort to be the controllers of present day life, instead of the inferior sex, I cannot understand those women who enjoy being spanked by their husbands. Most of the girls I associate with feel that it is *we* who should subjugate the men and administer discipline and punishment. Unfortunately little has been said, apart from kinky and erotic sexual pleasures, on the subject of female domination of the male.

This is something that has to be carried much further than sexual stimulation, and it must be devised on a pattern to create a complete domination in all domestic and home affairs. Recently we had a discussion on this matter and found that 90% of the girls and women had desires to be severe disciplinarians over their male friends and partners. Men are very easy to bring under control and once they have accepted their servile role they become perfect husbands and obedient lovers. The use of the cane or whip, however, is not enough, and one has to teach them complete subjection throughout the day and night. The correct procedure is to keep the partner in the nude, within the home, for to be without clothes is the symbol of subjection.

Another important symbol of subjection is making the male kiss the bottom and genital area while in a kneeling position. This should be done first thing in the morning, and at least twice in the evening, to make him realize that he is only a 'slave' and that any favors given are only granted because he pleases by his devotion. There should also be a list of punishments by cane or whip for every small failure to carry out his duties correctly, not, as some women believe, just for erotic stimulation.

There is also a necessity to chain him to the couch or bed, at times, and to masturbate him at one's pleasure and leisure. There are so many silly women who complain about the 'impotency' of their partners, but if they were to bind the male genitals tightly, with any form of strap or band, a firm and lasting erection would always follow. Even after ejaculation, this does not allow the organ to become flaccid, and he can perform the sex act again and again.

During the greatest period of female degradation it was the policy of the knights to place chastity belts on their women, and now the position is reversed and we are the superior sex. I find great pleasure in making sure that my male partner wears one. Any woman in control of her partner – as she now should be – can easily construct one of these. All that is needed is a long legged pantie girdle with a leather or plastic belt sewn to the top of it and a lock affixed. I always make sure that I keep the key; it is a wonderful feeling to know that I control his fidelity, and that he has to ask me to unlock it when he needs to go to the toilet. I can then make him kneel and ask for it in an obedient way and, if I feel like it, unlock it for a short time.

It is obvious that some women have not experienced the pleasure of complete female domination – it is far better than all kinky expressions and partner swapping. More important still it gives woman her rightful place in love and in the home.

Mrs. N.P.

SKILLFUL CANING

My wife and I have for many years enjoyed the delights of caning and spanking as part of our normal sexual life.

Since, clearly, people *will* cane each other, whatever sexual purists may say, could I offer, in all modesty, a few suggestions on technique?

1. The cane can be a vicious instrument of punishment, so see that you do cane on the moderate side. A few extra swishes can always be added if the victim has not had enough!

2. It is psychologically unhealthy to pretend that the caning is a punishment – it is, in fact, a form of sexual game and must be understood as such. (This does not preclude the pleasant little 'pretense' games played between understanding partners.)

3. There is only one safe place to apply the cane, low down on the buttocks where plenty of flesh protects bone and muscle. Too high, or too low, and severe bruising results and perhaps serious damage can be done to tissues.

4. The correct position to receive it is 'half bent over', i.e., lying over a chair. If touching the toes, or lying face down on a bed, some of the damage as in (3) can more easily occur.

5. Except for erotic purposes (i.e., a woman's panties) clothing should not be worn – in this way, the person caning can see where the strokes are landing.

6. The 'swishing' type of cane often preferred is, in fact, very hard to control, and a rather stiffer, shorter cane is much better for accurate placing.

N.M.

ABELARD AND HELOISE

Addicts of flagellation may take comfort from the fact that 800 years ago two of the most famous lovers in history, Abelard and Heloise, were devotees of their cult.

Abelard was the greatest philosopher of his day and Heloise, though only 16 when they first met, was also renowned for her learning, which was then most unusual for a woman. Abelard had been so preoccupied with his work that he had had no time for girlfriends; but having achieved all his ambitions by the age of 33 his thoughts began to turn to sex. Having heard that Heloise, besides being intelligent and learned, was also beautiful, he determined to seduce her and as a first step got himself accepted as a lodger in the house in Paris where she lived with her uncle, Fulbert. He also volunteered to tutor Heloise in his spare time.

Fulbert was so pleased and flattered that he placed the girl entirely under Abelard's direction and authorized him, 'if she were idle or careless, to chastise her into obedience'.

Corporal punishment by schoolmasters for both boys and girls was, of course, universal in the Middle Ages, and was usually administered with a birch on the naked buttocks. It might have been considered that Heloise was too old for such treatment, but evidently her uncle, who had probably given it to her often himself, did not think so.

Needless to say Abelard needed no further encouragement; and his nightly lessons were enlivened by frequent whippings followed by passionate lovemaking. The whippings must have been severe since Abelard tells us that he intended the sound of them to be heard by Fulbert, sitting in another room, in order to disarm the old man's suspicions. That they were also mutually enjoyable he makes clear when he writes that the strokes of his rod were 'sweet both to give and receive, with a sweetness surpassing that of all perfumes'.

All of which only proves that in the matter of sexual pleasure there is nothing new under the sun.

R.S.

P.S. The lovers were, of course, found out. Heloise had a baby and retired to a convent, while Abelard paid the price of castration.

DEVIATION

Sexual deviation is (quite rightly) frowned on by those who have not the need or the inclination to wander off the 'straight and narrow'. Those of us like myself, who do have this need, are given various degrees of classification depending on our particular 'kink'.

This only bothers me insofar as I object to the inference by medico-legal experts that we are 'sick'.

Deviation is a good word but is often misunderstood. In a roundabout way, we 'deviants' do achieve sexual satisfaction; and otherwise we live quite normally and cause no one any discomfort of any kind.

J.H.

The more experience I gain of other people's sexual needs, the more I begin to wonder whether the term 'normal' can really be applied to anyone. The difference between individual responses to all kinds of stimuli are so many and various that it is almost practically impossible to say that such-and-such a desire is normal, and that such-and-such is not.

It seems to me that the whole question of deviation needs rethinking and should be closely linked with the reeducation of those who somewhat smugly label themselves normal. What is involved after all? The satisfaction of a psychological need by a means of behaviour that is somewhat out of the ordinary. – F.

LOVE IN THE AFTERNOON

I'm what's commonly known I suppose as a happily and respectably married woman. I have been married for 12 years and have one daughter, aged nine and one son, aged seven. I am 34 years old and my husband is 36; he is an established professional man and therefore brings in more than enough money for us to be able to live in greater than average comfort, even luxury. I am of course very grateful for this.

Nevertheless, fairly soon after we were married, it became increasingly apparent to me that my husband's work demanded so much of his energy that he would come home, for example, very tired on many evenings and not wish to go out or make love. I tried many methods of attempting to soothe him and make him less tired. I always managed household affairs efficiently in order that he should not have to worry about them, and always looked after him well, giving him food that he enjoyed and talking with him on topics which interested him. Also, I used to devote much time and energy to making myself look attractive – something I still do because I enjoy it.

Eventually I told him that I was not satisfied with our life together, and gave as my reason the fact that he did not give me enough of his *physical* time. I told him I was young and enjoyed making love, and that I wanted to make love more than we had been, as well as to go out with him and be involved with him in more activities outside the home. To my astonishment, he was shocked when I told him this and at first became angry, calling me 'oversexed'. I told him that was nonsense and that, to my mind, what I was asking (simply that we be together more) was very reasonable. Eventually I became pregnant during which time our sex life came almost to a standstill.

After the baby was born I became involved in nursing the baby, while my husband devoted more time and energy than ever to his work, sometimes staying away for nights and weekends to attend conferences or deal with urgent matters. Sexually and in terms of attention from my husband, I grew more and more dissatisfied. When I told him of my dissatisfaction, he had a similar reaction to the previous occasion. Fairly soon after that, our second child was born.

Then, with two young children, my hands were really full. But I found myself growing lax and irritable, due, I felt, to an inadequate physical relationship with my husband. I took to masturbating regularly, but this was not at all sufficient to fulfill me.

A group of young mothers in the neighborhood, including myself, formed a mutual babysitting pool, which operated during the daytime as well as during the evening. I took advantage of this and began to travel by myself to London for daytrips. We live in a fairly accessible suburb, so this was not at all difficult. At first, I would window-shop, or go to a theater or cinema, or visit friends. My husband didn't seem to mind and, in fact, appeared rather pleased that I had something to occupy myself with.

I had by this time given up complaining to him about our life together because it just seemed to give rise to bad feelings between us, which the children easily picked up.

Then I grew bored with friends, cinemas and theaters, particularly since my visits to these became fairly soon habitual and began to remind me of the other habitual routine which I so much wanted to change from. So I started to go to clubs and pubs, at first in the West End and then in less fashionable parts of town. I knew deep down that I wanted to be picked up. I used to arrive in London somewhere around 11 in the morning, and knew that I would have to be back home by 7 p.m. at the latest to relieve my babysitter. I was therefore rather shocked at myself being honest enough to admit that what I was looking for was not a 'lover' in any regular sense of the word but the afternoon equivalent of a 'one-night-stand'.

When I finally admitted to myself what I wanted, I was able to go about looking for it more effectively and after very few visits allowed myself without too much guilt to be picked up and made love to by a young colored West Indian. The whole process took no more than about three hours. The approach, a few drinks, the journey to his room . . . then we made love, very passionately and rather gaily under the circumstances (on a creaky single bed), following which I went by bus to the station and took the train home, arriving there at my usual time.

Since then, I have spent similar afternoons, each time with a different man. And each time the man has been colored, mainly either African or West Indian, though occasionally American. Over five years, I should imagine I have had enjoyable sexual intercourse with well over a hundred men. As far as I am aware, neither my husband nor any of our mutual friends or acquaintances know anything about this second life that I lead.

Strangely enough, it's not just sexual enjoyment that causes me to gravitate toward Negroes. It's also (and perhaps more importantly), that colored people in general seem to stand for a completely different set of values than the average white Englishman. The afternoons I spend in the way that I've described are more often than not full of *physical engagement*, laughter and activity – not just sexual activity either, but activity also in the form of spontaneous dancing, talking, touching and even

410

manageable aggression, which I have acquired a natural liking for. None of these people have seemed bound to materialistic values in the way that my husband is, or to the extent that their vital energies are dissipated in competitiveness or in the need for commercial success.

I am not unique. I have met other white women, also 'respectable' who do the same thing I do and who also take their enjoyment where they can find it.

Perhaps if more anxiety-ridden Englishmen could creatively emulate our colored cousins there would be fewer secretly errant wives around – because, believe me, there are more than most people think, and I should know.

G.R.

DELICATESSEN SEX

My late wife was a great one for combining food and sex – I never knew just what to expect. I have had to eat swiss rolls, jam roly poly, celery, cucumber and all types of fruit attached to various parts of her body; likewise small cakes with a center hole, through which her nipple protruded and even jellies with a deep cavity to fit over her breasts. Sometimes I have even eaten salads and other foods placed on her tummy.

By experimenting she found that jam, syrup, salad cream, and some sauces can be used to stick food to the body. When cake baking she formed some in the shape of a penis and others to go over the penis, for her pleasure.

Condensed milk is a good sticker, as well as toffees and caramels. Soft cheese spread over the nipples or any part of the body with pieces of onion and gherkin embedded in it can always make a tasty dish, in more ways than one and can be used by either party.

F.F.

LOVE IN THE BATH

In *My Secret Life* Walter states categorically that it is impossible to make love underwater; a view many people seem to share. The difficulty is usually in achieving entry. My girlfriend and I frequently make love in the bath, and your readers might be interested in our method.

Before getting in I smear a little vaseline between the lips of

411

my girlfriend's vagina and some on my penis. Then I lie on my back under the water and my girlfriend straddles me and lowers herself gently onto my penis. In this position entry is easy, and the all-enveloping hot water adds a new dimension to the ensuing experience.

J.K.

FAIR EXCHANGE

I am 28 and have been happily married for the past six years to a very attractive wife. Last summer I struck up a friendship with another married man who lives quite near me. We used to meet every week for a drink in a local bar and he often used to quiz me about what my wife wore under her skirt. He would tell me in great detail about his wife's underclothes and would often produce from his pocket a little pair of flimsy panties for me to see.

He kept asking me to show him one of my wife's things, and after a few weeks coaxing, I slipped a pair of briefs into my pocket on the way to meet him. The result of all this is that I am now a fanatic about women's underclothes and I have seen every single item of his wife's collection. In return, he has been to my home a few times while my wife was out, and I have allowed him into our bedroom to inspect her undies.

We both thoroughly enjoy this relationship and now meet about twice a week by car to exchange small parcels which we return at an arranged time. As I write this letter I have in front of me the contents of his latest parcel – a black bra, white suspender belt, nylons, and red nylon panties that his wife wore yesterday. At this moment he has with him my wife's red bra, red pantie girdle, light tan tights and pink nylon panties. I get quite a sexual thrill when I see my wife wearing items that he has recently borrowed.

Of course, my wife knows nothing about this and I am certain she would not approve of what we are doing, despite the fact that it acts as a sexual stimulant and has improved our sex life. I wonder if this is an unusual 'hobby' or do many other married men indulge – or would they secretly like to indulge – in this practice?

W.T.

412

FIRST CLASS MAIL

I was very interested to read the letter from W.T. in which he states he exchanges items from his wife's underwear with a friend. Although this may seem to be a rather unusual hobby, several years ago I did exactly the same thing with a neighbor of mine. As in the case of W.T., our wives did not know of the swaps.

After some time, I became like W.T., a fanatic about women's underclothes. One evening, after making our twice weekly swap and being alone in the house, I could not resist the urge to try them on, which I did and found I got a terrific sexual thrill. For the first time since my childhood, at the time I was 29, I could not resist the urge to masturbate. I did not mention this to my neighbor, but every time we made our swaps, I did the same thing. I even started to wear the panties during the day.

Unfortunately, my friend moved to another state two years ago, and although at first we continued to swap by post, this has now stopped. I miss these swaps very much, and wish I could find somebody with whom to start again.

When they first moved away, I missed wearing his wife's underwear so much I went out and bought myself some panties of my own, a black lace pair and a frilly pink pair. Being able to wear these whenever I pleased only increased my desire to wear pretty things, and it was not long before I had built up quite a collection of bras, panties, suspender belts, slips.

About a year ago, I bought myself a navy blue minidress and a pair of black high heeled shoes. The thrill of dressing completely in women's clothes was tremendous, and after I had masturbated, washed and changed back to my normal dress, I could hardly wait for my wife to come home. That night we had a wonderful session.

Over the months, I added more dresses, skirts, blouses and sweaters to my collection, and I also bought a wig and some makeup. As my wife goes out several evenings a week, I am able to dress up quite frequently and each time I find it more exciting.

My wife does not know of this hobby of mine. The only other person who knows is the husband of my wife's best friend who called round to my house one evening when both our wives had gone out to evening class together. After a couple of beers and looking at some 'dirty' pictures he started to talk about homosexuals. He confessed he had feelings in this direction and in fact had several affairs both before and after his marriage. He asked me if I had any interests in this direction, and I told him about my desire to dress in women's clothes and about my collection.

He said he would like to see me dressed up, so I went into the bedroom and changed into frilly white undies, a pink minidress, stockings and high-heeled shoes, my wig and makeup. I went back to him in the lounge, and he seemed very pleased with my transformation. It was not long before he made a pass at me which I enjoyed. He then suggested we go to the bedroom and make love. Again I agreed, and he eventually had anal intercourse with me. It was my first time, and although it hurt I enjoyed it, and since then it has happened on several occasions, although he wants it more often than I do.

The homosexual side of this does not really interest me as much as the transvestite side which is really my main interest.

I am sure there must be quite a number of men, also happily married like myself, who are transvestites, and like me have to keep their interest in this to themselves.

A.H.

NARCISSISTIC TRANSVESTITE

I am a narcissistic transvestite. I have little body hair, tender soft white skin like a girl, am slim but well rounded, with good legs and a soft bottom. I am not young. I have always had a horror of becoming stout or pot-bellied and have avoided this by exercises and dieting.

Although I had my share of 'attention' from bigger boys at school I am not effeminate – I was in the school rugger team – but I have always been conscious of my liking my own body and my own figure. I have more than average male sexual virility, though not exceptional.

For years I had supremely happy normal sex relations with my wife. Then, during the war, in the Army, I spent five years in the East, detached in lonely small jungle camps with only one other white officer. We never even talked about sex. He was not that kind. We lived in separate tents, sometimes in small palm-leaf huts. The climate being hot. I spent usually an hour or so at midday and always all night nude with a loose loincloth.

Lonely, deprived of all sexual outlets after years of satisfying relations two or three times a week with my wife I fell in love

414

with my own body, caressing my own nipples, finding release with my penis squeezed between my legs.

At the end of the war I resumed happy marital relations, but was not averse to admiring myself in my wife's long mirror. Then my wife died suddenly. Much frustrated and desolate without her I started to try on some of her clothes. I soon became a transvestite – having corsets and dresses made for me, buying undies, tights, wigs, etc.

My main joy in transvestism was and still is to see *myself* as a desirable female in the mirror – and to feel like one – in two mirrors for preference so that I can see both front and rear view. Nothing excites my sexuality more than, with face made up, wig, and well-corseted figure, to watch myself do a striptease and to admire my own legs, curves, bosom and bottom.

I frequently tuck my manly parts back between my legs, presenting the frontal appearance of a woman. This especially excites me. I have no desire for another woman. I long to go to bed with myself, and have developed submissive homosexual desires as a result of my longing for the impossible – to make love to and to be made love to by myself.

Are not *all* transvestites really narcissistic, even if they do not realize it? Is this not in fact the basic urge from which trans-vestism springs?

I have come to feel that the only solution to my frustration would be a male lover who will treat me like a woman and make love to me (homosexually) as if I was one.

I would be most pleased to have your comments and advice.

R.M.

While narcissism is a constant feature of transvestite activity, it is not always present. For some, transvestism is secondary to homosexuality and there are expedient and political forms in which it is only necessary to be able to pass in society and be accepted as a member of the opposite sex. Narcissism also implies admiration, as clearly demonstrated by this writer. In burlesque forms of transvestism even a repulsive aspect is sometimes suggested.

Frequently the transvestite finds his appearance attractive, es-pecially when wearing clothing, makeup and wig produces a startling almost magical transformation so that the subject can barely recognize himself in the elegant, attractive figure reflected in the glass. As in the case of this correspondent he may fall in love with his female image; the ability to change the clothing from the elegant through the childish to the provocative and to act these roles before himself often provides the transvestite with stimulus and sexual arousal which leads to an act of masturbation or sometimes spontaneous ejaculation. — F.

SECRET DESIRE

I have a secret desire to stroll through the village where I was born wearing my transparent plastic exercise suit with nothing underneath. Maybe I will try it one night!

Have other readers any unusual wishes they would like to fulfill but cannot pluck up courage to do so?

Miss E.R.

This letter sounds like classic dream material except for its lack of disguise. In dreams most people disguise their exhibitionistic wishes by symbols. For example, a woman may dream she is dressed only in her bra, not completely nude. — H.G.

GOING BACKWARD

Just how enlightened is our present-day society in contrast to ancient civilizations? Perhaps the following brief description of the Egyptian New Kingdom 3,400 years ago might serve as a plausible answer: Women in that society appeared in public with unadorned breasts, and among the upper classes, nude serving girls were commonplace attractions during their various dinner parties and feasts.

As for the children, they were free to run totally unclothed until puberty. Sex and its physical manifestations were considered part of human existence totally devoid of shame or secrecy. All the senses were employed in deriving the greatest amount of pleasure from the sexual act. There was virtually no shame, guilt or sexual repression in that society.

And we call ourselves civilized!

Dr. M.T.

THE REAL VILLAINS

As a teacher for some 20 years, I have had ample opportunity to study children and their attitude toward sex. My main conclusion is that the real villains in society are those parents who regard sex as something unmentionable, and it is amusing but sad that girls of 10 and 11 – some with nipples no bigger than pinheads – turn their back lest teacher see their bare chests when they change in the classroom for physical education. I am sure that their shyness is due to their parents' conditioning. Many working class and lower-middle class attitudes to the naked body are little short of primitive.

As society becomes more enlightened, parents of this sort will, I hope, be arraigned for cruelty to children; poisoning of young minds by planting barbaric notions of sex with the result that some young people are literally ruined for life, their future marriages already marked down for failure. If perversions are in mind, it is surely some kind of perversion when, as is still not uncommon, husband and wife have never seen each other in the nude.

It must be the hope of every truly civilized person that (unless there is a backlash) children's minds – and hearts – will soon be opened to the full potentials of sex wherein they will find the unfolding of new worlds of sensual experience. This is their natural birthright.

The governing principle of young people's sexual enlightenment should be: let things develop naturally. Satisfy curiosity; reveal knowledge on request.

As a teacher, I now regard it as part of my mission in life to scotch the efforts of ignorant and bigoted parents to do harm to their children's sexual faculties. The idea that sexual knowledge is damaging to children is ludicrous. Junior children, particularly, are such jolly no-nonsense creatures that they can take pretty well anything. A bit of 'honest vulgarity' delights them enormously and the place of humor is important. It permits a constant release of feeling which is preferable to the discomfort of built-up tension which abortive attempts at a serious conventional lesson produce.

The secret is not to get too solemn about the subject. Lessons on sex are neither needed nor advisable. It is, after all, a social subject, not an academic one, and should be treated accordingly so that you have not a class but a social gathering – something warm which melts away incipient embarrassment.

In the realm of human sexuality, children – permitted their natural reactions – can teach adults a lot.

A.R.

SEX EDUCATION

One hears so much these days about narrow-minded mothers frightened of sex and instilling that fear in the minds of their children, especially daughters. Here am I with a problem I cannot explain clearly, even to myself. I grew up in a happy family and while my parents didn't actually encourage me to be alone with boys until I got married, they weren't strict. At 16 I lost my virginity without regrets or fears and had several affairs before I married. My husband and I had a wonderful sex life, all our children were wanted, though not planned.

When my husband died, I was desolate, but after about a year decided I was still too young to spend the rest of my life alone, that I had a great need for male companionship and sex. When I took my first lover after a couple of months, I let him stay at the house at night and didn't hide the fact I was sleeping with him from my children. Only my eldest boy seemed a bit put out by this, but he soon made friends with the man he thought was to be his stepfather. It didn't work out that way. We parted company and since then, I have had what seems in retrospect a long line of bed partners.

On one hand, I tell myself that it's natural to want sex, and I'm not hurting anyone and having a lot of fun, but on the other hand, I feel thoroughly ashamed of myself and want to teach my children not to be like me, especially my older ones. I want to tell them that sex is only beautiful in marriage and in love and that otherwise, it is degrading and meaningless. In some strange way, I want to live by a double standard, not as it is usually thought of, as a two way morality between man and woman, but between myself and my children. I have two boyfriends at the moment and am enjoying them both. I want to continue my sex life, and yet I want to stop my children from following in my footsteps. I spend many sleepless hours worrying about my daughter. I would be terribly hurt if she did the things I did in my teens, and my boys worry me too. I hate to think of them using someone else's daughter just for fun and telling tales about it. I hope none of them will follow my example, just as sometimes the children of alcoholics will never

418

touch a drink. And yet I don't want to lose their respect and love.

A lot of people would call me a hypocrite, because I don't practice what I preach, but I think there's an awful lot to be said for the old-fashioned concept of morality. Years ago, maybe a lot of couples didn't express themselves to the full sexually and got frustrated, but that's nothing compared to feeling emotionally washed out and in constant conflict with oneself, being continually lifted up and then let down again.

Teaching children about sex is so terribly difficult these days that it has become a matter for personal belief now there are no rules and no moral code. Often, as in my case, one's personal views are all mixed up.

Should I leave them alone and hope for the best or talk to them honestly, telling them how I really feel about sex after all the experience I've had?

L.S.

You should certainly talk to your children, but not try to force on them your conception of sex and sexual morality, which from your own statements reveals underlying sexual guilt, contradictions and personal confusion.

If you tell them of your own experiences and fears for their future course of action, you might also tell them the decision finally rests with them. They must be, as you say, aware of your lovers and the intensity and frequency of your sexual activity. This is likely to influence their attitudes whatever you tell them, however you phrase your warnings. The effects might be different just as their characters are different. Some might react with anger and dislike. Others might try and emulate you, especially as you have to be both mother and father to them. What is perhaps most important is that you encourage them at an early stage to come to you for advice and frank discussion. You obviously love them, and they must love you. This mutual bond will be strong enough, one hopes, to bridge any rift your sex life may have created. – F.

CORDUROY FETISH

I find corduroy sexually exciting and have been excited by it for as long as I can remember. I recall the thrill of watching the tight little buttocks of my friends at school encased in corduroy shorts. In those days, corduroy had a distinctive sweetish smell, and while I occasionally contrived to press my face against a corduroy-clad leg for a fleeting moment I never achieved my main desire which was to bury my face in a pair of corduroyed buttocks and to inhale the smell of hot buttocks through the sweet corduroy. As I grew up I lost interest in little boys – though not in corduroy.

I found new excitement in watching girls in cycling clubs who often appeared in corduroy shorts. I spent many hours stalking them with a camera to take sumptuous pictures of their buttocks. I married, lost interest in furtive titillation for years – though I still remained exceedingly attracted to corduroy. Now, however, at the dangerous age of 50 I find myself again attracted by boys in corduroy shorts.

The problem is this. I believe I have sufficient decency to overcome the temptation to assault a little boy – I have always resisted in the past and can rationalize myself out of temption by telling myself that they are smelly little buggers anyway. I am not so sure that I could resist the opportunity if the provocation were too great, however. Can you please tell me whether my case is following classic and disastrous lines (as I suspect) or whether it is possible for someone like me to live out a disreputable fantasy without putting it into practice? Do you think it would be possible to have psychiatric treatment to break my interest in little boys without destroying the love of corduroy which has been at the center of my sex life for so long?

I find deep satisfaction in dressing up in corduroys and masturbating into them and over them. Corduroy – which I feel was originally attractive because of the boys who wore it – is not an object in itself. Can I keep it that way?

H.M.

Your primary interest in corduroy as an erotic stimulant (which technically speaking is fetishism) is comparatively rare; most 'material fetishists' are usually attracted to the feel and texture of silk, satin and nylon. Psychoanalytically the corrugated nature of corduroy may symbolically represent the lining mucosa of the vagina, which is similarly ridged.

Your secondary predilection for young people's buttocks, preferably male but also female, is also an example of fetish-

ism. However in this case it is the shape, composition and warm smell that is erotically exciting. This attraction that little boys hold for you does not suggest to me, as you fearfully imply, a basic homosexual orientation; it is the buttocks rather than the sex of the possessor that seem crucial.

The problem that concerns you at present, namely the re-emergence of strong fetishistic desires, which following your marriage apparently lay dormant for years, is fairly common in middle, and more so in old age. Especially troublesome is the fear of succumbing to these temptations with all the possible legal and social sanctions that a hostile and uninformed public may unleash. Without a personal interview it is impossible to be dogmatic about causation; however a fairly common finding in a sizable proportion of cases is reduction in both the frequency of, and the pleasure derived from, heterosexual intercourse. In a few instances this may progress into coital abstinence or even impotence. The unavailability of a female sexual partner may also act as a trigger. A return to a previously practiced and much enjoyed mode of sexual stimulation (an example of regression) may represent an exercise in sexual self-reassurance – to the effect that one is still rousable and capable of responding fully.

Regarding your fear about succumbing, there is of course a world of difference between fantasy and reality; sexual fantasies which may occasion great satisfaction and happiness are perfectly harmless and can be indulged without fear or remorse. On the information provided in your letter, I think it unlikely that you will 'act out' your erotic desires. If you think it feasible it may be helpful to communicate your preferences to your wife. In one case I know of, following discussions, the wife regularly dressed in corduroy shorts to enhance her husband's sexual pleasure. Both seemed perfectly content with the arrangement.

Regarding your question of psychiatric treatment to break your interest in little boys, but not in corduroy, without a detailed interview it is again impossible to do other than generalize. Generally, however, removing sexual interest in one specific object only is difficult to achieve, since the aversion induced is often transferred to other or, rarely, to all sexual objects. – F.

421

APHRODITE CALLIPYGOS

Despite the cries that surely there are other things as interesting as the 'bum' – well, I'm afraid there aren't! The bottom is here to stay.

Take a look at any magazine. Examine holiday pictures, scanty undies prints, notorious girls in sensational stories, and the banned 'porno's'. The final accent is – you've guessed it – on the female derriere. As a great artist once said, 'There are many unshapely legs and busts, but few such bottoms. Mayhap our Creator intended that the entrance to love's citadel should be erotic spheres of soft symmetry, most tempting to eye and hand – for my work too is better for it.'

Since Eve first wore the proverbial fig leaf, nearly all males have involuntarily gazed in awe at that part of the female anatomy and desired to touch, to stroke, to kiss – yes, and to pat and smack as well. Why else do you think girls silently try to outdo each other with their minis, their frothy panties just showing and the glimpses of bare flesh they allow?

J.S.

THE FEMALE BOTTOM

Just how widespread among men is the erotic appeal of the female bottom? Personally I am almost devoted to it and like many others I am seeking reassurance I'm not abnormal.

I will walk far out of my way to follow a particularly delightful pair of buttocks in a tight skirt or jeans, and when meeting an attractive girl for the first time or for the thousandth time, my greatest joy is to observe her from the rear.

There is nothing sadistic in my desire. The idea of inflicting punishment on a girl's bottom repels me. I have been fortunate in meeting many women who have allowed me to kiss and fondle their buttocks, but after an hour or so of this activity even those who appeared to enjoy it expressed surprise that I could obtain so much pleasure from it.

I have several large scrapbooks filled with pictures of girls displaying their bottoms, either bare, or in panties, tight skirts, or jeans, and get a great deal of pleasure from them when I am alone.

Should I worry about this desire which I cannot suppress, or should I just relax and enjoy it?

G.P.

Relax and enjoy it. You are in good company: the Greeks, for instance, had a great cult devoted to Aphrodite Callipygos – the goddess with the beautiful bottom.

In a third century Roman manuscript there is a description of the beauty and effect of female buttocks that might explain their fascination:

'What a sight! Even Venus Callipygos would have been envious of such charms! Delicious curves full of promises formed a harmonious and supple sphere. It was grace itself. Above all, this was the irresistible domain of the feminine flesh...' – F.

PAIN GAME

On the subject of pain-pleasure, I agree with those who say that it must be a mutually agreeable game.

My fiancée was an awful tease, until finally she went too far. I hauled her over my knees, tossed up her skirts, and spanked her panty-clad bottom.

I expected this to be the end of our engagement, but instead the girl who got up from my lap rubbing her smarting seat, was loving and passionate. I was lucky to have found a woman who shared my tastes, but there must be many men who are not so fortunate. Let's face it, to invite a young lady to place herself across your knee is to invite a rebuff, and be labeled as kinky! To take action as I did is to invite a charge of assault!

For the first few months of our marriage, I lost no opportunity of spanking my wife's pretty bottom, but soon this seemed to lose its excitement, as there was no element of compulsion.

So we decided to make up a game. We play a game of cards, and the loser of each hand or point must draw a card from a special set we have made; this shows the position to be adopted. clothing to be worn, and the number of whacks and with what object. An evening's cards like this leaves us both smarting pleasantly and highly aroused.

For my own part, I have no time for the vicious whippings some advocate; with canes and birches; I am quite happy with my wife bent over my knees, skirts up, panties down, her bottom bouncing under the impact of my flattened palm, and equally so with her grasping her ankles for a few noisy whacks with a slipper on the taut seat of her skirt or ski pants.

Let me add that there is also a therapeutic effect on regular spankings for the female bottom. Thanks to my constant attention, my wife is the proud owner of the prettiest and most pattable bottom I have ever seen; it is indeed a pleasure to follow her down the street, watching her firm rounded buttocks bouncing merrily beneath her slim skirt.

M.E.B.

MUSIC FOR LOVERS

I wonder whether spanking devotees have ever considered using a musical accompaniment. This would certainly improve their rhythm and I am sure that the buttocks would prefer to dance to music.

Some years ago a Hollywood star applied for a divorce because her husband spanked her bottom while singing the First World War song, 'Keep the Home Fires Burning'. The words were very appropriate, but I think that the music and timing was rather slow. A quick step or rousing march would be ideal.

When my doctor was treating me for sciatica he said that it was a pity that I was not married as I could have asked my wife to spank me. He said that the heat so generated would have soothed the sciatic nerve which runs through the buttock.

B.S.

I find your musical suggestions interesting but I don't believe that medical science has established spanking as the treatment of choice for sciatica yet. – H.G.

MÉNAGÉ À TROIS

Living with us is the widow of my closest friend. When he died in a car accident last year, his wife went into shock and it took a good while till she regained the will to live. We insisted she come live with us and my wife couldn't have been more loving and understanding in this time of need. Loneliness is a terrible thing, and we just couldn't see this woman living by herself. We insisted she live with us, and it was obvious she was delighted to do so.

My wife is a marvelous and understanding woman. She was

well aware of our guest's sexual needs, especially in view of the fact that the latter is in her middle 30's, and is very highly sexed. After a decent interval, my wife arranged several dinner parties to which she invited men whom she thought were eligible. As it turned out, nothing came of these arrangements.

One night, while the three of us were celebrating my wife's birthday, consuming in the process a considerable amount of champagne, and with all inhibitions lessened, the conversation turned to sex. In a moment of complete honesty, our friend let slip out the fact that she was terribly frustrated sexually and that it was making her very nervous. Without thinking, and obviously under the influence of the champagne, my wife suggested that I offer my services! After all, she was our closest friend and was now part of our family. Ironically, I was the one who was slightly inhibited, but fortunately, that soon passed. The following events were so natural and fulfilling for the three of us that we kicked ourselves for not having thought about it sooner.

Sexually, the arrangement has worked out to everyone's satisfaction. Because there are two women with whom I can now enjoy sexual relations, I haven't the slightest desire to cheat on my wife. How many men married for over 15 years can honestly make that statement? Sexually, I have always been more demanding than my wife, and if our threesome arrangement had not come about, it was inevitable that I would indulge in extramarital affairs. This situation also suits my wife, not only because she no longer feels guilty about not keeping up with me sexually, but also because she knows how much pleasure it is giving our third partner. For the time being, the latter is quite content with the arrangement. She has plenty of love and security which she wouldn't have had, were she living alone. The three of us truly love one another and there hasn't been the slightest jealousy from any of us.

To expect a marital relationship to remain stimulating and the partners to remain sexually faithful to one another for 50 years or so is to demand the impossible. For that reason, I feel that those couples whose marriages are basically healthy should not be deterred from experimenting with new techniques or relationships because of fear or guilt. If whatever they do is agreeable to both and makes their marriage more exciting and happier, then I say good luck to them.

J.R.

CLIMB EVERY MOUNTAIN

An article I read and enjoyed two years ago, written by a married woman, described in detail her erotic experiences during a weekend. Both she and her husband regularly exchanged partners with another married couple almost invariably at weekends.

On a certain occasion, the other wife was away for the weekend visiting relatives, but due to a compromise between the two males, the available wife was asked to make a trio. Here I must quote her reactions and account of her 'most glorious weekend'.

'The prospect of going to bed with both men made me feel apprehensive and inadequate. However, I decided to try it, and for the very first time, I achieved the peak of sexual and sensual satisfaction. Lying naked between two virile males afforded me hours and hours of pure pleasure and gratification. Only when a woman is being shared by two passionate males, and enjoying their dual offerings does she realize she has reached the Utopia of erotic ecstasy between the sexes. No one man can satisfy a woman so completely in the manner in which her secret urges and desires long to be satisfied. The supreme joy of enjoying two organs simultaneously and reveling in their urgency is truly wonderful.

'To have one man exploring the upper regions while feeling the lower parts being similarly engaged is sensational. The hands and mouths, exciting and titillating two different areas simultaneously is beyond description. And the erotic act of being entered vaginally from the rear while engaged in visual and oral satisfaction with the other erection left nothing to be desired. Subsequently, the glorious climax far surpassed anything I had ever known or imagined. I had many that weekend, and my partners exchanged their positions.

'Later,' she continues, 'when my husband and I were alone, he assured me he had enjoyed the experience as much as I had. The intimate action of watching me being entered and the subsequent engagement, coupled with the oral pleasure I afforded him far exceeded anything he had ever known. The advantages of a third party enabled him to achieve something which was not possible with only one partner. By the dual joys of both oral and visual pleasures, he was transported to the highest pinnacle of erotic ecstasy.'

L.S.

AN UNHYGIENIC BUSINESS

I do not recall ever hearing it said that sex is a most unhygienic business. Romantic sex is even worse, for one has no thoughts when one's head is in the clouds.

Even if both participants take a bath first, germs from a kiss on the breasts pass by hand to the vaginal opening in foreplay. Then there is the question of circumsion, as the foreskin harbors germs. I have read that while cancer of the cervix is a common occurrence in countries where many are not circumcised, it is almost unknown among the Jews.

It is difficult to visualize a completely hygienic sex technique. Both should bathe first. The mouth should be reserved for above-waist play only. The hands should be kept for below-waist play only. The genitals should be kept only for their counterparts. Not very romantic! Not very much fun!

Much emphasis nowadays is being placed on the importance of fellatio and cunnilingus in sex practice, but little or nothing is said about the hygiene involved. As a dentist, my thoughts are focused on the mouth. In health, the mouth is teeming with germs which do no harm so long as they are confined to the mouth, just as *B. Coli* does not harm as long as it is kept to the colon. A mouthwash will reduce the number of germs in the mouth but not for long, and they are back to full strength within half an hour. In fellatio, there is perhaps little danger to the male, as saliva on the penis soon dries, killing most of the bacteria, and any which do enter the urethra will be washed out at the next visit to the toilet.

In cunnilingus, the situation is quite different. For the female, any germs placed in or near the vagina will thrive in the warm moist environment. Then they can either penetrate the uretha and reach the bladder or enter the uterus and fallopian tubes via the vagina.

Other than the normal mouth organisms, venereal disease can perhaps be discounted as a hazard of any sex encounter, but what of flu, pneumonia, the infectious fevers, thrush and many others?

Last but not least, I have been allowed to practice cunnilingus but once in my life. I shall always consider it to be one of the peaks of my sexual existence. It was beyond description it was so good, but what germs did it introduce into my wife's body? Was it the cause of a later hysterectomy and cystitis?

T.M.

The world around us is a bacteriologist's nightmare – but for most people common sense prevails.

We lick our fingers to flick over a germ-ridden telephone book, wipe our hands on a grossly contaminated handkerchief before putting a chocolate in our mouths, we wipe our cutlery on filthy tea-towels – and our sexual organs are inevitably mixed up with our excretory functions physically and psychologically. And yet on the whole we remain well.

This is because the natural defenses of our body are always at work protecting us from ourselves. It is common sense to accept no unnecessary risk – here we should wash our hands after toilet and always before meals, we should keep our skins clean and free from our natural secretions, and apply the usual sensible precautions to the preparation of our food, i.e. wash our fruit, ensure our meat is fresh, etc.

In our sexual activities we should apply the same principles – we should wash ourselves before the act, paying particular attention to our sexual parts, and clean our teeth. Such activities should not normally spoil the spontaneity of the act and indeed the washing process can become a part of the pre-coital sexual play when partners wash each other – in which case it can be done to their own satisfaction.

I can assure the writer that nothing he did is likely to have had any bearing at all upon the subsequent illness of his wife and he should put his mind completely at rest on this point. Guided by common sense and the normal habits of a cultured society, he should enjoy his life and remember that in spite of the myriads of germs around us, most are not the cause of disease. The few that are have to penetrate the body defenses first and man has probably been on this earth for a million years and hasn't done too badly so far. – F.

BREAST DEVELOPER

Mention of the idea that swallowing semen improves the breasts prompts me to tell you of my own experience a few years ago in the army. I met a woman considerably older than myself to whom I was initially attracted.

She wasn't a beautiful woman, but being of White Russian descent she had raven black hair, the biggest bosom I'd ever seen, and a vivacious, sparkling personality that made her very desirable to men.

I took her out several times and eventually was invited back to her flat. It turned out that her husband was away at sea for long periods – which made me think I was on to a good thing!

Her flat was tastefully furnished – the main feature of the room being a large black leather settee on which she made herself comfortable and invited me to come and sit alongside her on a small seat. She wore a black satin button-up dress, and I saw that the two top buttons were already undone. I made to kiss her but she told me not to. Instead she calmly undid her dress, whipped off her bra and exposed her enormous breasts, at the same time taking my hands to her nipples and instructing me to pinch them hard. This I did, and under my manipulation they grew to the size of acorns. I tried to remove her briefs and get down to serious business, but was instead given an ordinary lead pencil (which she had removed from behind the cushions) and told to tap each nipple alternately. I did this for about seven minutes during which her excitement increased until she began to writhe about in a series of orgasms, without any other stimulation.

Naturally, I was extremely aroused, and she knew this, but still would not let me proceed further with removing her panties. Instead, motioning me onto the settee beside her (where I lay full length) she quickly undid my zip and performed fellatio, swallowing the semen. She explained this extraordinary maneuver as being good for her bosom, saying that in her province of origin it was standard practice for all women.

R.F.

GOOD FOR THE BOSOM?

About two years ago, during our lovemaking, after a prolonged genital kiss, my wife insisted on keeping my penis in her mouth when I ejaculated.

She later told me how much she had enjoyed the sensation of warm semen filling her mouth. Subsequently, she developed a very definite liking for the semen, with the result that ever since she insists on fellatio at least twice a week.

When my wife and I started this form of intercourse my wife's breasts were underdeveloped. They were, in fact, extremely small; practically nothing but nipple and aureole.

However, they have now developed to a reasonable size, and are quite firm. I have wondered if the intake of semen has anything to do with this improvement.

This is one subject on which information seems scarce; most sex books usually dismiss it in a sentence or two. Do you have any theories which might explain the above?

W.G.

Many people are still under the false impression that human semen contains various remarkable properties. In fact, the only function of semen is to fertilize the human ovum. Therefore ingestion through swallowing can do neither harm nor good.

A possible explanation might be that W.G.'s wife is now obtaining the full sexual satisfaction previously denied her. This could improve her well-being, both physically and psychologically. Thus her hormone balance would be improved. This in turn can result in more regular menstrual periods, efficient ovulation and development of secondary sex characteristics, including the breasts.

It may then be assumed that W.G.'s wife who is said to once have possessed 'underdeveloped' breasts may have benefited from hormonal stimulation which tends to be the result of a fully adequate sex life. – F.

SECRET FOR FIRM BREASTS

Now that women and their braless breasts are in the news, and the fashion looks like catching on, I have decided to reveal my closely kept secret for firm breasts, whatever age they may be.

Each night before retiring, I go to the bathroom, fill up the hand basin with *cold* water. I then proceed to bathe each breast in turn for five minutes. When they start to tingle, I pat them dry with a rough towel. That's all there is to it.

Cold water tightens the muscles and skin, keeping the breasts from sagging. It will keep them healthy and firm.

This is also a wonderful treatment for men and women starting to show double chins. Hold your face over the basin, wet hands well with the cold water, slap well under chin. After one month of this treatment you will be delighted with your new face.

I am 45 years old, the mother of three, and a grandmother. I wear no bra or restraining garment of any kind. Yet my breasts are as firm as a 20-year-old's. This brings much delight to my husband, and my own satisfaction whenever I go swimming at the seaside.

Mrs. B.W.

DOCTOR NO HELP

I am twenty-five years old and have been married eighteen months. I have a problem which is turning me into a nervous wreck, has caused tremendous unhappiness and frustration and might destroy my marriage. I'm referring to my problem of premature ejaculation.

I've had this problem ever since my first sexual experience at the age of eighteen. Because of my disability, I seldom indulged in sex until my marriage. I thought perhaps that with a steady partner, I would be cured. But such has not been the case. In fact, it has become somewhat a vicious circle. The more tense and insecure I become, the less I am able to control my ejaculation.

I've discussed my problem with our doctor, but he wasn't able to help me. I would sincerely appreciate any advice you might offer.

H.H.

There is at present no agreed meaning for premature ejaculation. Some medical specialists consider a man to be a premature ejaculator if he cannot sustain the sex act for 30 seconds. Others agree that a full minute is the criterion for sexual performance. Dr. William Masters, whose pioneer laboratory studies of human sexual response are world famous, states: 'We consider a man to have a premature ejaculation problem if he cannot control his sexual processes for sufficient time to satisfy his individual partner' – in at least half of their attempts.

It is Dr. Masters' contention that premature ejaculation often begins with early sex experiences that were furtive and hurried, such as frantic encounters with casual dates in parked cars, or visits to prostitutes. As a result, many men have not learned to enjoy a leisurely sexual pace, or to adapt themselves to their partners' needs.

In treating this type of problem, Dr. Masters and his associate, Mrs. Virginia Johnson, try to encourage 'real, direct husband-wife communication' and the return to 'sensate focus'. Very often the wife of a man who rushes toward his own satisfaction, soon learns to freeze at her husband's approach. Since she is understandably reluctant to do anything that might stimulate him too rapidly, she develops what Mrs. Johnson calls a 'don't-touch attitude' toward her husband.

Dr. Masters and Mrs. Johnson have educated wives in the methods of helping their husbands to develop control. The husband is also trained to signal the wife when he realizes he is near the stage of 'ejaculatory inevitability' – a few seconds before orgasm.

They also train the wife to watch for certain physical signals that this stage is imminent. What the wife can then do is relatively simple – although, unlike the rest of the Masters–Johnson therapy, it does include a physical technique. This is taught to each wife so she can bring her husband back temporarily from the verge of orgasm. – F.

'SQUEEZE' TECHNIQUE

I am unable to understand the Masters and Johnson theory that the 'squeezing' of the frenum or foreskin can be a cure for premature ejaculation.

As described, when the man's penis has been stimulated to full erection, the woman should place her thumb on the frenum or foreskin (if uncircumcised) and her fingers round the coronal ridge and then squeeze it, and squeeze hard. If this is done properly, we are told, the man will soon lose his desire to ejaculate.

I have never read such nonsense, and I can think of no better way by which to stimulate a man's penis – and if the 'squeeze' technique is continued, it would be an abnormal man who could prevent himself from ejaculating. I would have thought that, anyway, it would be harmful to prevent or suppress a man from ejaculating at the moment when he felt ready for it.

The only cure for premature ejaculation is the practice of self-control and the avoidance of too much precoital play involving stimulation of the penis.

T.G.

The technique described was developed by the American sex researchers Masters and Johnson at their clinic for sexual inadequacy.

They treated 186 premature ejaculators with the 'squeeze technique'. Of these 182 were cured – in other words, learned sufficient control 'to provide orgasmic opportunity for the sexual partner during approximately 50% of the coital opportunities'. This is a success rate of 97·8% – even more remarkable when one remembers that most of the cases Masters and Johnson treated were those of long standing who had tried many other methods – including psychotherapy – without success.

I think T.G. may not realize that the penis must be squeezed really hard with more pressure than a man would ever be likely to use during masturbation. Masters and Johnson say: 'The amount of pressure necessary to depress a man's ejaculatory urge would be somewhat painful if the penis were in a flaccid state, but causes no similar level of discomfort when the penis is erect.'

As for any risk of physical injury – Masters and Johnson have been using this technique for 11 years and have followed up all their cases, and have found no evidence that this method of treatment can be harmful.

Nearly all the men who went to the sex clinic for cure had tried, and failed, to cure themselves by the 'practice of self-control and the avoidance of too much precoital play involving stimulation of the penis. – F.

A DANGEROUS PRACTICE

All married persons must come up against that vexed question of promoting, and then retaining, a firm erection.

I discovered the perfect way years ago, in the bath, when my nurse, by way of a joke, slipped her engagement ring on my penis and told me that we were married. On being dried after the bath, she became attentive to the organ, and I soon had a very firm erection. I noticed that when she touched me the organ was more sensitive than normally. It was then that I had my first orgasm.

After ten minutes or so, I still had an erection and nurse tried to get her ring off. After much application of soap and squeezing of the penis we did manage to remove it, but we were scared to try it again. With experiment, any couple can find the correct size of ring. A key ring nearly an inch in diameter is about the right size. The tip of the penis must be grasped firmly and stretched as far as possible while the ring is pushed right down the shaft to the body. If the ring fits tightly all the way down the shaft it will be the right size. This operation must be carried out before any lovemaking can take place at all and while the organ is quite soft. After a little loveplay, the blood will push the ring away from the body. All that is necessary then is to give the ring a push back towards the body, and the blood will flow into the penis and it will start to swell. More blood will come, and again by pushing the ring back to the body, the penis will swell more. In a few minutes you will have a penis larger than you have ever had before, with a glans large and shiny enough for any lover. You will also find that the organ is more sensitive. The beauty of this system is that the ring is so small and stays outside the female body so that it does not interfere with intercourse. During sex play it will be noticed that there is no leak of liquid from the penis and at orgasm too not a drop of semen escapes.

I must warn others that when choosing a ring, it must not be so small that it causes pain to push it along the shaft of the penis because when the organ is enlarged you cannot get the ring off there and then, and you will have to wait for some time to elapse for the penis to return to normal before you can get the ring off.

As a matter of fact, I have an account of a man with a flaccid penis $7\frac{1}{2}$ inches in length and $1\frac{1}{2}$ inches in diameter, who had to go to the surgeon to have a ring of $\frac{3}{4}$ inch removed.

J.W.

There is the likelihood of considerable danger in this practice. Sooner or later it will become impossible to remove the ring without cutting it, and anesthesia may be required. A key ring is particularly dangerous as the steel is most difficult to cut.

If the ring is too tight there is the possibility of the blood clotting in the damaged veins in the penis – thrombosis giving rise to priapism. This causes severe pain and disability. It can also lead to permanent damage.

It is very undesirable to have a constriction so tight that it obstructs the semen at the time of ejaculation.

However, constriction of the shaft of the penis, if done sensibly with something easily removed in an emergency, such as a rubber band, cord, strap etc., can be very helpful in some cases and will avoid these very real dangers. – F.

RUBBER RING

I have a very long foreskin and even when my penis is erect, it hangs over the tip of the glans by at least $\frac{1}{4}$ inch. At one time, during intercourse, instead of the foreskin staying back and leaving the glans bare, it moved backward with my movements. Hence, I ejaculated after only a short time.

I then learned that many people who were circumcised could prolong intercourse for long periods. Two years ago I started the practice of keeping back my foreskin by the use of a rubber ring. The ring is placed at the end of my penis and the end of my foreskin folded back over it. The ring and foreskin are then rolled down the shaft towards my scrotum. When my penis is fully erect the ring is halfway down the shaft.

After using this ring for three months my staying power during intercourse improved dramatically. I can now last for as long as half an hour.

During intercourse the chafing of the ring against the walls of my wife's vagina greatly excites her. We now have a wonderful sex life.

H.L.

The use of rubber rings around the penis is a well-known method of increasing the stimulation for the woman, and so indirectly the pleasure of the man. It is quite safe. – F

BENEFITS FROM TRAINING

I would like to say that I have masturbated since my schooldays and learned control of ejaculation through a desire for prolonging the whole process to the extent that I could go on for an hour sometimes.

I am engaged and having sexual intercourse with my fiancée frequently. I have found that this same control which I developed at school still works for me with her to the same extent.

My fiancée enjoys prolonged intercourse, but preferably with herself sitting in an armchair and myself kneeling, whereby she enjoys one or more orgasms to my one.

In this position, it is enjoyable for both of us to indulge in mutual anal stimulation both before and during intercourse. I use either my finger or the tip of my penis which she grips fiercely with her sphincter muscle giving great pleasure to both of us! We discovered this form of stimulation by accident as apparently have most couples.

I think that had I not masturbated and developed this contact, my performance would probably be sadly lacking, as apart from my fiancée, I am a virgin. This is probably a good thing as we both were and have developed sexually together. Therefore we can now control our desires or succumb very quickly to them, for example, after a prolonged separation.

A.M.

VAGINAL SORENESS

We have been married for 25 years and have had a full and varied sex life. We have the problem, though, that if we have intercourse twice in succession, my wife is sore for some days. The flow of natural lubricant has always been rather limited, so we have used a wide variety of alternatives, none of which has proved satisfactory.

The situation has now worsened to the extent that soreness results from a single performance of only a few minutes' duration. The soreness occurs in a narrow band right around the vaginal entrance. Perhaps you could recommend a suitable lubricant which would overcome this difficulty (I should add that the use of different contraceptives – sheath, cap, and gel, and in later years the Pill – has made no difference).

A.R.

It is impossible to tell from the facts in your letter whether or not your wife's problem might stem from psychological causes. Disinclination on her part, causing tension of the vaginal muscles, could lead to pain on entry and soreness afterwards.

If this doesn't seem to be the cause, then it would be advisable for your wife to have a physical checkup. Several minor infections (not forms of venereal disease) could cause the symptoms you describe. Both monilia *and* thrush, *for example, can*

436

be present without any discharge or other obvious sign except soreness during and after intercourse. Very often, in fact, a woman can go for years without suspecting the presence of such infection, especially in the case of thrush which tends to lie latent for long periods, emerging at times of fatigue or ill-health. Another possibility is atrophic vaginitis, *in which the skin of the vagina becomes thin and dry as a result of hormone deficiency and the production of natural secretions can almost cease, leading to soreness. This can be treated by a local application of hormone cream.*

If no physical cause can be found, there are local anesthetic creams, available on prescription, which would dull the soreness without seriously affecting your wife's pleasures. – F.

ICY LOVE

Letters concerning the embellishment of wives' erogenous zones with various forms of confectionery reminded me of occasions when my wife enjoyed being penetrated by an ice-cold sherry decanter stopper of about two inches in diameter.

From an outside viewpoint it really would seem quite kinky but when we do it, it seems perfectly ordinary and natural, as in fact, acts between lovers in pursuit of mutual enjoyment are.

B.L.

WATER TREATMENT

I would be interested to know if there are those who use the bathtub or full-sized, floor-to-ceiling shower as an area for sexual exploits.

My first baptismal experience was in a bathtub and started me off with a bias, but when I moved into a house with a large built-in shower, I realized that I had fully graduated.

The all pervading and insinuating sensation of the water in the tub is great, but the incessant Freudian reminder of the pounding, inescapable water in the shower makes strong men weak.

Had my impressions been based on isolated instances, I would have hesitated to comment on my preference. However, after various bathtubs and showers, I fancy myself something of an expert . . . In a way I have 'done my thing',

D.S.

THE WIFE'S TALE

I was originally jealous of my wife's previous lovers until one night, while making love to her in the rear entry position, I asked her if she had ever done it that way with others. When she replied 'no', I then wanted to know exactly what she had done, and while she told her experiences, I had the most wonderful climax.

This we repeated several times. We find the best excitement can be obtained when my wife tells of how she lost her virginity. Although, of course, her boyfriend had had access to her breasts and panties in places like darkened rooms and cinemas, they had not had much opportunity to be alone until my present mother-in-law left them at home one night to attend a bridge party. Although expecting 'heavy petting', my wife quickly found out that her young man was not going to be satisfied with just her naked breasts and at his insistence allowed her panties to be slipped down to her thighs. She said that the man was gentle and pleased she was a virgin. In their lovemaking on future occasions, while telling my wife 'not to be shy', he would gently spread her thighs, until at their widest, then with his fingers he would open her inner lips and gaze at her for some time. She found it exciting to offer herself thus without inhibition.

Throughout their relationship, which lasted two years, my wife's lover refused to permit her to wear panties in his presence, as he said he preferred her naked beneath her skirt ready to accept him at his wishes.

On many occasions I have appreciated the glances which have been slipped up my wife's nyloned thighs as she mounts the stairs of buses or gets out of the car.

If a bit of exhibitionism with its subsequent voyeurism brings some pleasure and excitement to those concerned, I say, why not?

W.J.

SENSUAL BLISS

My idea of sensual bliss is to be led to a darkened, preferably underground room and there stripped, bound, trampled upon and mercilessly whipped by a booted but otherwise naked woman whose identity is concealed behind a black mask and who, before leaving me to lick my wounds, orders me to satisfy her with my tongue after her appetite has been whetted by the flogging.

Although my craving to undergo such treatment cannot be gratified more than once in a blue moon (the fees these girls charge nowadays!) I get immense satisfaction simply by imagining such scenes, especially in the office where I'm surrounded by delectable dollies at whose feet I often picture myself groveling in abject subjugation. In fact, I had to forgo coffee the other afternoon as I'd fantasized about being treated in my favorite way by one of our typists (they're *asking* to get raped, the length they wear their skirts these days!) and had induced an erection which it would have been hard to conceal in the coffee line.

M.G.

DANGEROUS VISIONS?

As far back as I can remember I have had a colorful imagination. During my schooldays, I spent hours in the classroom dreaming up various fantasies, not all of which were actually sexual.

As an adolescent, whenever I masturbated I indulged in my fantasy world, but it never occurred to me that I would continue with my fantasies after I got married.

Yet, when at the age of 25 I married, and after the initial excitement of discovering lovemaking was over, I found that I needed these fantasies in order to become fully aroused. I confided this to my wife and she was extremely shocked and hurt. She said that I should not need wild imaginings in order to make myself want her.

Consequently, I never mentioned the matter to her again and for the past five years have implemented my imagination without her knowledge.

When we make love I find it necessary to pretend to myself that we are in a room full of people who, after watching us for a while, all begin to make love themselves. Another of my fantasies is imagining that my wife does not really want me and that I am taking her by force. Often I wish that I could tell her of all this and that she would agree to act out some of my fantasies. But I know that she considers my 'visions' to be perverted and abnormal. Is my need for way-out sex fantasies a kind of perversion?

P.M.

No, it is not. If you need your fantasies to achieve an erection and/or thereby orgasm, sexually satisfying your wife, no one should deprive you of them – or has any ethical reason to do so. Such fantasies are very often uncontrollable and can be provoked by a chance sight, sound or touch. Whether you should insist involving your wife in them is another matter. If their 'trigger effect' exists without your telling her, you can safely keep them to yourself. But, perhaps you might be able to educate your wife sufficiently so that even if she will not share them, at least she will accept your 'wild imaginings'. – F.

MARITAL RX

My wife and I have a prescription for sexual excitement which works every time. All it requires is imagination, fantasy and honesty. During our prolonged loveplay, we both indulge in the most erotic sexual fantasies, which we then describe to one another. The sexual heat generated in the telling and listening to these wildly sexual 'happenings' is close to boiling point.

With our imaginations, we can place ourselves in any kind of position with anyone, anywhere. Because it is fantasy, there is no jealousy on either side when we recount erotica which may even involve people we know. We've fantasized everything from the most buxom movie queens to wild orgies.

This sexual prelude requires the most articulate communication between the couple, a complete release of one's libido and the employment of all the senses. Once you've experienced these pleasures, leading to eventual coital orgasms, all previous loveplay will seem like child's play!

F.L.

Psychologist Albert Ellis tells the story of a couple who had been married for 25 years. They had got along splendidly, sexually and otherwise. To celebrate their 25th wedding anniversary, they spent a night on the town – dinner, the theatre, dancing, and lots of drinks. They could not remember ever having enjoyed themselves more. Eventually they went home and went to bed, where, after nearly half an hour of coitus, they found themselves getting nowhere – the man wasn't even approaching orgasm, and neither was his wife. Finally she looked up at him and sighed: 'Well, dear, on this day of all days I guess you're having trouble thinking of someone else, too!'

We relate this story as an illustration of the widespread practice of sexual fantasy. Few adults have not at some time or another during their lives engaged in fantasies of a sexual nature. Some, during coitus, have fantasized a different partner, or a different sex act with the same partner – perhaps an act the actual performance of which was blocked by personal inhibitions.

On the autoerotic level, many young people have fantasized during masturbation, or while not engaged in any overt sex act – for example, while lying in bed before falling asleep. But, the person who has never fantasized, under any circumstances, is rare indeed – if he exists at all. Dr. John S. Yankowski, in his Report on Premarital Sex, found that 100% of all male respondents and 99% of all female respondents reported having engaged in fantasies of coitus while still in their teens. – F.

GUARANTEE OF SATISFACTION

This letter may be of interest to women who find it hard to reach a climax during intercourse. I discovered the method while reading a book on the 'Art of Marriage', but have never seen it described in any other book.

Take up the normal position for intercourse, then, the man having entered and thrust well home, the woman straightens her right leg fully, while the man lifts his left leg. She brings her leg inside. The man then lowers his left leg, which is now on the outside of hers. Do the same with the other leg and the man should be on the outside, the woman inside.

At this stage, while the penis is still inside the vagina, the woman puts her hands down between the bodies, and parts the lips of the vagina. The penis is now touching the clitoris. Now commence intercourse. If the woman keeps her legs together, as tightly as possible, it is also a great thrill for the man. A must in this position is a gentle stroking of each nipple. The woman will then experience orgasm within a few minutes.

This method is a 'guarantee of satisfaction', especially for women who, like my wife, will not tolerate cunnilingus for long.

G.T.

A guarantee of satisfaction, especially in sex, is almost impossible. But thanks for sharing the recipe. – R.G.

PLEASURE ANXIETY

I am interested in sexual sociology and investigating the further principles of orgasm therapy, as well as analyzing and classifying the qualitative differences in sexual experience. The fact is that Man is the only species who has destroyed his own natural sexual function. That is his trouble.

Social adjustment still requires the suppression of genital sexuality. This creates the damming up of life energy which animates pathological drives, for it would certainly be true to say that abnormal modes of sexual satisfaction do not guarantee full pleasure and the adequate release of tension.

The principle of freedom applies to the vital, spontaneous impulses. People must not confuse secondary distortions, such as those exemplified in pornography, with healthy sexuality. It would be as well to bear in mind that condemnations of sex often refer to its caricature.

Many of us brought up in an anti-sexual atmosphere acquire a Pleasure Anxiety, which means that the fear of pleasurable excitement has become structured internally, Repairing the damage done by social frustration is hard, but surely there will be no genuine human happiness until man is permitted the satisfaction of his natural orgastic gratification. Individuals who are capable of orgastic potency are known by their kindness and gentleness. The sexual process and the life process are identical. Do we really intend to go on permitting our sexual freedom to be retarded by life-negating ideologies?

Sexual love affords the most intense sensations of pleasure. Instinctual forces can be self-regulating, making compulsion unnecessary. What is required is a fresh concept of living, where social activity is centered around an interest in sex, making the sexual embrace an experience richer each time.

In order to expand the frontiers of sexuality beyond the limits set by an obsolescent social morality, a more open and liberal attitude towards the subject is required. I mention this because of my own inner emotional burdens at having to check present orgasmic excitation and block off biological currents of genital stimuli. I need some help from others (female) to restore my organic capacity for pleasure. The therapeutic function of orgasm is a matter I take very seriously. I want to improve my existing sexual structure, which is in many ways rigid and blocked. I believe this can only be done through an inner change of moral opinion.

P.G.

The author of this letter seems to be influenced by the writings of Wilhelm Reich, originally a Freudian psychoanalyst, who stressed the importance of the orgasm in explaining many types of neurotic problems. Reich's book, The Function of the Orgasm, *probably contains his most complete statement on the subject: 'Psychic health depends upon orgastic potency, that is on the capacity for surrender in the acme of sexual excitation in the natural sexual act. Its basis is the un-neurotic character attitude of capacity for love. Mental illness is a result of a disturbance in the natural capacity for love. In the case of orgastic impotence from which a vast majority of humans are suffering, biological energy is dammed up, thus becoming the source of all irrational behavior.'*

Wilhem Reich also developed a system of nonverbal therapy which he called vegeto-therapy, now slightly altered by Alexander Lowen as bioenergetic therapy, which seems to be a combination of chiropractic and psychoanalytic techniques. Lowen also works on the premise that due to sexual statis, neurotic difficulties express themselves in physical rigidities. In order to bring back the repressed memories which are believed to be the cause of the neurotic difficulty, the vegeto-therapist or the bioenergetic therapist attacks the muscular rigidities directly through pressure, breathing exercises and other physical methods. A recent development very closely related to Reichian therapy is that of Janov's Primal Scream.

The assumption that there is a connection between physical rigidities and other problems may be so, but unfortunately many of the Reichian and bioenergetic people seem to have become fanatically devoted to this one approach and consider all other approaches irrelevant.

Not many psychologists and psychiatrists agree with Wilhelm Reich and his followers that all neurotic problems arise out of inadequate orgasm. I have found that a singleminded search for the perfect orgasm is not conducive to development as an individual. – H.G.

FACT OR FICTION

The male orgasm is one subject one cannot discuss with one's friends. At least, I find myself unable to discuss my problem with my friends. In reading literature, especially fiction, it is not unusual for the author to describe the male orgasm as 'the earth moving' or using adjectives which describe an immense catyclysm within the hero's body.

During my five years of marriage, my orgasms have not been of the earthmoving variety. For the most part, the feeling has been limited to the genital region, and the sensations are anything but overpowering or convulsive. Although I try to keep my true feelings from my wife, I'm sure she's aware of the lack of intensity of my climax. As a result, my desire for sex is not as strong as I think it should be.

On the other hand, is it possible that the so-called overpowering orgasm is just a figment of our writers' imaginations? After all, ever since the beginning of time, man has exaggerated his sexual prowess, if for no other reason than to convince himself of his 'manhood'.

I would appreciate an honest opinion on the subject of the male orgasm. If the majority of men experience the same intensity of orgasm I describe above, I will at least be reassured that I'm normal.

J.S.

Kinsey lists six kinds of orgastic response in his study dealing with the male. None of them is a full orgastic response. They include:

1. A mild reaction limited to the genitals, with little or no body reaction. In the penis there are a few throbs, and the semen flows out without the normal ejaculatory, pulsatile squirts. The climax is one without any significant feeling. Kinsey states that about one-fifth or more of all males experience this most inadequate response. It would appear from his letter that J.S. belongs to this category.

2. The climax said to be most common involves some 'tension or twitching of one or both legs, of the mouth, of the arms or of other particular parts of the body'. In this response, the whole body becomes rigid. There are a few spasms, but no aftereffects. This reaction is said to occur in about 45% of all males. The body is rigid which prevents an orgastic convulsion.

3. This is the same nature as the preceding one, but the reac-

tion is more violent. The descriptive terms used by Kinsey, based on statements of his subjects, are: 'legs often become rigid with muscles knotted and toes pointed, muscles of abdomen contracted and hard, shoulders and neck stiff and often bent forwards, breath held or gasping, eyes staring or tightly closed ... whole body or parts of it spasmodically twitching, sometimes synchronously with throbs or violent jerking of penis.' In addition, there may be groans, sobs or violent cries. The aftereffects are not marked. This type of response was reported by about one-sixth of Kinsey's subjects. A famous British psychiatrist referring to this type of climax wrote: *'Rigidities, tensions and spasms are contrary to the nature of the orgastic reaction. How pleasurable can a climax be if it is accompanied by violent manifestations? One would expect such reactions from a person undergoing torture rather than the delights of an ecstatic experience. This is not orgasm but fear – fear of an orgasm that threatens to overwhelm the ego.'*

4. A small percentage of males whose reactions were hysterical, including those of laughter, talking, sadistic or masochistic feelings and rapid motions *'culminating in frenzied movements'*. About 5% of the males.

5. A small group of males also reported the above reactions but *'culminating in extreme trembling, collapse, loss of color, and sometimes fainting of subject'*.

6. According to Kinsey, a number of males complained of pain and fear at the approach of orgasm. It seems that the penis became very sensitive just before orgasm, and Kinsey says that *'some males suffer excruciating pain and may scream if movement is continued or the penis even touched'*. Some of these males may fight away from the partner at the approach of the climax, although they report *'definite pleasure'* in the whole experience. – F.

VICTORIOUS SURRENDER

Last night I had a real orgasm. For the first time in my life I was able to release the years of tension and feelings that I have been unable to shed. I never knew in all my searching and trying for orgasm, that it was to be found inside me and a thing of my own control. All these years, and all these men, and I could have surrendered to it if only I had realized what had to be done. Last night my vagina became myself, and then a cave and then a tunnel in the side of a mountain, with everything rushing through it – me rushing through it – and out into freedom. I have surrendered.

I never knew I had to surrender. I never knew you had to give your whole self to gain this freedom. I can see clearly now that to surrender to a man does not make one weaker as a woman. It is the *only* way to be a woman.

I have always been too aware of men and confused by the fear of letting things get out of my control, of losing the 'upper hand'. My relationships with men have been a long battle which I have always had to win, verbally and sexually. I have always thought that one man would someday come along and give me this orgasm, like a present – now I know that all along it was my gift to give it to him.

All the pretense and performances I've put on in all my considerable sexual involvements have been a pathetic attempt to save my pride. I could never bear the thought of letting a man know that I was unable to carry out my complete role in intercourse. I don't know yet whether the fear of rejection was greater than the fear of being hurt before I could hurt them, but I was unable to allow any man to be better at fucking than I was. While it is obvious to me now, the desire to give completely of myself was never there. I wanted to take, not to give. I never realized before that my potential and sexual freedom was as a woman – not as a man.

Being able to surrender for the first time and leave 'self' behind has unlocked in one day that which all the 'erotica' in the world could not have achieved. Afterward, in the full realization and clarity of the mental and physical release I had gained, I could see myself from the outside. I could look back in the long battle with men which started the moment my sexuality developed. My only way of conquering men and overcoming my own inadequacy was to hurt them first. By their orgasms they laid offering all over me; but I was giving nothing, and thereby 'winning'.

I shall now try to find out what has happened to me, why I have spent so much time without ever wanting or being able to surrender to man. I know, through the stripping away of the layers of guilt and lies that came with the orgasm, that since my childhood I have been unable to relate myself to any man – more than likely starting with my father. I don't know much about this yet, but I shall find out.

This morning when I woke up, in bed with my lover, and looked at him sleeping, I thought: I know you don't love me – this is all right. For the first time, I won't punish you for it. *I love you* and it doesn't matter that you don't love me or want me there forever, or that you don't want to support me and swear undying love. You are not using me. I don't have to fight anymore, because I have laid down my arms, the battle is over. I am loving you, and giving to you and so, I have been released. I can love you now for what I can give to you, not for what I've been trying to get from you for so long. I want you to take my gift – there aren't any strings attached to it anymore. It is a gift I've been trying to give, without even knowing exactly what it was. I know now that what I had to give was myself and that only by giving myself can I find myself as a woman.

Miss S.L.

This is an eloquent description of one way to achieve full sexual pleasure. There is much in this letter from which men as well as women can profit. – H.G.

The ability to give up the 'battle' is frequently a most promising way to ensure sexual pleasure. Unfortunately all too often men and women will use sex as one of the major weapons in their struggles with each other. – R.G.

HOME FORUMS

We have successfully conducted Home Forums for the past three months among our married friends and have found these evenings to be the most stimulating and interesting we have ever had. Initially, we were embarrassed to broach the subject to our friends – thinking it would also embarrass them or that they would misinterpret our intentions.

Fortunately for me, my wife is a very frank and open person and she decided, rightly so, to ask the wife of one of our closest friends if she and her husband would care to come over for an evening of coffee/cake and a discussion of sex. When the invitation was eagerly accepted, my wife then found it easier to approach several more of our friends' wives with the same invitation.

Our first attempt at a Home Forum saw our living room bursting with 18 people, all married. It appeared several of our friends brought along some of their own friends. The evening couldn't have been more successful. We discussed and argued about the Pill, adultery, group sex, sex education for our children, drugs and alcoholism, and other subject matters. Instead of leaving at midnight as planned, most of them stayed until two a.m. and would have remained even later if we had allowed it.

For many of the couples, it was the first time they had ever discussed sex openly. I sensed a feeling of exhilaration as we argued with no holds barred about such sensitive areas as man's need for more excitement and stimulation as his marriage tends to become stale and repetitious. Most of the couples were in their 40s. It was fascinating to see when the subject of group sex was being discussed, or should I say, argued, how most of the men were in favor of trying it, while most of the wives were against the idea. If nothing else, it showed the women something about their husbands' desires.

I learned later most of the couples present never discussed their sexual feelings and problems among themselves when they were alone. I find this terribly sad, especially if it applies to many other marriages in our country today. Fortunately, my wife and I have never kept anything from one another from the day we were married, and this fact, more than anything else I feel, has kept our marriage healthy and vibrant.

L.S.

We hope that many couples will use this book to organize similar Home Forums. – H. and R.G.

WHAT'S WRONG?

We are a young unmarried couple, very much in love, who have been together for the last eight months. In this time we have been avid readers of Forum, especially the letters section. Having digested the views of your readers (whom we are sure represent a large proportion of the educated and informed majority of this country) we have finally decided to put our problem to you.

We find that we spend most of our time making love (both sexually and mentally), favor the most popular position, do not need sexual aids, respond to the same stimulus, find no need for flagellation, have not considered troilism, are not overtly stimulated by the sight of rubber, and are still excited by the prospect of making love to each other.

What's wrong with us?

P.O. and Miss C.C.

NOTHING LEFT

I am 20 and am having an affair with a married man of 30. This has been going on for over 18 months. Everything is perfect but for one small problem. We have a very happy sex life, have tried everything in the books and now we have come to an end. Nothing else to try. Can you help us? We seem to be looking for something new all the time.

Miss B.L.

Your letter is very touching. The search for external stimulation is indeed a widespread problem in our time and culture. If man does not live by bread alone, neither does he live by sex alone. While sex can be lovely, exciting, enjoyable, for most people it does not seem to be enough to give complete fulfillment to their lives. – H.G.

INDEX

Note: Almost every letter in this book deals with more than one sexual feeling or behavior pattern. Many cross-references are given; however, the reader who wishes to search out any specific topic should look for it under related subject headings.

453

454